TWENTIETH CENTURY WAR MACHINES

SEA

CHRISTOPHER CHANT

ILLUSTRATIONS BY
JOHN BATCHELOR

TWENTIETH CENTURY WAR MACHINES

SEA

CHANCELLOR
PRESS

This edition published by Chancellor Press
an imprint of Bounty Books, a Division of the
Octopus Publishing Group Ltd,
2-4 Heron Quays, London, E14 4JP

© Graham Beehag Books

Printed in 1999
by Tat Wei Printing Packaging Singapore Pte Ltd

Contents

The Battleship and Battle-Cruiser

A
s its name suggests, the battleship was the modern successor of the type of capital ship known in the navies of the sailing era as the line of battle ship which, with its armament of 60 or more guns on two or more decks, was regarded as the arbiter of naval warfare fought between fleets of ships operating in lines of battle. As sail power was replaced by steam power and as wooden construction was superseded by iron (later steel) construction in the second and third quarters of the nineteenth century, the term battleship was introduced to reflect the new type of modern warship, whose creation was also facilitated if not actually made inevitable in the 1840s and 1850s by the development of the rifled gun supplementing and then replacing the short-ranged and less accurate smooth-bore gun, and of the explosive shell replacing the less damaging solid shot. In short, the development in little more than 25 years of iron (for additional protection and then as the primary structural medium), steam propulsion, the rifled gun and the explosive shell rendered obsolete the line of battle ship that had reigned supreme on the world's seas for more than three centuries.

The first such ship of this type was perhaps the French *Gloire* which was launched in 1859, but this was built primarily of wood with her sides provided with additional protection by a plating of iron. It is generally accepted, therefore, that the first true battleship was the British *Warrior*, which was launched in 1860, with a hull of iron construction. Both of these ships were officially rated as frigates and were completely ship-rigged, but this should not be allowed to disguise the fact that they were the harbingers of a new type of naval warfare, for with their auxiliary steam propulsion arrangements they could steam at 13 knots, which made it possible for them to overhaul, outmanoeuvre and thereby gain a decisive tactical advantage over any line of battle ship with its greater multitude of guns on several decks.

This should not be construed as suggesting that there was an immediate shift to the new concept of warship as a fully fledged type, however, for in the absence of any major European war that might otherwise have provided both the stimulus and the operational validation of the concept, the process was gradual. The transition from ship of the line to battleship was thus characterised by the conversion of many line of battle ships toward the newer standard by the addition of iron protection plating on the outside of the hulls and the lengthening of their hulls to allow the incorporation of a primitive steam propulsion arrangement that supplemented but certainly did not replace their original sailing ship rig, and also by the creation of new iron-hulled and steam-powered battleships which nonetheless retained the sailing ship rig and massive gun batteries of the earlier generation's ships.

Thus it was only with the development of improved and more reliable steam propulsion arrangements, offering greater power as well as radically

The capital ship of World War II is seen in classic form in this painting of the German battle-cruiser *Scharnhorst* in action with heavy ships of the British Home Fleet in northern waters.

improved economy of operation, that the battleship began to emerge in the third quarter of the nineteenth century as a type radically different from the line of battle ship. The new breed of battleship was made possible not only by its new steam propulsion arrangement but also by the adoption of more advanced guns with breech rather than muzzle loading, rifled rather than smooth-bore barrels, and efficient smokeless nitrocellulose propellant in place of the inefficient smoke-producing black powder. Steady improvements in metallurgy allowed the construction of larger ships whose armoured sides provided better protection against incoming fire, and the evolution of more advanced propulsion arrangements and hull designs facilitated higher speeds. (Although hull designs were generally improved in terms of a better underwater line and a higher length-beam ratio, an anachronism that lasted well into the twentieth century, at least in vestigial form, was the ram bow: this had apparently proved itself by deliberate and successful use in the second Battle of Lissa in July 1866, when the Austro-Hungarian flagship rammed and sank the Italian *Re d'Italia*, and by accidental but also successful use in 1893 when the *Victoria*, flagship of the Mediterranean Fleet, was rammed and sunk by another British battleship.)

The first battleships relying on steam rather than sail as their prime mover were generally known as mastless ships, and the first of these was the British *Devastation* launched in 1869 as what was really a sea-going monitor as it was very low in the water and lacked any forecastle or poop. The masted and mastless ships were still produced in parallel however, and the last masted iron battleships survived until the late 1880s.

Even so, technical progress made in the period between 1870 and 1890 in the development of steam power, gun technology and armour protection ensured that the battleship began to appear as a distinct type with the main guns mounted in trainable turrets. It was at this stage that the battleship

Designed in the UK by Mackrow as an improved 'Majestic' class battleship of the pre-dreadnought type, the *Hatsuse* is seen here on trials shortly after being launched on the River Tyne in 1899. The *Hatsuse* and her near-sister *Shikishima* differed only in their hull forms, and the details of the Imperial Japanese navy's *Hatsuse* included a full-load displacement of 15,255 tons, length of 439ft 0in (133.8m), armament of four 12in (305mm) guns in two twin turrets, fourteen 6in (152mm) guns in single mountings, twenty 3in (76mm) guns in single mountings, twelve 47mm guns in single mountings and four 18in (457mm) torpedo tubes, protection in the form of a 9.05in (230mm) belt, 14in (355mm) barbettes and 4in (102mm) deck, propulsion in the form of triple-expansion steam engines delivering 14,500hp (10,810kW) to two shafts for a speed of 18 knots, and complement of 740.

emerged from experimental status to be built in classes by the world's major powers. Each of these classes introduced improvements in capability that were reflected in greater size and displacement, the latter increasing typically from the 9,200 tons of the *Warrior* to the 15,000 tons of the *Majestic*, a British battleship launched in 1895. Whereas the *Warrior* was a single-ship type 420ft (128m) long, fully ship-rigged with an auxiliary steam powerplant delivering 5,267hp (3,927kW) to one propeller for a speed of 14.1 knots, protected by 4.5in (114mm) of iron over 18in (457mm) of wood, and armed with ten 110lb (49.9kg) and four 70lb (31.75kg) breech-loading guns as well as twenty-eight 68lb (30.8kg) muzzle-loading guns, the *Majestic* was the lead vessel of a 10-ship class to a design that included a length of 421ft (128.32m), triple-expansion steam engines delivering 12,000hp (8,947kW) to two propellers for a speed of 16.1 knots, protection based on steel up to 14in (357mm) thick, and an armament of four 12in (305mm) breech-loading guns in two centreline turrets supported by twelve 6in (152mm) breech-loading rifled guns in casemated mountings, sixteen 12pdr quick-firing guns and twelve 3pdr quick-firing guns.

The 'Majestic' class marked the start of a battleship type that became standard, with local changes, in most of the world's major navies and was built in large numbers in the period up to 1905 with changes limited mainly to greater size, thicker protection, more power for slightly increased speed, and secondary and tertiary gun batteries increased in calibre: this last factor is reflected in the two 'Swiftsure' class ships of 1904 with a secondary battery of fourteen 7.5in (191mm) guns, the eight 'King Edward' class ships of 1905 with a secondary battery of four 9.2in (234mm) guns and ten 6in (152mm) guns, and the two ships of the 'Lord Nelson' class of 1907 with a secondary battery of ten 9.2in guns. The largest-calibre guns were seen as the primary weapons for the engagement of opposing battleships, with the secondary battery adding to the weight of fire and also providing a capability against secondary targets such as armoured cruisers, which could also be hit by the tertiary battery that was provided mainly for the protection of the battleship against the attentions of torpedo boats. These boats were regarded as a major threat to the battle fleet, as they operated in flotillas designed to exploit their speed and manoeuvrability to get in close and decimate the battle fleet with waves of potent torpedoes.

Seen in the period leading up to World War I, the *Indefatigable* was lead ship of a class of three battle-cruisers designed to an improved 'Invincible' class standard for the Royal Navy, with a full-load displacement of 22,080 tons, length of 590ft 0in (179.8m), armament of eight 12in (305mm) guns in four twin turrets, sixteen 4in (102mm) guns in single mountings, four 3pdr guns in single mountings and two 18in (457mm) torpedo tubes, protection in the form of a 6in (152mm) belt, 7in (178mm) barbettes and turrets, 2.5in (64mm) decks and 10in (254mm) conning tower, propulsion in the form of steam turbines delivering 44,000hp (32,805kW) to four shafts for a speed of 25 knots, and complement of 800. Although fast and moderately well armed, the ships were woefully deficient in protection.

The performance of these guns was considerable: the 12in (305mm) weapon, for example, could fire an 850lb (386kg) projectile to a range of more than 20,000yds (18,290m). Yet it was still standard at the beginning of the twentieth century to think of fleet engagements at ranges of only a few thousand yards. This meant that virtually every gun on a battleship would be capable of striking its opponent, and this raised the enormous difficulty of spotting the fall of shot, for with guns of three or more calibres hitting the target ship it became crucially important to differentiate the explosions of the shells fired by the various guns: there was little point in an enemy capital ship being blanketed in the fire of the 6in (152mm) or smaller guns of the tertiary battery, which could inflict relatively little decisive damage, if this obscured the fact that the fire of the secondary and primary batteries was not hitting the target.

That this might well be the case was illustrated by Captain Percy Scott, a decided advocate of accurate gunnery at a time in which the Royal Navy, followed by most other navies, believed that protracted gunnery practice was expensive and unnecessary for the type of short-range engagements that were envisaged, with rate of fire and general accuracy more important than truly aimed fire, and that gunnery practice also damaged the ship's paintwork and brightwork. Even so, it came as a shock in 1899 when Scott's command, the cruiser *Scylla*, achieved 80 per cent of hits with her 4.7in (120mm) guns in the Mediterranean Fleet gunnery competition, easily winning over ships whose average score was a paltry 30 per cent.

Scott's technique was based on the use of a telescopic sight on each gun and the following of the target through his own ship's roll rather than firing only when the guns of his own ship were brought to bear by the ship's roll. Scott also devised an effective training system for his gunners, who trained with the 'otter', 'loader' and 'deflection teacher' aids for practice in roll, loading and allowance for the target ship's horizontal movement. Such was Scott's success that the inertia of other commanders and the Admiralty was overcome and by 1902 most British warships were using the same methods. Scott became Inspector of Target Practice in 1905, and in 1907 the average number of hits being secured by British ships had risen to 81 per cent. Scott returned to sea in 1908 as commander of a cruiser squadron in the Channel Fleet, but his involvement in an extraordinary vitriolic quarrel between Admiral Sir Charles Beresford and Admiral Sir John Fisher, respectively the commander of the Channel Fleet and the First Sea Lord, ended his active career. Fisher

Seen in her original form in 1913, the *Kirishima* was a 'Kongo' class battle-cruiser of the Imperial Japanese Navy, but in 1933 and 1934 was reconstructed as a fast battleship. The four ships were designed in the UK, and the lead ship was also built in that country as the last Japanese capital ship constructed outside Japan. The specification for the four ships, as completed to an improved 'Lion' class design offering superiority to all current capital ships in the arrangement of the main armament, weight of the secondary armament and extent of the protection, included a full-load displacement of 32,200 tons, length of 704ft 0in (214.6m), armament of eight 14in (356mm) guns in four twin turrets, sixteen 6in (152mm) guns in single mountings, sixteen 3.1in (78mm) guns in single mountings and eight 21in (533mm) torpedo tubes, protection in the form of an 8in (203mm) belt, 10in (254mm) barbettes, 9.1in (230mm) turrets and 10in (254mm) conning tower, propulsion in the form of steam turbines delivering 64,000hp (47,720kW) to four shafts for a speed of 27.5 knots, and complement of 1,220.

was well aware of the importance of Scott's thinking, however, and Scott was encouraged to continue with his most important work: this was the creation of the director sight.

This concept took overall control of each ship's gunnery into a gunnery control position mounted in the battleship's foretop, now located at the junction of a sturdy tripod mast to ensure rigidity, from which a good view of the engagement could be obtained and the laying and firing of all guns could be controlled in replacement for the individual aiming that was otherwise standard despite the fact that each gunner was located relatively low in the ship and could have his sight of the target obscured by spray, smoke, cordite haze, and mist or fog, especially as ranges began to increase as a result of the Scott-inspired improvement of gunnery accuracy. Director firing involved the use of a single telescopic sight in the director position. The target was held in this sight, which was located above most obstructions to its field of view, and the individual gunners then had to align their gunsights with a pointer controlled from the director position: once each gunsight had been aligned with the pointer it was accurately laid in azimuth and elevation, and then all the guns were fired electrically and in unison from the director position, which ensured a higher level of accuracy and also simplified the spotting of the fall of shot and thus the generation of error corrections.

Scott perfected the system in 1910, but met with considerable opposition from officers who claimed that reliance on a single director position and electrical controls opened the way to a disastrous failure in the event of a single shell hit, for reliance on this system would have ensured that little training was given to individual gunners. The matter was settled in 1912 during trials between two battleships, one using the Scott system of director firing and the other relying on individual aiming: the director-equipped ship scored six times as many hits at a range of 9,000yds (8,230m), and director firing was adopted by the British in 1913, only later being utilised by the Germans and Americans. It is worth noting that the accuracy of director firing was considerably enhanced from 1913 by the simultaneous adoption for the director position of Captain Frederic Charles Dreyer's 'fire-control table', which was in essence a mechanical computer for the solution of fire-control problems on the basis of inputted data for target bearing, bearing rate change, range, range rate change, and speed.

The director firing concept would have been useful for the type of battleship described above with its three or even four calibres of guns, but in fact came into its own with a new type of conceptually simpler but tactically superior

The 'Bellerophon' class battleships of the Royal Navy were the first class-built dreadnoughts to enter British service, and the three ships were completed to an improved 'Dreadnought' class standard with two tripod masts, a full-load displacement of 22,100 tons, length of 526ft 0in (160.3m), armament of ten 12in (305mm) guns in five twin turrets, sixteen 4in (102mm) guns in single mountings, four 3pdr guns in single mountings and three 18in (457mm) torpedo tubes, protection in the form of a 10in (254mm) belt, 9in (229mm) barbettes, 11in (280mm) turrets and conning tower, and 4in (102mm) decks, propulsion in the form of steam turbines delivering 23,000hp (17,140kW) to four shafts for a speed of 20.75 knots, and complement of 735.

battleship that first appeared in October 1906 with the completion of the British ship *Dreadnought*.

The impetus for the creation of this new type of battleship can be traced to 1896 and the passing of the First Naval Law designed to pave the way for the creation of a German navy that would eventually rival that of the UK. This led to a numerical and strategic destabilisation of the naval *status quo* in Europe at a time when the UK was already becoming concerned about the threat to its pre-eminent world position posed by Germany's growing industries and mercantile marine, and coincided with the simultaneous introductions of several new technologies that were all to exert considerable influence upon naval warfare. These technologies included the 'locomotive torpedo' in a perfected form, the submarine, radio communication, the internal-combustion engine including its safe and very economical diesel engine form, oil- rather than coal-fired boilers, steam turbines in place of triple-expansion engines for smoother running as well as higher power in less volume, and, from 1903, the aeroplane.

These and other factors combined to make inevitable the introduction of what might reasonably be called the 'all big gun' battleship with its primary and secondary batteries (typically four 12in/305mm primary guns in two centreline turrets fore and aft of the central superstructure, and ten 7.5in/190mm secondary guns in casemated mountings round and below the superstructure) replaced by a larger number of turreted main guns located on or as close to the centreline as possible and complemented by large numbers of small guns. The task of the main guns was to deal with major adversaries, and the function of the small guns was to provide protection

against the attentions of torpedo boats, which were thought to offer a significant threat but were lightly built in order to secure high speed, and were thereby vulnerable to the fire of quick-firing weapons such as 12pdr guns.

A primary armament of single-calibre guns had been tested in the 1870s in a few British and Italian battleships, but the failure of these vessels had led to the general retention of at least three main calibres for battleship armament. Then in 1904-05 the Russo-Japanese War revealed the limitations of such a mixed armament: the primary guns were used accurately at the unprecedented range of 20,000yds (18,290m), and spotting of the fall of shot of the secondary and tertiary batteries proved almost impossible even at considerably shorter ranges.

The lesson was clear to all who considered the implications of the Japanese victory in the Russo-Japanese War: the day of the secondary and tertiary batteries as offensive weapons was over, and it was therefore sensible to concentrate all the offensive firepower in a larger number of main guns, which could concentrate an overwhelming weight of fire at very long range and sink or disable an enemy before it could close to a range at which its medium-calibre guns might become effective. The Japanese were in the position to reach this conclusion before anyone else, and laid down the first 'all big gun' battleships as the *Aki* and *Satsuma* with a planned armament of twelve 12in (305mm) guns in two centreline twin turrets and, on each beam, one twin and two single turrets. Completion of the ships was delayed not only by Japan's limited industrial capacity, however, but also by the realisation that it was not cost-effective to have two four-gun beam batteries that would never be used simultaneously: these were therefore replaced by an intermediate-calibre battery of twelve10in (254mm) guns in three twin turrets on each beam. It was therefore the British, now thoroughly concerned about the pace and extent of Germany's growing naval strength, who produced the first 'all big gun' battleship as the *Dreadnought*, with the Americans close behind them with the 'South Carolina' class and the Germans also in the running with the 'Nassau' class.

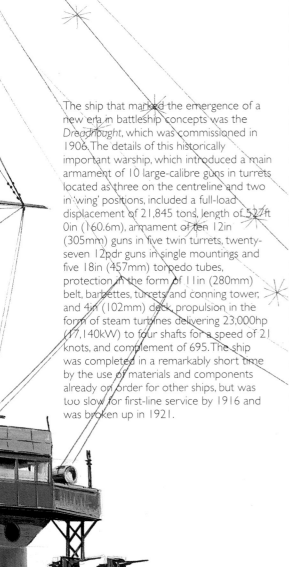

The ship that marked the emergence of a new era in battleship concepts was the *Dreadnought*, which was commissioned in 1906. The details of this historically important warship, which introduced a main armament of 10 large-calibre guns in turrets located as three on the centreline and two in 'wing' positions, included a full-load displacement of 21,845 tons, length of 527ft 0in (160.6m), armament of ten 12in (305mm) guns in five twin turrets, twenty-seven 12pdr guns in single mountings and five 18in (457mm) torpedo tubes, protection in the form of 11in (280mm) belt, barbettes, turrets and conning tower, and 4in (102mm) deck, propulsion in the form of steam turbines delivering 23,000hp (17,140kW) to four shafts for a speed of 21 knots, and complement of 695. The ship was completed in a remarkably short time by the use of materials and components already on order for other ships, but was too slow for first-line service by 1916 and was broken up in 1921.

This was the eighth ship of this name in the Royal Navy, and certainly the most important as she ushered in a new type of warship. The *Dreadnought* gave her name to the new type of 'all big gun' battleship, the ships of the previous generation with mixed batteries becoming known as 'pre-dreadnought' battleships. The ship was laid down at Portsmouth Dockyard in October 1905 and launched in February 1906 for completion later in the year, and this was a truly remarkable construction effort made possible only by using matériel already ordered and built for other ships. The ship was described by Fisher, her conceptual father, as "the hard-boiled egg — because she cannot be beat". The ship was the first capital ship in the world to be fitted with steam turbines as her primary propulsion arrangement, in this instance four sets of turbines delivering 23,000hp (17,150kW) to four shafts for a maximum speed of 22 knots, which was considerably faster than any 'pre-dreadnought' battleship despite her longer length of 526ft (160.3m) and greater displacement of 20,700 tons at full load. Fisher had a penchant for major warships that secured their advantage through an offensive combination of firepower and speed rather than ta defensive strength of thick armour, and the *Dreadnought* was therefore only modestly well protected with a maximum thickness of 11in (280mm) on the waterline belt. It was in her armament that the *Dreadnought* excelled, however, for the primary battery comprised ten 12in (305mm) guns installed in five twin turrets as one forward and two aft on the centreline, and the other two in 'wing' positions abreast the superstructure for a broadside of eight 12in guns. Intended only for the task of repelling torpedo boats, the secondary armament comprised twenty-four 12pdr guns in single mountings.

The completion of the ship was a matter of enormous pride for the British people, but also a subject of much anxiety as the ship had, at a stroke, revolutionised naval warfare by making all 'pre-dreadnought' battleships obsolete. This meant that the Royal Navy currently enjoyed a numerical advantage of only one in terms of its best battleship strength, and naval superiority would therefore go to the country which could build 'dreadnought' battleships more quickly in what came to be called the 'naval race'.

The primary threat was Germany, but by striking first the UK had secured a significant advantage, and by the time Germany had completed its first class of four 'dreadnoughts', the UK had seven as well as three examples of the battle-cruiser, a still more revolutionary and controversial type of capital ship. The origins of the battle-cruiser can be traced back to 1896 and the suggestion of Emile Bertin, the great French ship designer, for a large warship combining the speed and protection of the armoured cruiser with the main-calibre guns of the battleship to create a type notable for its great offensive power (speed and firepower) but only limited defensive capability. The concept appealed strongly to Fisher, who considered offensive capability to be all-important and saw in the proposal a means of producing a cost-effective type

The Austro-Hungarian *Viribus Unitis* was the last unit of the four-strong 'Tegetthof' class of dreadnought battleships completed from 1913 as comparatively small but nonetheless useful ships with their main armament in two pairs of superfiring triple turrets. The details of the class included a full-load displacement of 21,595 tons, length of 499ft 4in (152.2m), armament of twelve 12in (305mm) guns in four triple turrets, twelve 5.9in (150mm) guns in single mountings, eighteen 2.6in (66mm) guns in single mountings, two 47mm guns in single mountings and four 21in (533mm) torpedo tubes, protection in the form of an 11in (280mm) belt, barbettes, turrets and conning tower and 1.4 in (36mm) deck, propulsion in the form of steam turbines delivering 25,000hp (18,640kW) to four shafts for a speed of 20 knots, and complement of 1,045.

Based on misleading information put out by the British about its 'Invincible' class battle-cruisers, the *Blücher* was a neat but badly undergunned and underprotected ship that lay in the bracket between armoured cruiser and battle-cruiser. The ship's specification included a full-load displacement of 17,500 tons, length of 530ft 10in (161.8m), armament of twelve 8.3in (210mm) guns in six twin turrets, eight 5.9in (150mm) guns in single mountings, sixteen 3.4in (88mm) guns in single mountings and four 17.7in (450mm) torpedo tubes, protection in the form of a 7.1in (180mm) belt and turrets, 9.8in (250mm) conning tower and 2.75in (70mm) deck, propulsion in the form of triple-expansion steam engines delivering 34,000hp (25,350kW) to three shafts for a speed of 24.8 knots, and complement of 890.

that would be able to function in typical cruiser roles (scouting for the main fleet and protection of British maritime trade routes all over the world) and have the capability for active participation in fleet engagements as a result of its powerful and long-ranged main battery.

The result was the battle-cruiser, of which the first three were laid down in 1906 as 'armoured cruisers'. Completed at three-monthly intervals in 1908, the ships of the 'Invincible' class were then revealed as vessels altogether different from anything that had gone before. Although their protection was along armoured cruiser lines, with a maximum armour thickness of 7in (178mm), the main armament of these ships, each displacing 19,940 tons at full load, was eight 12in (305mm) guns in four twin turrets of which two were located on the centreline fore and aft of the superstructure and the other two in echeloned 'wing' positions on each beam. A secondary armament more capable than that of the *Dreadnought* was installed, in the form of sixteen 4in (102mm) guns, and the other primary distinguishing features of these handsome ships were their fine lines on a length of 567ft 0in (172.82m) and the high speed of 26.6 knots provided by the delivery of 41,000hp (30,570kW) to four shafts by four sets of steam turbines.

In overall terms, the battle-cruiser was basically a development of the 'dreadnought' battleship with one less main turret, a considerably reduced area and thickness of armour, and a combination of a longer hull and a more powerful propulsion arrangement for notably higher speed. The result was a highly impressive type of warship designed to outfight any ship it could not outrun, and outrun any ship it could not outfight, but as operations in World War I (1914-18) were to prove, the lack of effective protection was a fatal flaw in the concept of these fine vessels.

The 'dreadnought' ships that followed in the period up to 1910 were the British 'Bellerophon' class of three ships based on the *Dreadnought* but with two tripod masts and a secondary armament of sixteen 4in (102mm) guns, the 'St Vincent' class of three ships with slightly thinner bow and stern armour as well as 50- rather than 45-calibre main guns for higher muzzle velocity and greater penetrative capability, the Japanese Satsuma interim type with its hybrid armament, and the German 'Nassau' class of four ships with a main armament of twelve 11in (280mm) guns in six twin turrets located as two centreline units fore and aft of the two superstructure blocks and four 'wing' turrets, a secondary armament of sixteen 3.4in (88mm) gun, protection up to a maximum of 12in (305mm), and a propulsion arrangement based on triple-expansion reciprocating steam engines delivering 26,244hp (19,568kW) to three shafts for a speed of 20 knots.

It is interesting to note that the Germans had considered that the protection of the British ships was too light, and therefore opted for better protection using the weight saved by the adoption of a slightly smaller-calibre main gun that nevertheless possessed a high muzzle velocity as well as the flatter trajectory that simplified the creation of a valid fire-control solution and also permitted the use of a lower and therefore lighter turret design.

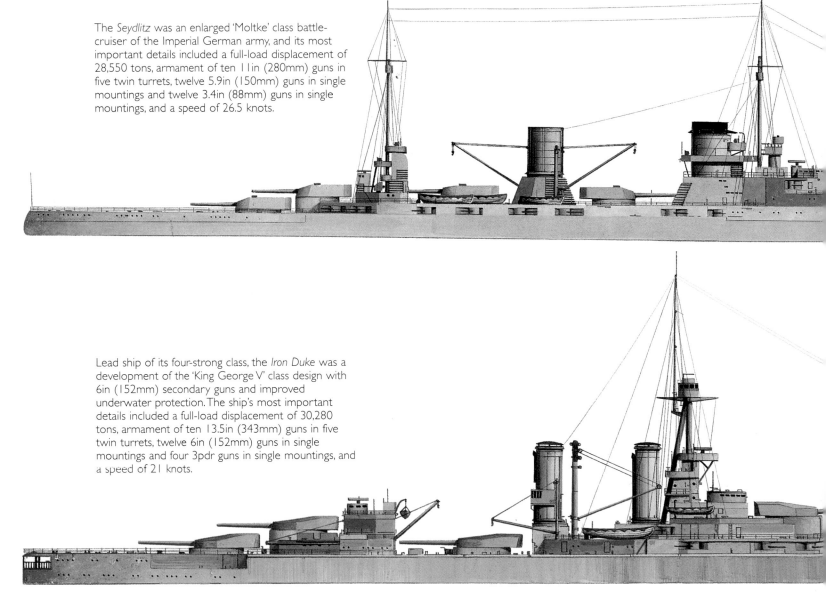

The *Seydlitz* was an enlarged 'Moltke' class battle-cruiser of the Imperial German army, and its most important details included a full-load displacement of 28,550 tons, armament of ten 11in (280mm) guns in five twin turrets, twelve 5.9in (150mm) guns in single mountings and twelve 3.4in (88mm) guns in single mountings, and a speed of 26.5 knots.

Lead ship of its four-strong class, the *Iron Duke* was a development of the 'King George V' class design with 6in (152mm) secondary guns and improved underwater protection. The ship's most important details included a full-load displacement of 30,280 tons, armament of ten 13.5in (343mm) guns in five twin turrets, twelve 6in (152mm) guns in single mountings and four 3pdr guns in single mountings, and a speed of 21 knots.

The *Rheinland* was one of the four 'Nassau' class ships that were Germany's first dreadnought battleships with a full-load displacement of 20,535 tons, armament of twelve 11in (280mm) guns in six twin turrets, twelve 5.9in (150mm) guns in single mountings and sixteen 3.4in (88mm) guns in single mountings, and a speed of 19.5 knots.

Another unit of the 'Nassau' class, the *Westfalen* was typified by armour protection in the form of an 11.4in (290mm) belt, 11in (280mm) turrets, 12in (305mm) conning tower and 3.15in (80mm) deck. The ships were shorter and beamier than the *Dreadnought*, possessed a more old-fashioned propulsion arrangement, were less well armed, and had a poor main armament disposition with only two centreline and four 'wing' turrets that limited the broadside to eight guns.

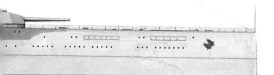

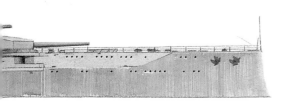

The completion of the *Dreadnought* gave the UK an early lead in the 'dreadnought race' within the 'naval race'. From the end of the first decade of the twentieth century, the pace of naval rearmament increased in direct proportion to the decrease in international relations as the UK's rapid start was now matched by developments in other countries. The first evidence of this world-wide response to the British lead was the commissioning of the 'Nassau' class ships in 1909 and 1910, and then of the two 'South Carolina' class battleships for the US Navy with a main armament of eight 12in (305 mm) guns in four centreline turrets. Further 'dreadnoughts' were: the two 'Minas Gerais' class ships built in the UK for Brazil; the two 'Delaware' class ships for the USA with ten 12in guns in five centreline turrets; the four ships of the 'Helgoland' class for Germany with twelve 12in (305mm) main guns in six twin turrets disposed as in the 'Nassau' class, the single ship of the 'Neptune' class for the UK with an armament of ten 12in main guns in five two-guns turrets installed as three (including a superfiring after pair) on the centreline and echeloned 'wing' turrets for the possibility of a 10-gun broadside, the two 'Colossus' class ships for the UK similar to the 'Hercules' class but with only one tripod mast; the two ships of the 'Florida' class for the USA as an improved version of the 'Delaware' class with rearranged cage masts and turbine propulsion on four shafts rather than triple-expansion engines on three shafts; the two ships of the 'Kawachi' class for Japan with an armament of twelve 12in main guns disposed as in the 'Helgoland' class, the two ships of the 'Wyoming' class for the USA with a main armament of twelve 12in guns of a longer design in six twin-gun centreline turrets installed as a superfiring pair forward and two superfiring pairs aft; the four ships of the 'Viribus Unitis' class for Austria-Hungary with an armament of twelve 12in main guns in four triple turrets located in fore and after superfiring pairs; the six ships of the 'Kaiser' class for Germany with an armament of ten 12in guns in five twin turrets located as three on the centreline (with the two after units in a superfiring arrangement) and two echeloned 'wing' turrets; the single ship of the 'Dante Alighieri' class for Italy with an armament of twelve 12in main guns in four triple turrets on the centreline; the three smallest-ever 'dreadnoughts' of the 'España' class for Spain with an armament of eight 12in main guns in four twin turrets located as two on the centreline and two in echeloned 'wing' positions; the four ships

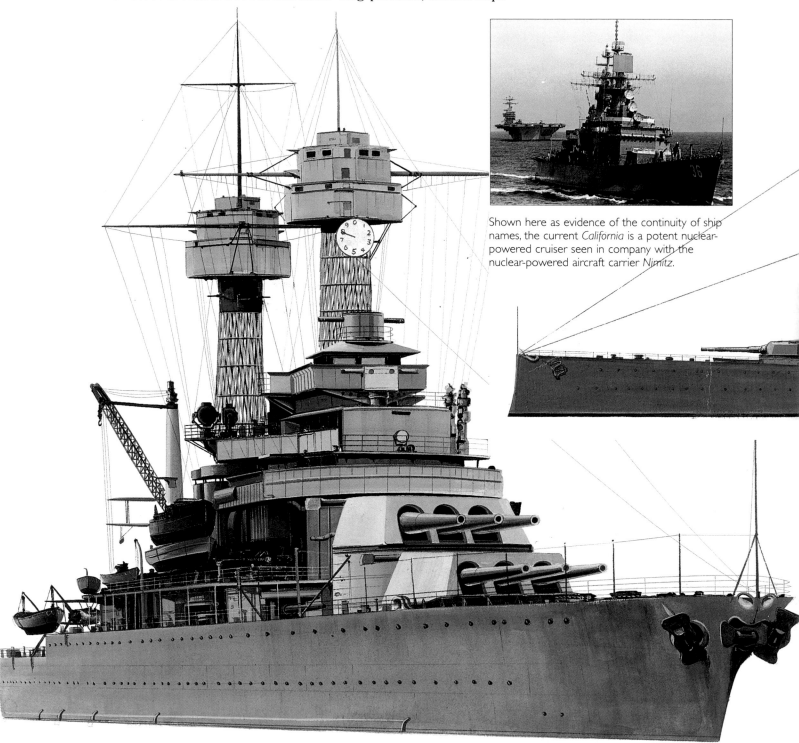

Shown here as evidence of the continuity of ship names, the current *California* is a potent nuclear-powered cruiser seen in company with the nuclear-powered aircraft carrier *Nimitz*.

Completed shortly after World War I and seen here in 1920, the *Hood* was reckoned to be the greatest and most beautiful capital ship of its time. The type was a battle-cruiser based on an enlarged version of the 'Queen Elizabeth' class battleship design to counter the Germans' planned 'Mackensen' class battle-cruisers, and with a full-load displacement of 42,500 tons and speed of 32 knots, it carried an armament of eight 15in (381mm) guns in four twin turrets backed by twelve 5.5in (140mm) guns in single mountings.

of the 'Courbet' class for France with an armament of twelve 12in main guns in four triple turrets installed on the centreline in forward and aft superfiring pairs; the four ships of the 'König' class for Germany with an armament of ten 12in (305mm) main guns in five twin turrets located on the centreline; the single 'Rio de Janeiro' class ship built for Argentina but taken over by the UK with an armament of no fewer than fourteen 12in main guns in seven twin turrets located as five on the centreline (a superfiring pair forward and three aft including one superfiring pair) and two echeloned 'wing' turrets; the two ships of the 'Rivadavia' class for Argentina built in the USA with a main armament of twelve 12in main guns in six twin turrets located on the

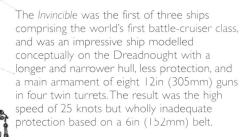

The *Invincible* was the first of three ships comprising the world's first battle-cruiser class, and was an impressive ship modelled conceptually on the Dreadnought with a longer and narrower hull, less protection, and a main armament of eight 12in (305mm) guns in four twin turrets. The result was the high speed of 25 knots but wholly inadequate protection based on a 6in (152mm) belt.

One of the definitive American 'super-dreadnought' classes, the two-ship 'Tennessee' class (here epitomised by the *California*) was an improved version of the 'New Mexico' class with two thinner funnels and a hull line clear of gun ports. The ship has the type of cage masts typical of American capital ships of the period, and its details included a full-load displacement of 33,190 tons, length of 624ft 6in (190.3m), armament of twelve 14in (356mm) guns in two pairs of superfiring triple turrets, fourteen 5in (127mm) guns in single mountings, four 3in (76mm) guns in single mountings and two 21in (533mm) torpedo tubes, protection in the form of a 13.5in (353mm) belt, 13in (330mm) barbettes, 18in (457mm) turrets, 16in (406mm) conning tower and 3.5in (89mm) deck, propulsion in the form of turbo-electric drive delivering 26,800hp (19,880kW) to four shafts for a speed of 21 knots, and complement of 1,085.

centreline and including superfiring forward and after pairs, the four ships of the Russian 'Gangut' class with an armament of twelve 12in main guns in four triple turrets located on the centreline; the two ships of the 'Caio Duilio' class for Italy with a main armament of thirteen 12in main guns in three triple and two twin turrets on the centreline with the twin turrets firing over the forward and after triple turrets; the two ships of the 'Conte di Cavour' class for Italy with basically the same armament as the 'Caio Duilio' class ships; and the three ships of the 'Imperatritsa Maria' class for Russia with a similar main armament to the 'Gangut' class ships but in a revised layout, thicker protection, a heavier secondary armament of eighteen 5.1in (130mm) guns in place of sixteen 4.7in (120mm) guns, and reduced speed and range as the ships were designed for service exclusively within the confines of the Black Sea.

The same period saw the spread, although not to so large an extent, of the battle-cruiser concept. In the UK the three ships of the 'Invincible' class were followed by the single ship of the 'Von der Tann' class for Germany with an armament of eight 11in (280mm) main guns in four twin turrets located as two on the centreline and the other two in echeloned 'wing'

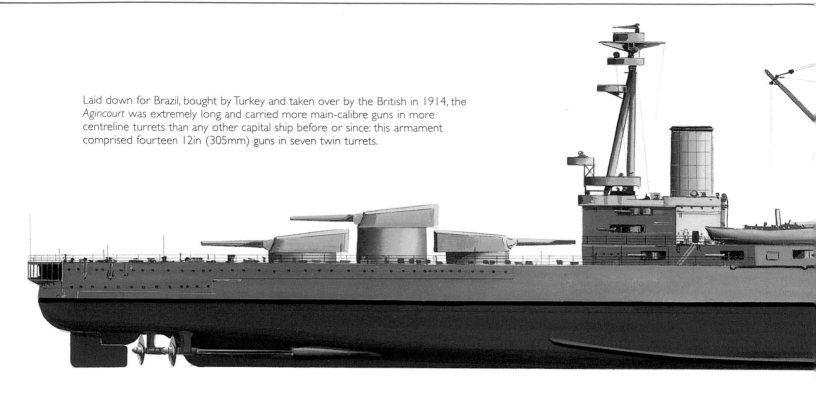

Laid down for Brazil, bought by Turkey and taken over by the British in 1914, the *Agincourt* was extremely long and carried more main-calibre guns in more centreline turrets than any other capital ship before or since: this armament comprised fourteen 12in (305mm) guns in seven twin turrets.

positions. By comparison with the British battle-cruisers, the German ship had a lower combination of freeboard and superstructure (which made it difficult to secure a good range figure), better armour protection and, for the first time in German practice, a propulsion arrangement based on two sets of steam turbines driving four shafts for high speed and great reliability. The British followed the 'Invincible' class with the 'Indefatigable' class of three ships that differed from their predecessors mainly in the greater echeloning of their 'wing' turrets, making possible an eight- rather than six-gun broadside. The Germans countered with the two ships of the 'Moltke' class to an enlarged 'Von der Tann' design and with a fifth 11in (280mm) twin turret in a superfiring after position for a total of ten such weapons. The single ship of the 'Seydlitz' class that followed was basically an improved 'Moltke' class unit with the same armament on a longer and narrower hull for improved speed and better sea-keeping qualities. The final vessels of the pure 'dreadnought' type of battle-cruiser were the three ships of the 'Derrflinger' class for Germany, which differed quite significantly from the 'Moltke' and 'Seydlitz' class ships in being flush-decked and in having their eight 12in (305mm) main guns in twin turrets located in superfiring pairs

A fine example of a late-generation armoured cruiser that verged on the pre-dreadnought battleship, the Japanese *Ibuki* of 1904 was a member of a two-ship 'Kurama' class and was the first Japanese ship completed with turbine propulsion. The full-load displacement was 17,200 tons, the armament was four 12in (305mm) guns in two twin turrets complemented by eight 8in (203mm) guns in single mountings, the protection was based on a 7in (178mm) belt, and a speed of 21.5 knots was achieved on the 24,000hp (17,895kW) delivered to two shafts.

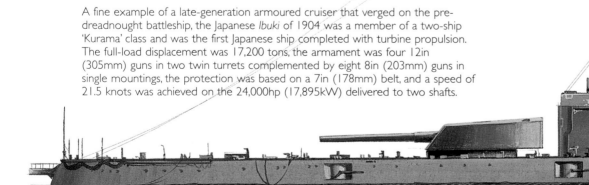

forward and aft of the superstructure, which contained the considerably enhanced secondary battery of twelve 5.9in (150mm) guns.

In the last stages of the 'dreadnought' era's first stage, the building race between the UK and Germany was complemented by a technological race in which each side sought to create successive classes of capital ship in which each succeeding class offered advantages over its predecessor. Thus the Germans, who had initially been content to rival the British 12in (305mm) gun with their 11in (280mm) weapon firing a lighter shell at a higher muzzle velocity for a flatter and therefore more aimable trajectory for roughly comparable armour-penetration capability, soon planned the switch to a 12in weapon firing an 893lb (405kg) shell to a maximum range in the order of 21,000yds (19,200m) for increased penetrative effect at longer range.

Anticipating such a move by the Germans, the British had planned a development of the 'dreadnought' into the 'super-dreadnought' type of battleship with a primary armament of 13.5in (343mm) guns. This weapon fired a larger shell than the 12in (305mm) weapon and at a lower muzzle velocity, resulting in more than adequate hitting power at long range in combination with greater accuracy and lower barrel erosion, the last factor providing a significant increase in barrel life. The first result of this process was the 'Orion' class of four ships, which introduced the new gun in five twin turrets located on the centreline (superfiring pairs of turrets fore and aft with a singleton turret amidships), increased the height as well as the thickness of the armour belt, and despite a significant increase in displacement was able to attain a higher speed than the *Dreadnought* as the result of its improved propulsion arrangement, in which four steam turbines delivered 27,000hp (20,130kW) to four shafts for a speed of 21 knots.

The British capitalised on the availability of the new 13.5in gun by adopting it for a series of battleship and battle-cruiser classes. Among the battleships were the four ships of the 'King George V' class with the same basic armament but an improved pattern of main gun; the four ships of the 'Iron Duke' class with the same main armament as the 'King George V' class but with the improved secondary armament of twelve 6in (152mm) guns in place of sixteen 4in (102mm) guns supplemented – for the first time in a

Below left: Lead unit of a three-ship class of *Panzerschiffe* known in the English-speaking world as pocket battleships, the *Deutschland* was completed in 1933 as a long-range commerce-raiding ship that could outrun anything that it could not outfight, and outfight anything that it could not outrun. With a full-load displacement of 15,900 tons and length of 610ft 3in (186.0m), the ship carried an armament of six 11in (280mm) guns in two triple turrets, eight 5.9in (150mm) guns, three 3.4in (88mm) anti-aircraft guns and eight 21in (533mm) torpedo tubes.

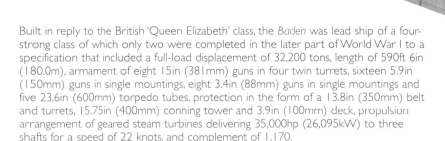

Built in reply to the British 'Queen Elizabeth' class, the *Baden* was lead ship of a four-strong class of which only two were completed in the later part of World War I to a specification that included a full-load displacement of 32,200 tons, length of 590ft 6in (180.0m), armament of eight 15in (381mm) guns in four twin turrets, sixteen 5.9in (150mm) guns in single mountings, eight 3.4in (88mm) guns in single mountings and five 23.6in (600mm) torpedo tubes, protection in the form of a 13.8in (350mm) belt and turrets, 15.75in (400mm) conning tower and 3.9in (100mm) deck, propulsion arrangement of geared steam turbines delivering 35,000hp (26,095kW) to three shafts for a speed of 22 knots, and complement of 1,170.

British battleship class – with anti-aircraft armament in the form of two 3in (76mm) high-angle guns; the single ship of the 'Reshadieh' class built for Turkey but taken over by the UK as the *Erin* with the same basic armament as the 'Iron Duke' class; and the single ship of the 'Admiral Latorre' class built for Chile but taken over by the UK as the *Canada* with a primary armament of ten 14in (356mm) guns in the same dispositions as the British ships with 13.5in (343mm) guns.

The first battle-cruisers with 13.5in guns were the three ships of the 'Lion' class, which were known as the 'splendid cats' and were the largest warships yet planned when they were laid down in 1912 and 1913 with a full-load displacement of 29,680 tons and a length of 700ft 0in (213.36m). The main armament comprised eight 13.5in weapons in four centreline turrets, of which the forward two were installed as a superfiring pair, and this was complemented by a secondary armament of sixteen 4 in (102mm) guns. Protection was provided by armour up to 10in (254mm) thick, and the

Completed in the late 1920s and seen here in 1930, the *Norfolk* was designed as the lead ship of a four-strong class of heavy cruisers of which only two were completed to a standard that included a displacement of 9,925 tons, length of 630ft 0in (192.0m), armament of eight 8in (203mm) guns in four twin turrets, eight 4in (102mm) anti-aircraft guns in four twin turrets, sixteen 2pdr anti-aircraft guns in two octuple mountings, eight 0.5in (12.7mm) machine guns in two quadruple mountings and eight 21in (533mm) torpedo tubes in two quadruple mountings.

propulsion arrangement comprised four sets of steam turbines delivering 73,800hp (55,025kW) to four shafts for a speed of 27 knots. The *Tiger*, planned as the fourth unit of the class, was completed slightly later to a design that resulted from a measure of revision in light of British knowledge of the Japanese 'Kongo' class, of which four were being built in the UK. The *Tiger* therefore appeared with the improved secondary armament of twelve 6in (152mm) guns and slightly greater beam and displacement to allow an enlargement and reorganisation of the machinery spaces to allow the delivery of 108,000hp (80,525kW) to four shafts for a speed of 20 knots. Detractors of the battle-cruiser's protective arrangements felt that too much offensive power and performance had been built into the 'splendid cats', but

it is worth emphasising that at the Battle of Jutland in May 1916, the *Tiger* took hits from 21 shells (including 17 large-calibre) without suffering major damage, and was repaired in less than one month.

The major increase in operational capability represented by the 'Orion' class, together with her battleship and battle-cruiser successors, meant that other navies had to respond to the 'super-dreadnought' concept by adopting larger-calibre main guns, improved defensive measures (secondary armament and armour) and, where they had not already done so, a centreline disposition for the main armament.

First off the mark was Japan with the four battle-cruisers of the 'Kongo' class, of which the lead ship was built in the UK largely so that Japan could become accustomed to the latest design and construction techniques used by the British. The design was derived from that for the Turkish 'Reshadieh' class battleship and resulted in the most powerful battle-cruiser of its time, considerably improving on the standards set by the 'splendid cats' in terms of protection (with a longer, deeper and thicker belt closed off at the ends by armour bulkheads as well as considerable internal compartmentalisation) and gun power, which was based on a primary armament of

From front to back, this quartet of Japanese battleships photographed in the period leading up to World War II comprises the *Nagato*, *Kirishima*, *Ise* and *Hiuga*. Most noticeable are the enormous 'pagoda' foremast arrangements.

An 'armoured ship' or pocket battleship of the 'Deutschland' class, the *Admiral Scheer* was launched in April 1933 and completed in November 1934. During World War II the ship was used initially for anti-commerce raids into the Atlantic and Indian Oceans before being transferred to the Arctic coast of Norway in 1942 and then into the Baltic late in 1944. The ship was bombed at Kiel during April 1945 and then capsized.

eight 14in (356mm) guns in four twin turrets on the centreline with the forward pair in a superfiring installation, a secondary armament of sixteen 6in (152mm) guns and a tertiary armament of sixteen 3in (76mm) guns. With 64,000hp (47,720kW) delivered by four sets of steam turbines to four shafts, the ships had a speed of 27.5 knots.

The battle-cruisers were matched by four battleships, namely the vessels of the two-ship 'Fuso' and 'Ise' classes that were originally to have been four units of the 'Fuso' class. Entirely designed and built in Japan with Japanese weapons and equipment, the ships confirmed the full arrival of the Japanese navy to world class status, for the 'Fuso' class battleships outgunned the contemporary 'Texas' and 'Oklahoma' class battleships of the US Navy and were basically equal to the 'Pennsylvania' class battleships. The Japanese ships were less well protected than these American counterparts and carried their main armament in twin rather than triple turrets: the main battery of 12 guns required six turrets rather than the American ships' four turrets, which required additional length. The resulting finer hull line, however, which translated into higher speed: 23 knots was attained on the 40,000hp (29,825kW) delivered by the steam turbines to four shafts. Other details of the 'Fuso' class battleships included a secondary armament of sixteen 6in (152mm) guns and a maximum armour thickness of 13.75in (349mm).

Although planned as standard 'Fuso' class ships, the last two units were completed to a standard that differed from that of the 'Fuso' class sufficiently for them to be recategorised in their own 'Ise' class. The main changes were the relocation of the two amidships twin gun turrets as a superfiring pair, and the replacement of the 6in guns of the secondary battery by more modern 5.5in (140mm) weapons.

The USA also opted for the 14in (356mm) main gun, but avoided the concept of the battle-cruiser, which ran contrary to American notions. The Americans therefore opted for maximum firepower and maximum protection even if this meant a sacrifice in speed to typical battleship levels. The first of the US Navy's ships built to the 'super-dreadnought' standard were the two vessels of the 'Texas' class, with the typical US flushdecked design derived from that of the beamy 'Wyoming' class and originally designed for a primary armament of fifteen 12in (305mm) guns in five centreline triple turrets. Then the advent of the 'Orion' class forced a rethink

The *Bismarck* was the lead ship of the two-strong class whose other unit was the Tirpitz, and these were the only German battleships completed in the lifetime of the Third Reich. The ships were visually impressive and exercised a horrid fascination on the minds of the British Admiralty despite the fact that they had an unfortunate propulsion arrangement, possessed a considerable weight of armour that was not particularly well disposed, and had a cluttered deck arrangement in its combination of secondary and tertiary gun batteries (due to the German navy's lack of dual-purpose guns and fire-control systems). The specification for the Bismarck included a full-load displacement 50,900 tons, length of 813ft 8in (248.0m), armament of eight 15in (380mm) guns in four twin turrets, twelve 5.9in (150mm) guns in six twin turrets, eight 4.1in (105mm) anti-aircraft guns in four twin mountings and sixteen 37mm anti-aircraft guns in single mountings, protection in the form of a 12.6in (320mm) belt, 14.2in (360mm) turrets, 13.8in (350mm) conning tower and 4.7in (120mm) deck, propulsion in the form of geared steam turbines delivering 138,000hp (102,895kW) to three shafts for a speed of 29 knots, and complement of 2,400.

on the US Navy, which then opted for a primary armament of ten 14in guns in five centreline twin turrets (superfiring pairs forward and aft with a singleton unit amidships), and a secondary armament of twenty-one 5in (127mm) guns. Protection was provided by well-arranged armour up to 14in (356mm) thick, but a retrograde step – forced on the Americans by the inability of US turbine manufacturers to meet the exacting official requirement – was the use of reciprocating machinery delivering 28,100hp (20,950kW) to two shafts for a speed of 21 knots.

Further development along the same lines resulted in the two ships of the 'Nevada' class, which carried basically the same armament as the 'Texas' class battleships but were considerably better protected (firing trials against an old battleship revealed that light and medium armour were no protection against large-calibre shells). The Americans therefore adopted the 'all or nothing' principle for armour protection, demanding that all armour protecting the ship's vital spaces and other essential areas should be proof against penetration by large-calibre shells fired at typical ranges, and that other areas should receive no protection at all. This meant that the Americans now began to produce battleships with excellent firepower and protection although this inevitably meant a slight sacrifice in theoretical performance to typical battleship levels, and effectively ended any possibility of American battle-cruisers. The two ships of the 'Nevada' class

The *Bismarck* rides through the North Atlantic swell in May 1941, somewhat low in the bows after suffering damage and taking on water, in the aftermath of the Battle of the Denmark Strait in which its accurate long-range gunfire sank the Hood, still the pride of the Royal Navy despite its age and lack of adequate horizontal protection against plunging fire.

had armour up to 18in (457mm) thick. The propulsion arrangement was now based on steam turbines, in this instance delivering 26,500hp (19,760kW) to two shafts for a speed of 20.5 knots.

The final expression of the American 'super-dreadnought' concept was to be found in the five ships of the two-ship 'Pennsylvania' and three-ship 'New Mexico' classes completed in the early part of World War I and while the USA was still a neutral nation. The 'Pennsylvania' class design was basically an improved version of the 'Nevada' class with the earlier type's combination of two triple and two twin superfiring turrets replaced by four triple turrets in superfiring pairs. The same armament of 12 main-calibre guns was carried in the contemporary 'Fuso' class for the Japanese navy, although in

Above: The most famous of the three 'Deutschland' class 'pocket battleships', the *Admiral Graf Spee* was launched in June 1934 and completed in January 1936, and was scuttled off Montevideo in December 1939 after suffering only modest damage in the Battle of the River Plate, against a force of three British cruisers, at the end of a commerce-raiding cruise in which the German ship had sunk or captured nine British merchant ships.

Only two of the four 'Richelieu' class battleships, planned in the late 1930s as the major surface fighting element of the French navy were completed. This is the *Richelieu*, seen in partially completed state off Dakar in French West Africa during 1941 after the ship's hasty departure from France in June 1940. The ship's details included a full-load displacement of 47,500 tons, length of 813ft 0in (247.8m), armament of eight 15in (380mm) guns in two quadruple turrets, nine 6in (152mm) guns in three triple turrets, twelve 3.9in (100mm) anti-aircraft guns in six twin turrets and sixteen 37mm anti-aircraft guns in eight twin mountings, protection in the form of a 12.9in (327mm) belt, 15.9in (404mm) barbettes, 16.9in (430mm) turrets, 13.3in (340mm) conning tower and 6.7in (170mm) deck, propulsion in the form of geared steam turbines delivering 155,000hp (115,570kW) to four shafts for a speed of 30 knots, and complement of 1,550. The design was a development of that evolved for the smaller 'Dunkerque' battleships, with better protection and heavier armament based on a primary battery of eight guns in two superfiring quadruple turrets forward of the superstructure and a secondary battery of nine guns in three triple turrets abaft the superstructure.

Below: The *Gneisenau* was the second of the two 'Scharnhorst' class battle-cruisers completed in Germany in the late 1930s as highly impressive ships with a full-load displacement of 34,900 tons, length of 754ft 0in (229.8m), armament of nine 11in (280mm) guns in three triple turrets, twelve 5.6in (150mm) guns in six twin turrets, fourteen 4.1in (105mm) anti-aircraft guns in seven twin mountings and sixteen 37mm anti-aircraft guns in eight twin mountings.

this instance the guns were carried in six twin turrets that demanded an additional 65ft (19.8m) of length and additional 15,000hp (11,185kW) of power for a speed 2 knots higher on the same displacement.

The 'New Mexico' class design was a much improved version of the 'Pennsylvania' class design with basically the same armament, although the main guns were mounted in separate sleeves to allow individual rather than collective elevation and the secondary guns were installed one deck higher. The main improvements in the class were a more refined hull, which introduced an elegant clipper bow and a bulbous forefoot, increased internal compartmentalisation for greater survivability and, in the New Mexico, the first installation in a capital ship of a turbo-electric propulsion arrangement in which two steam turbines powered electrical generators supplying current to the four electric motors that delivered 27,500hp (20,505kW) to four shafts for a speed of 21 knots. Although bulky and heavy, the turbo-electric drive was highly economical and a decided asset to manoeuvrability.

The French had lagged somewhat behind in the 'dreadnought race', and it was only in May 1912 that the first of three 'Provence' class 'super-dreadnought' battleships was laid down. This was based on the hull design of the 'Courbet' class 'dreadnought' battleship to save in design time, but

Second of a two-strong battle-cruiser class whose other unit was the lead ship *Scharnhorst*, the *Gneisenau* was launched in December 1936 and completed in May 1938. In the early months of World War II the two ships undertook a raid into the North Atlantic before being damaged by the fire of the British battle-cruiser *Renown* off Norway in April 1940; the *Gneisenau* later sank the British aircraft carrier *Glorious* and was damaged when the destroyer *Glowworm* rammed it. Further damage resulted from a torpedo hit from the submarine Clyde in June 1940, and after this more serious damage had been repaired, the two German battle-cruisers made a further sortie into the North Atlantic during the first three months of 1941 before returning to Brest. The two battle-cruisers, together with the heavy cruiser Prinz Eugen, made a classic run up the English Channel to Germany in February 1942, suffering mine damage near the end of the trip and then bomb damage while in dock at Kiel. The ship was decommissioned in July 1942, and expended as a blockship at Gdynia in March 1945.

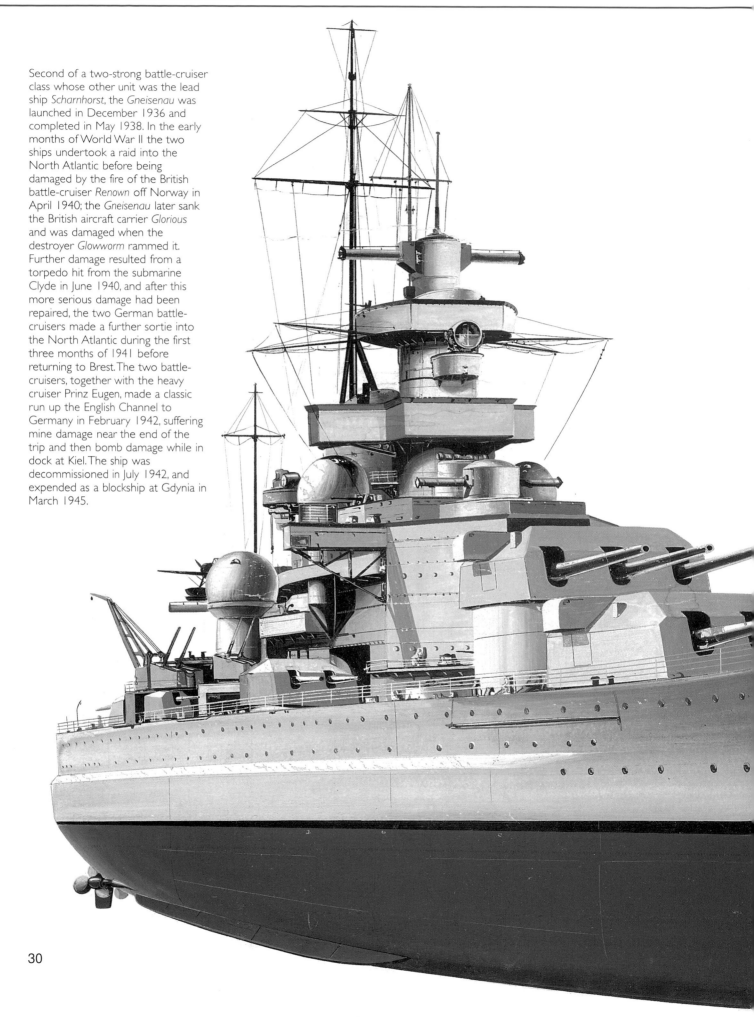

made a new departure for the French as it was armed with ten 13.4in (340mm) main guns in five centreline twin turrets (superfiring pairs forward and aft with a singleton unit amidships).

Meanwhile, the British had been pushing ahead with their next development in response to the latest German ships. These were now armed with 12in (305mm) main guns, which the British deemed to be comparable in operational terms to their 13.5in (343mm) weapons as the German guns had a higher muzzle velocity for greater range and penetrative power in combination with a flatter trajectory that made for greater accuracy. The British response was the 15in (381mm) gun designed to provide a significant measure of advantage over the German 12in weapon and also the 14in (356mm) gun that was entering service with other navies. The 15in gun proved itself an excellent weapon, with a 1,920lb (871kg) shell fired at a muzzle velocity of 2,655ft (809m) per second to attain a range of 35,000yds (32,005m); moreover, the gun soon revealed the additional advantage of suffering little barrel wear even in protracted firing, and this offered excellent economics. The additional weight of this larger gun, its mounting and the turret required to carry them in a twin installation

Operation 'Cerberus'

OPERATION 'Cerberus' was the German designation for the dash up the English Channel between 11 and 13 February 1942 by three major German warships, namely the battle-cruisers Scharnhorst and Gneisenau with the heavy cruiser Prinz Eugen, all of which had arrived in the Breton port of Brest after commerce-raiding cruises into the Atlantic, resulting in the sinking of 22 British ships. Brest had since suffered a protracted series of British bombing raids, including one on April 10 during which the Gneisenau had been hit by four bombs and another on July 22 in the course of which the Scharnhorst had been hit by five bombs. Although Grossadmiral Erich Raeder, commander-in-chief of the German navy, was convinced that the ships should be left at Brest for further raids into the Atlantic, Adolf Hitler demanded that they be brought home to Germany as insurance against the expected British invasion of Norway, and it was decided that a high-speed dash under massive fighter protection offered the best chance of breaking through the inevitable British attacks. The squadron sailed at 22.45 on 11 February, and caught the British so completely by suprise that it was not until 11.30 on 12 February that the German squadron was positively identified and marked for attack. By this time the German units were off Boulogne, and managed to fight through determined but unco-ordinated British air and surface attacks to reach Wilhelmshaven (Scharnhorst) and Brunsbuttel (Gneisenau and Prinz Eugen) on the morning of 13 February. The Gneisenau was slightly damaged after hitting one mine, but the Scharnhorst was more seriously affected by striking two mines. British aircraft losses were heavy as a result of the ships' massive anti-aircraft armaments and the superb fighter escort provided by the Luftwaffe. The Scharnhorst was repaired and re-entered combat in September 1943, when the ship bombarded Spitsbergen, but in December of the same year, the British battleship Duke of York and an accompanying cruiser and destroyer force caught up with the German battle-cruiser off the North Cape. The resulting battle ended with the sinking of the Scharnhorst and the loss of 1,803 German officers and men.

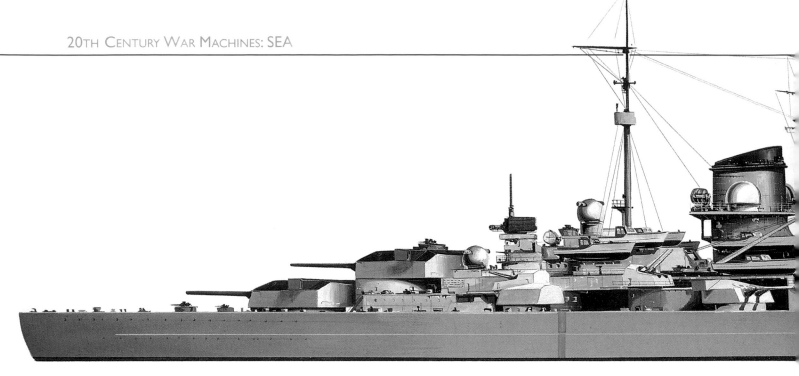

demanded a ship somewhat larger than had become the norm. The result was the 'Queen Elizabeth' class of five ships based on a hull design adapted from that of the 'Iron Duke' class, with an additional 2,500 tons of displacement provided by a lengthening of 20ft (6.1m) and a widening of 6in (0.15m). Another development was the introduction, for the first time anywhere in the world, of boilers that were exclusively fired by oil. The elimination of the bunkerage previously required for coal saved a considerable amount of weight, and this was used to improve the protection, which was based on a deeper belt up to 13in (330mm) thick, five armoured decks that yielded a greater overall thickness than the individually thicker decks of the 'Iron Duke' class ships, and two longitudinal bulkheads to provide improved underwater protection. On this massive hull, with a full-load displacement of 33,020 tons and capable of 23 knots on the 75,000hp (55,920kW) delivered to four shafts, the 'Queen Elizabeth' class battleships carried a main armament of eight 15in main guns in four centreline turrets (superfiring pairs forward and aft) and a secondary armament of sixteen 6in (152mm) guns.

The 'Queen Elizabeth' class ships opened the definitive period in the development of the 'all big gun' battleship, for further progress was now based not so much on any conceptual developments but rather on increased

Below: The *Tirpitz* was the sister-ship of the *Bismarck*, from which it differed only in details such as a full-load displacement of 52,600 tons, length of 823ft 6in (251.0m) and the addition of eight 21in (533mm) torpedo tubes. The ship was launched in April 1939 and completed in February 1941, and its sole success in World War II (apart from tying down large numbers of British capital ships) was a bombardment of Spitsbergen in September 1943. The ship was damaged by British midget submarine attack later in that month, damaged by aircraft attack in April 1944 (with the loss of 122 men after being hit by 14 bombs), rendered unseaworthy by further aircraft bombs in September 1944, and finally sunk in November 1944 when the ship capsized with the loss of 902 men after being hit by 'Tallboy' bombs.

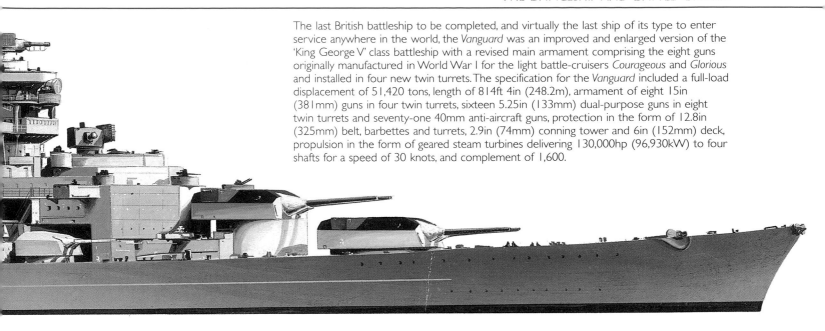

The last British battleship to be completed, and virtually the last ship of its type to enter service anywhere in the world, the *Vanguard* was an improved and enlarged version of the 'King George V' class battleship with a revised main armament comprising the eight guns originally manufactured in World War I for the light battle-cruisers *Courageous* and *Glorious* and installed in four new twin turrets. The specification for the *Vanguard* included a full-load displacement of 51,420 tons, length of 814ft 4in (248.2m), armament of eight 15in (381mm) guns in four twin turrets, sixteen 5.25in (133mm) dual-purpose guns in eight twin turrets and seventy-one 40mm anti-aircraft guns, protection in the form of 12.8in (325mm) belt, barbettes and turrets, 2.9in (74mm) conning tower and 6in (152mm) deck, propulsion in the form of geared steam turbines delivering 130,000hp (96,930kW) to four shafts for a speed of 30 knots, and complement of 1,600.

size for the greater power and thicker (as well as better disposed) armour that provided a higher speed and improved protection, in combination with a centreline main armament arrangement often involving larger-calibre guns, a better secondary armament arrangement in which casemated single-purpose guns were generally replaced by turreted weapons that were often of the dual-purpose type, and a tertiary armament arrangement designed to supplement the secondary armament with a dedicated anti-aircraft fit to provide protection against the warplane, which became the primary threat to the capital ship after the end of World War I.

This was still in the future, however, as countries started to respond to the British lead exemplified by the battleships of the 'Queen Elizabeth' class and then exploited by the five ships of the 'Royal Sovereign' class, which was a further development based on the hull design of the 'Iron Duke' class with a primary armament of eight 15in (381mm) guns in four twin superfiring turrets (forward and aft) and a secondary armament of fourteen 6in (152mm) guns. Revisions were incorporated to improve the design's steadiness, to improve protection by an increase in the depth of the belt, the enhancement of the internal underwater protection and, in the last ship of the class, the introduction of the external 'bulges' that became standard in the 1920s and 1930s. With a speed of 22 knots on the 42,650hp (31,800kW)

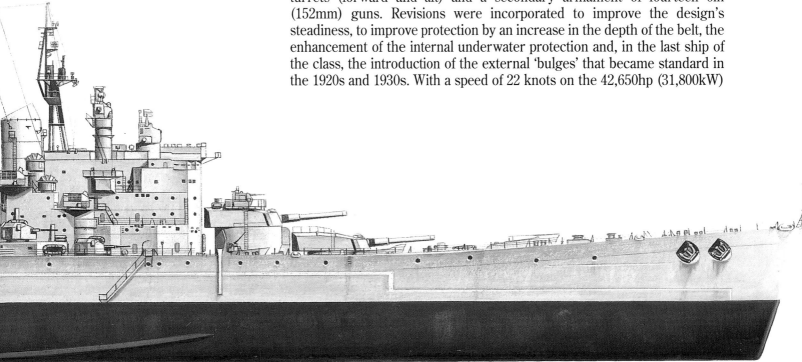

Eventually numbering four out of a planned six ships, the
'Iowa' class battleships were without doubt the most capable
battleships ever designed, even though the two completed units
of the Japanese 'Yamato' class were larger and more heavily armed.
Exemplified here by the *Iowa*, the class carried basically the same
armament as its predecessors but was better protected on a longer hull
whose high length/beam ratio allowed the attainment of speeds never exceeded
by other battleships. The specification of the ships as completed included a full-load
displacement of 55,250 tons, length of 887ft 3in (270.4m), armament of nine 16in
(406mm) guns in three triple turrets, twenty 5in (127mm) dual-purpose guns in ten twin
turrets and eighty 40mm anti-aircraft guns, protection in the form of a 12.2in (310mm) belt, 17.3in
(440mm) barbettes, 17in (432mm) turrets, 17.5in (445mm) conning tower and 5.5in (140mm) decks,
propulsion in the form of geared steam turbines delivering 212,000hp (158,065kW) to four shafts for a
speed of 33 knots, and complement of 2,750. The ships were retained after World War II for further
operational service in the Korean and Vietnam Wars, and were finally decommissioned only in the early 1990s after
having been updated to a considerably more potent form with provision for Tomahawk cruise and Harpoon anti-ship
missiles. The two photographs, taken in the late 1980s, show the *Iowa*'s forward main turrets – that on the left
in action and that on the right after suffering a turret explosion and fire.

delivered to four shafts, the 'Royal Sovereign' class battleships were for a time considered inferior to the 'Queen Elizabeth' class ships, but were in fact superior as a result of their improved protection and siting of secondary armament.

The battleships armed with 15in main guns were complemented by battle-cruiser equivalents, starting with the two ships of the 'Renown' class with a main armament of six 15in guns in three centreline twin turrets (a superfiring pair forward and a singleton unit aft), armour up to a maximum of 11in (280mm) but only 6in (152mm) on the belt, and a speed of 32.7 knots on the 126,300hp (94,170kW) delivered to four shafts. The last three British battle-cruisers of World War I were distinctly eccentric ships, reflecting Fisher's obsession with speed and firepower to the detriment of protection and, in this instance, his desire to undertake a landing, in collaboration with Russian forces, on the north German coast in the Baltic with the support of shallow-draught battle-cruisers. This resulted in the three ships of the 'Glorious' class. The first two of these were completed with a main armament of four 15in guns in two twin turrets and a secondary armament of eighteen 6in guns in six triple turrets, an armoured belt whose maximum

The *Ferre* is a British 'Daring' class destroyer of the Peruvian navy, which received two such ships in 1969. Manned and operated almost as light cruisers, the class numbered eight ships completed in the early 1950s with a full-load displacement of 3,580 tons, length of 390ft 0in (118.8m), armament of six 4.5in (114mm) dual-purpose guns in three twin turrets, up to six 40mm anti-aircraft guns in up to three twin mountings and one 'Squid' anti-submarine projector, propulsion in the form of geared steam turbines delivering 54,000hp (40,260kW) to two shafts for a speed of 34.75 knots, and complement of 330.

thickness was only 3in (76mm), and a speed of 32 knots on the 93,780hp (69,920kW) delivered to four shafts: they were a pair of magnificent but wholly impractical ships whose basic concept was taken to the limit, or indeed beyond it, by their half-sister *Furious* in which the main armament comprised two 18in (457mm) guns in single turrets and the secondary armament eleven 5.5in (140mm) guns. Before completion, the *Furious* was modified into a hybrid aircraft carrier with the forward main-gun turret replaced by a long flightdeck, and in 1918 the ship was revised as a true aircraft carrier, a standard to which the two half-sister ships were modified in the 1920s.

The German response to the British ships with 15in guns was the 'Baden' class projected at four units of which only two were completed. The design of this class reflected a change in German thinking from an original capital ship philosophy of gun power inferiority but protective superiority vis-à-vis British ships, to an equality of gun power and protection. This philosophy was posited on the new 15in gun developed by Krupp, which was in fact inferior to the British gun of the same calibre as it fired a lighter 1,653lb

Opposite top: One of three 'Tourville' or 'C67' class guided missile destroyers completed for the French navy in the mid-1970s, the *Tourville* is a multi-role destroyer optimised for the anti-submarine role with a full-load displacement of 5,745 tons, length of 501ft 0in (152.5m), armament of two 3.9in (100mm) dual-purpose guns in single turrets, six MM.38 Exocet anti-ship missiles, one Crotale octuple launcher for twenty-six surface-to-air missiles and one Malafon launcher for thirteen anti-submarine rockets, propulsion in the form of geared steam turbines delivering 54,400hp (40,560kW) to two shafts for a speed of 31 knots, and complement of 305.

Epitomised here by the *Zeeland*, the Dutch 'Holland' class of destroyers totalled four ships completed in the mid-1950s to a specification that included a full-load displacement of 2,765 tons, length of 371ft 0in (113.1m), armament of four 4.7in (120mm) guns in two twin turrets, one 40mm anti-aircraft gun and two 14.75in (375mm) anti-submarine mortars, propulsion in the form of geared steam turbines delivering 45,000hp (33,550kW) to two shafts for a speed of 32 knots, and complement of 250.

Below: Completed for the French navy in the late 1950s, the five destroyers of the 'Duperré' or 'T53' class were produced to a standard evolved from that of the 12 destroyers of the 'Surcouf' or 'T47' class and are epitomised here by the *Jaureguiberry*. The details of this important multi-role type included a full-load displacement of 3,740 tons, length of 422ft 0in (128.6m), armament of six 5in (127mm) dual-purpose guns in three twin turrets, six 57mm anti-aircraft guns in three twin mountings, two or four 20mm cannon in single mountings, one 14.75in (375mm) anti-submarine rocket launcher and six 21.7in (550mm) torpedo tubes in two triple mountings, propulsion in the form of geared steam turbines delivering 63,000hp (46,975kW) to two shafts for a speed of 34 knots, and complement of 345.

(750kg) shell at the lower muzzle velocity of 2,297ft (700m) per second to the shorter range of 22,200yds (20,300m) at an elevation of 16 degrees. Eight of these guns were located in four centreline twin turrets installed as superfiring pairs, and the secondary armament was sixteen 5.9in (150mm) guns in casemated mountings. The hull was basically an improved version of that developed for the 'König' class but with greater length and beam for a larger displacement and space for a more powerful propulsion arrangement, with three sets of steam turbines delivering 52,000shp (38,770kW) to three shafts for a speed of 22.25 knots.

German plans for the completion of the remaining two ships of the class, and also for the construction of other ships with 15in guns, were overtaken by the end of the war, but British assessment of these and other German ships after the war revealed that they were basically inferior to their British counterparts in structural integrity as well as in a number of operational features.

The end of World War I, brought about by the political, social, economic and military collapse of Germany and its Central Powers' allies, most

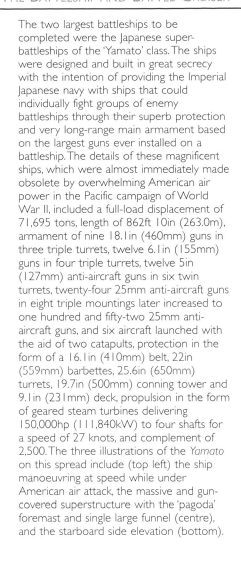

The two largest battleships to be completed were the Japanese super-battleships of the 'Yamato' class. The ships were designed and built in great secrecy with the intention of providing the Imperial Japanese navy with ships that could individually fight groups of enemy battleships through their superb protection and very long-range main armament based on the largest guns ever installed on a battleship. The details of these magnificent ships, which were almost immediately made obsolete by overwhelming American air power in the Pacific campaign of World War II, included a full-load displacement of 71,695 tons, length of 862ft 10in (263.0m), armament of nine 18.1in (460mm) guns in three triple turrets, twelve 6.1in (155mm) guns in four triple turrets, twelve 5in (127mm) anti-aircraft guns in six twin turrets, twenty-four 25mm anti-aircraft guns in eight triple mountings later increased to one hundred and fifty-two 25mm anti-aircraft guns, and six aircraft launched with the aid of two catapults, protection in the form of a 16.1in (410mm) belt, 22in (559mm) barbettes, 25.6in (650mm) turrets, 19.7in (500mm) conning tower and 9.1in (231mm) deck, propulsion in the form of geared steam turbines delivering 150,000hp (111,840kW) to four shafts for a speed of 27 knots, and complement of 2,500. The three illustrations of the *Yamato* on this spread include (top left) the ship manoeuvring at speed while under American air attack, the massive and gun-covered superstructure with the 'pagoda' foremast and single large funnel (centre), and the starboard side elevation (bottom).

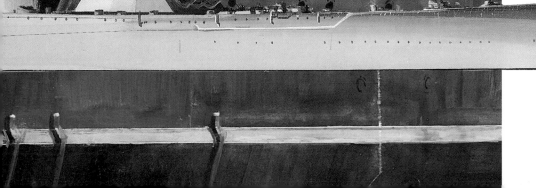

notably Austria-Hungary and Turkey, was a relief for the almost equally exhausted Allied powers, especially France and the UK. For a variety of reasons, none of these countries could consider large-scale naval development or construction in the years following World War I, and this left the USA and Japan to move up in the 'naval race'. The USA now felt itself compelled to operate a navy 'second to none' as a protector of its world-wide mercantile interests and main bastion of democracy, while Japan had grown enormously in power across the eastern Pacific during the war and now felt that parity with the USA was a realisable and indeed worthy objective that was reflected in the so-called 8-8' programme to build eight new battleships and eight battle-cruisers by the end of the 1920s. Moreover, despite its exhaustion the UK felt in the early 1920s that it could not allow its naval superiority to be challenged without any British response, and thus it appeared that a new 'naval race' might be in the making.

Efforts to prevent such a race, with its financial burdens and destabilising influences, resulted in the Washington Naval Conference of 1921-22 that resulted in a treaty signed in February 1922. This was a far-ranging document that sought to impose artificial limits on the tonnage of warships

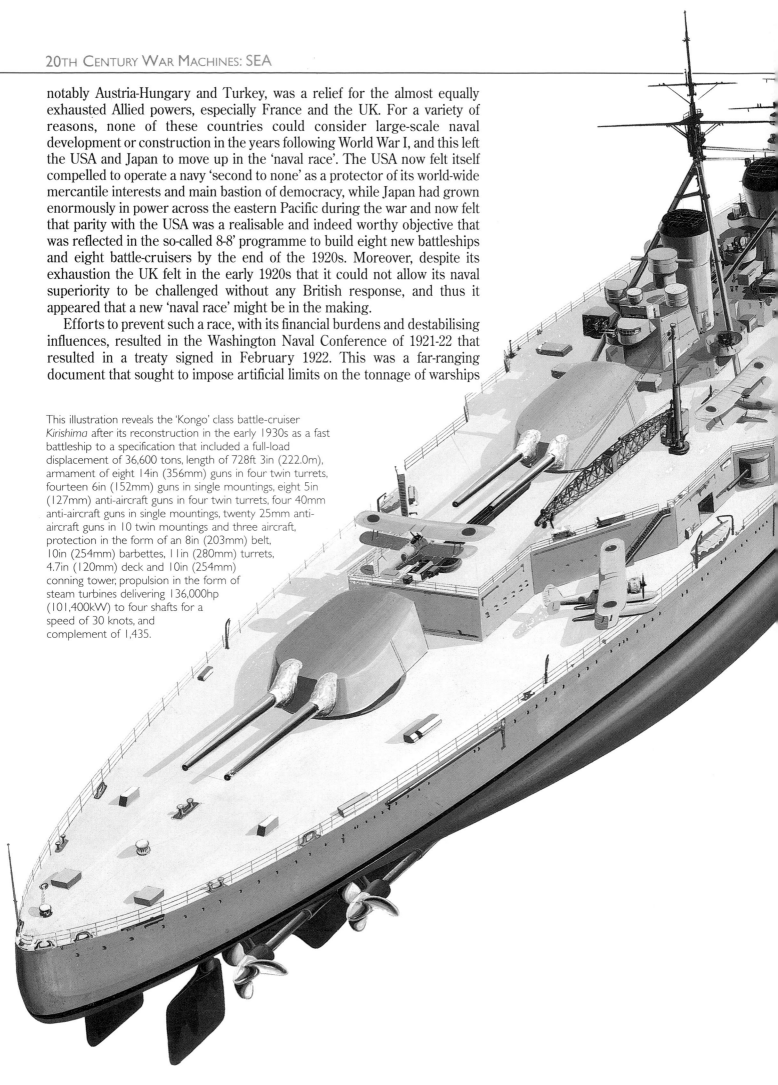

This illustration reveals the 'Kongo' class battle-cruiser *Kirishima* after its reconstruction in the early 1930s as a fast battleship to a specification that included a full-load displacement of 36,600 tons, length of 728ft 3in (222.0m), armament of eight 14in (356mm) guns in four twin turrets, fourteen 6in (152mm) guns in single mountings, eight 5in (127mm) anti-aircraft guns in four twin turrets, four 40mm anti-aircraft guns in single mountings, twenty 25mm anti-aircraft guns in 10 twin mountings and three aircraft, protection in the form of an 8in (203mm) belt, 10in (254mm) barbettes, 11in (280mm) turrets, 4.7in (120mm) deck and 10in (254mm) conning tower, propulsion in the form of steam turbines delivering 136,000hp (101,400kW) to four shafts for a speed of 30 knots, and complement of 1,435.

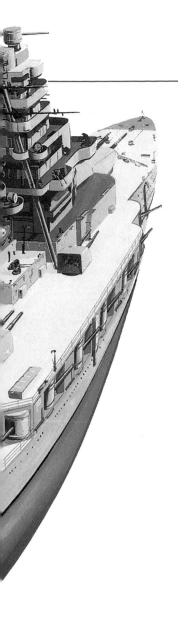

that could be built and on the calibre of the weapons that they might carry. In qualitative terms the treaty fixed 35,000 tons and 16in (406mm) as the maximum displacement and maximum gun calibre that might be used, and in quantitative terms it imposed limits so acute that an immediate result was the scrapping of many American, British and Japanese capital ships then under construction or being planned. These types, some of which were converted into aircraft carriers, included the American 43,200-ton 'South Dakota' class battleships with an armament of twelve 16in (406mm) guns and the 43,500-ton 'Lexington' class battle-cruisers with an armament of eight 16in guns; the British 48,400-ton 'G3' class battle-cruisers with an armament of nine 16in guns and the 48,500-ton 'N3' class battleships with an armament of nine 18in (457mm) guns; and the Japanese 40,640-ton 'Amagi' class battle-cruisers with an armament of ten 16in guns and the 40,570-ton 'Tosa' class battleships with an armament of ten 16in guns.

As well as the disruption caused by their politically inspired changes and limitations, capital ships' designers now had to come to terms with a number of changed technical factors. On the offensive side these were basically the revision of turrets and their guns to allow firing at higher elevation angles for the type of longer-range engagement that was now increasingly the norm, the replacement of casemated secondary-armament guns by turreted guns installed at a higher level for greater range and continued operability in a seaway, the adoption of director firing for the secondary armament, and the increased sophistication of the main armament's director firing system with a longer-base rangefinder for the maintenance of accuracy at longer ranges and a gyroscopic platform whose electric output was used to keep the guns in the same position relative to the horizon despite the ship's roll, thereby much enhancing the accuracy of fire to a given range.

On the defensive side, the designers had to come to grips with the changed protective requirements imposed by the potential arrival of projectiles at higher impact angles (shells fired at longer range and therefore descending at a more acute angle, and aircraft-dropped bombs arriving at a near-vertical angle). The latter threat demanded an increase in horizontal protection to resist the penetration of these high-angle weapons, although no loss of vertical protection could be entertained because of the continued threat of short-range fire, the torpedo and the mine. Early trials with bombs dropped by warplanes had been largely discounted because of their inaccuracy under all but artificial conditions, but the tendency to ignore the air-launched bomb and its effects was regretted in the early days of World War II (1939-45), when the bomb delivered with considerable accuracy by the dive-bomber became a decisive weapon that was matched later in the war by the bomb dropped by the level bomber. The fact that the threat of the warplane was not ignored, however, was shown by modest improvements in horizontal armour and the introduction of larger numbers

Spain's two 'Roger de Lauria' class destroyers, here epitomised by the lead ship, were completed in the late 1960s after having been laid down as the second and third units of the 'Oquendo' class that comprised only one ship, the other six units having been cancelled. The 'Roger de Lauria' class ships were completed with American weapons and electronics to a specification that included a full-load displacement of 3,785 tons, length of 391ft 6in (119.3m), armament of six 5in (127mm) dual-purpose guns in three twin turrets, six 12.75in (324mm) tubes in two triple mountings for lightweight anti-submarine torpedoes, two 21in (533mm) tubes for heavyweight anti-submarine torpedoes and one helicopter, propulsion in the form of geared steam turbines delivering 60,000hp (44,735kW) to two shafts for a speed of 31 knots, and complement of 320.

The triple turret and three 16in (406mm) Mk 7 Mod 0 guns carried by the 'Iowa' class battleships weighs 1,700 tons complete with its mounting, has a crew of 79, can fire at the rate of two rounds per minute per gun, and can fire its 2,700lb (1,225kg) armour-piercing projectile to a maximum range of 40,185yds (36,745m), or alternatively its 1,900lb (862kg) high-capacity projectile to a maximum range of 41,625yds (38,060m).

of dedicated anti-aircraft guns. The standard in the later part of World War I had generally been two 3in (76mm) or similar weapons, but during the 1920s the numbers of anti-aircraft guns were increased significantly in the forms of larger-calibre weapons for the engagement of high-flying attackers at longer ranges, and smaller-calibre weapons, often of the multiple type, for the creation of a barrage through which any low-level attacker would have to fly at shorter ranges. As the navies of the world and their designers were dealing with the limits imposed on them by the Washington Naval Treaty, the last of the World War I capital ships were being completed. The finest of these, and arguably the most beautiful, was the British battle-cruiser *Hood*, which resulted directly from the revelation in 1915 that the Germans were preparing a battle-cruiser design with 15in (381mm) main guns. The

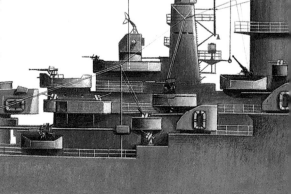

Admiralty decided to respond not with larger-calibre weapons, but rather with a battle-cruiser that combined superior speed, greater firepower than was available in the 'Renown' class ships and greater protection than was afforded in the 'splendid cats'. The result was a design that was in effect a 'Queen Elizabeth' class battleship with a longer and less thickly armoured hull containing a more potent propulsion arrangement for significantly higher speed despite a full-load displacement of 44,600 tons. Four of the class were ordered in April 1916, but the only unit to be completed was the *Hood*, which had a main armament of eight higher-angle 15in guns in four superfiring twin turrets on the centreline as well as a secondary armament of twelve 5.5in (140mm) guns, a maximum armour thickness of 12in (305mm) including a measure of inclined armour to provide protection against plunging fire, and steam turbines powered by more efficient small-tube boilers for the delivery of 151,280hp (112,795kW) to four shafts for a speed of 32.1 knots.

Whereas it was generally the British who had led the way with capital ship design up to this period, the Japanese led the way to the adoption of the 16in (406mm) gun in the two ships of the 'Nagato' class that entered service in the early 1920s. These were excellent examples of the 'fast battleship' concept, for the adoption of eight 16in main guns in two pairs of superfiring twin turrets permitted a significant reduction in armament weight by comparison with the ships of the 'Hyuga' class with their primary armament of twelve 14in (356mm) weapons in six turrets. The broadside weight of the 'Hyuga' class ships was 17,857lb (8,100kg) in comparison to the 'Nagato' class ships' 17,513lb (7,944kg). The 'Nagato' class was based on the same hull as the 'Hyuga' class, but this was revised with significantly more and better disposed armour and a propulsion arrangement in which four steam turbines delivered 80,000hp (59,650kW) to four shafts for a speed of 26.75 knots. Other improvements over the 'Hyuga' class included a secondary armament of twenty 5.5in (140 mm) guns and a control top located on what came to be called a 'pagoda' foremast, after this highly distinctive feature of the Japanese capital ship.

American battleships completed in this period included the two ships of the 'Tennessee' class that were in essence improved versions of the 'New Mexico' class ships with turbo-electric drive and the secondary armament of fourteen 5in (127mm) guns located one deck higher: although one-third less than that of the 'New Mexico' class in purely numerical terms, the secondary battery of the 'Tennessee' class was operationally superior because of its higher siting. There followed the ships of the 'Maryland' class that was basically a repeat of the 'Tennessee' class with the twelve 14in (356mm) guns replaced by eight 16in (406mm) guns. The class was to have totalled four ships, but the completion of the fourth unit was overtaken by the Washington Naval Treaty. The incomplete ship was therefore used for tests into explosions and blast, and as such probably played as important a part in the development of the American battleship as she would have done if completed.

The two American battleships of the 'Tennessee' class, here epitomised by the lead ship later in its career during World War II, were planned in the early part of World War I as improved versions of the two 'New Mexico' class battleships and were completed to a specification that included a full-load displacement of 33,190 tons, length of 624ft 6in (190.3m), armament of twelve 14in (356mm) guns in four triple turrets, fourteen 5in (127mm) guns in single mountings, four 3in (76mm) anti-aircraft guns in single mountings and two 21in (533mm) torpedo tubes, protection in the form of a 13.5in (343mm) belt, 13in (330mm) barbettes, 18in (457mm) turrets, 16in (406mm) conning tower and 3.5in (89mm) deck, propulsion in the form of turbo-electric drive delivering 26,800hp (19,980kW) to two shafts for a speed of 21 knots, and complement of 1,085. Both ships were completely rebuilt in 1943 to emerge as potent escort and gunfire support vessels with a full-load displacement of 40,300 tons, beam increased from 97ft 4in (29.67m) to 114ft 0in (34.75m), and an armament of twelve 14in guns in four triple turrets, sixteen 5in dual-purpose guns in eight twin turrets, forty 40mm anti-aircraft guns in 10 quadruple mountings, fifty-two 20mm cannon in single mountings, and three aircraft.

In the years following World War II, the rapid development of the 'Cold War' between the superpower blocs of the USA and the USSR led to the US Navy's retention of its better World War II destroyers in a form optimised for the escort of major surface forces. Two of the fleet destroyer classes that were taken in hand for adaptation to ocean escort standard were the 'Fletcher' and 'Allen M. Sumner' classes. Seen (top) is the 'Fletcher' class destroyer *Halsey Powell* in 1962 after its conversion but before its 1968 transfer to South Korea as the *Seoul*. Seen (above) is the 'Allen M. Sumner' class destroyer *James C. Owens* in 1969 before its transfer to Brazil as the *Sergipe* in 1973.

The first country to design a battleship without the constraints of the Washington Naval Treaty was the UK with the two-strong 'Nelson' class, which was designed to provide parity with the Japanese 'Nagato' and American 'Maryland' class ships. The design was basically a cut-down version of the projected 'G3' class battle-cruiser with the same primary armament and level of protection, although displacement limitations meant that thick armour was applied to a reduced area and the propulsion arrangement was considerably down-rated. The principal expedient adopted to provide adequate protection over the vital spaces was the grouping of all three triple turrets, each carrying three 16in guns, ahead of the superstructure block, resulting in a very truncated stern. The propulsion arrangement comprised just two sets of steam turbines delivering 45,000hp (33,550kW) to two shafts for a speed of only 23.5 knots.

This was basically the extent of capital ship construction in the 1920s as limited by the Washington Naval Treaty, although considerable effort was expended by the major powers on improvements to the capabilities of their existing ships, especially in terms of their defensive capabilities – for which an additional 3,000 tons of displacement were permitted per ship – which included enhanced anti-aircraft capability in the form of additional armour and extra anti-aircraft weapons, and improved anti-torpedo capability in the form of bulges on and below the waterline. Other changes that were effected were a revitalisation of the propulsion arrangement, with oil-fired boilers replacing surviving coal-fired units, and the addition of one or more catapults for the launch of floatplanes that could extend the parent ship's search horizon and also serve in the gunnery spotting role in long-range engagements. Some countries also went to the trouble and expense of virtually gutting their older battleships and battle-cruisers so that they could be revised into altogether more modern and capable warships. The Japanese, for example, rebuilt their 'Kongo' class ships with a lengthened hull for the improved length-beam ratio that allowed considerably higher speed, while the Italians revised their 'Conte di Cavour' and 'Caio Duilio' class battleships virtually out of recognition with extended and reshaped bow lines, heavier main armament achieved by boring out the original weapons, a completely new secondary armament arrangement, and a totally rebuilt superstructure. This last revision was also a feature of Japanese battleships, which all began to sport a 'pagoda' type of superstructure. British battleships were also extensively revised with new superstructures and main batteries in which the guns' maximum elevation angle was increased to 30 degrees from the original 20 degrees as a means of extending their range.

Plans were also laid in the 1930s for more extensive rebuilds of older ships, but these were generally curtailed on the outbreak of World War II, when the ships were required for immediate service, and the combination of dockyard facilities and other resources were earmarked for more important programmes such as the construction of new vessels and the rapid repair of damaged ships.

A revitalisation of battleship-building programmes resulted from the 1929 decision by Germany, prohibited by the terms of the Treaty of Versailles from building warships with a displacement of more than 10,000 tons, to build a class of armoured ships (*Panzerschiffe*) that were really cruisers with a main armament of 11in (280mm) guns. This led to the First and Second London Naval Conferences of 1930 and 1935-36, together with the resulting treaties that sought to maintain the basic concept of the Washington Naval Treaty but added a number of provisos allowing individual countries to react in various ways in response to the actions of other countries. The First London Naval Conference involved Japan, the UK and the USA while the

The *Perkins* was another FRAM II conversion to the ocean escort role, in this instance from the 'Gearing' class fleet destroyer standard. The ship is seen here in 1969 before its 1973 transfer to Argentina, in whose navy it became the *Py*. In its modernised form, the ship had a full-load displacement of 3,945 tons, length of 390ft 2in (119.0m), armament of four 5in (127mm) dual-purpose guns in two twin turrets, one ASROC anti-submarine rocket system with 17 weapons, six 12.75in (324mm) tubes in two triple mountings for lightweight anti-submarine torpedoes and one DASH remotely piloted helicopter, propulsion in the form of geared steam turbines delivering 60,000hp (44,735kW) to two shafts for a speed of 32 knots, and complement of 310.

In some respects resembling a destroyer of the period after World War II, the Italian navy's *San Giorgio* was completed in 1943 as a light cruiser named *Pompeo Magno*, but was renamed when converted into a training ship in the mid-1960s. The ship was deleted in 1980, and in training ship configuration had a full-load displacement of 4,450 tons, length of 466ft 6in (142.2m), armament of four 5in (127mm) dual-purpose guns in two twin turrets, three 3in (76mm) dual-purpose guns in single turrets, six 12.75in (324mm) tubes in two triple mountings for lightweight anti-submarine torpedoes and one Menon three-barrel launcher for anti-submarine rockets, propulsion in the form of a CODAG arrangement with four diesels and two gas turbines delivering 18,000hp (13,420kW) and 15,000hp (11,185kW) respectively to two shafts for a speed of 27 knots, and complement of 315 excluding 130 midshipmen.

Second Conference involved France, the UK and the USA, and with hindsight both can be appreciated as attempts to re-establish a situation that was already disappearing even if it had not actually disappeared.

The first result of the Germans' decision to build a class of three 'Deutschland' class *Panzerschiffe* was the French order for two 'Dunkerque' class fast battleships with a main armament of eight 13in (330mm) guns in two quadruple turrets ahead of the superstructure, and a secondary armament of sixteen 5.1in (130mm) dual-purpose guns in three quadruple turrets aft and two twin turrets amidships. Protection was on the light side, with a maximum of 13.6in (345mm) on the barbettes and 9.5in (240mm) on the belt, but this allowed the ships to achieve 29.5 knots on the 112,500hp (83,880kW) delivered to four shafts by four sets of steam turbines.

This was a period of steadily deteriorating relations between France and Italy, and the former's decision to build two ships was soon followed by the latter's order for two more potent 'Vittorio Veneto' class battleships with a main armament of nine 15in (381mm) guns in three triple turrets and a secondary armament of twelve 6in (152mm) guns in four triple turrets located in beam pairs abreast the superfiring unit of the two forward main-gun turrets and the after main-gun turret. The Italians preferred to rely on speed and manoeuvrability for protection, and the armour of the two 'Vittorio Veneto' class ships was therefore on the thin and light side by contemporary standards, but this permitted a speed of 31.4 knots on the 134,616hp (100,370kW) delivered to four shafts by four sets of steam turbines.

The final nails were put into the 'battleship holiday', which had started

Lead ship of possibly the last type of 'battleship' to be built, the Soviet battle-cruiser *Kirov* is seen here during its trials in February 1981. This class was the USSR's first nuclear-powered surface combatant type, and with the exception of aircraft carriers and major amphibious warfare vessels is the largest type of surface warship built since the end of World War II.

with the Washington Naval Treaty, by the German decision to renounce the terms of the Treaty of Versailles and start a programme of rearmament that included two improved *Panzerschiffe*, namely the battle-cruisers of the 'Gneisenau' class, and by the revelation that Japan had no intention of abiding by the terms of the 1936 London Naval Treaty, which ordained that signatory countries could build as many battleships as they liked so long as none of these ships exceeded a displacement of 40,000 tons and a main gun calibre of 14in (356mm). The Treaty also contained a provision that in the event of a Japanese non-ratification, the signatories could switch to 16in (406mm) main guns, but American and British moves in this direction were hampered by their continued attempts to limit battleship displacement to 45,000 and 40,000 tons respectively. In the event, all these negotiations were overtaken by the outbreak of World War II in September 1939.

Another attempt to limit the growth of Europe's fleet of expensive capital ships was the Anglo-German Naval Treaty of 1935, in which the UK agreed to a measure of German rearmament in exchange for a German agreement to limit its capital ship programme to the two battleships of the 'Bismarck' class with an armament of eight 15in (381mm) guns in four twin turrets against which the British laid down the first of its 'King George V' class of modern battleships with a main armament of ten 14in guns in two quadruple turrets and one superfiring twin turret. This British effort was designed to persuade other countries to limit their main gun calibre to 14in, but the fact that the originating country did not have much confidence in the success of its effort was signalled by the preparation of plans for the 'Lion' class battleships with an armament of nine 16in guns in three triple turrets, but these were later cancelled because of the exigencies of the war.

The two 'Gneisenau' class battle-cruisers were planned as the fourth and fifth units of the 'Deutschland' class of 'pocket battleships' before it was decided to develop them into altogether larger and more powerful ships to give the Germans parity with the French 'Dunkerque' class of fast battleships. Further delay was occasioned by Adolf Hitler's initial insistence that the ships should have the same main armament as the 'Deutschland' class vessels, namely six 11in (280mm) guns in two triple turrets and the German navy's demand that the minimum feasible armament for ships of this type should be nine 11in weapons in three triple turrets. The navy had really wanted a larger calibre of gun, and was hard pressed to justify its resistance to Hitler's next demand, which was that the ships should be designed and built with provision for subsequent rearmament with 15in weapons when these became available. The basic design was modelled on that of two uncompleted battle-cruiser designs of World War I, which were the most advanced types of which Germany had direct experience, with a number of improvements to features such as the disposition of the armour, the introduction of considerably more modern fire-control systems, and provision for catapult-launched aircraft. Completed in the second half of the 1930s and later revised with a clipper bow for improved seakeeping capabilities, the two ships were small but nonetheless impressive vessels of their type, and their details included a primary armament of nine 11in guns in three triple turrets including a superfiring pair forward of the superstructure, a secondary armament of twelve 5.9in (150mm) guns, a tertiary armament of fourteen 4.1in (105mm) anti-aircraft guns, armour up to a maximum thickness of 13.8in (350mm), and a propulsion arrangement in which three sets of steam turbines delivered 160,000hp (119,360kW) to three shafts for a speed of 31 knots. A propulsion arrangement based on diesel engines had originally been considered for very long cruising range, the ships being designed for extended commerce raiding capability in the Atlantic, but this was rejected in favour of the higher speed provided by steam turbine propulsion.

Epitomised here by its lead ship, the 'Georges Leygues' or 'F70/ASW' class of seven ships is the French navy's most advanced type of anti-submarine destroyer, these ships having entered service between 1979 and 1990 with a full-load displacement of 4,380 tons, length of 455ft 11in (139.0m), armament of one 3.9in (100mm) dual-purpose gun in a single turret, two 20mm cannon in single mountings, four MM.38 Exocet anti-ship missiles, one Crotale octuple launcher for 26 surface-to-air missiles, two 21in (533mm) tubes for heavyweight anti-submarine torpedoes, and two helicopters, propulsion in the form of a CODOG arrangement with diesels and gas turbines delivering 10,400hp (7,755kW) and 42,600hp (31,765kW) respectively to two shafts for a speed of 21 or 30 knots respectively, and complement of 220. There are also two ships of the 'Cassard' or 'Type F70AA/A' class of anti-aircraft half-sisters with basically the same hull but with a diesel powerplant and a different combination of sensors and primary weapons.

The two 'Gneisenau' class battle-cruisers were followed by the two 'Bismarck' class battleships. These were designed and built with commendable speed on the basis of theoretical work which German naval architects had completed during the period in which Germany was prohibited from the construction of warships displacing more than 10,000 tons, but reflected the fact that Germany was short of practical experience in the design, construction and use of modern battleships. The most important aspect of this limitation was that the basic hull concept of the World War I 'Baden' class was reused, albeit in a more refined form with a greater length-beam ratio to allow a higher speed. Considerable development of the basic hull allowed the incorporation of much-improved underwater protection and an enhanced armament fit, which now comprised a main battery of eight 15in (381mm) main guns in two pairs of superfiring twin turrets, a secondary battery of twelve 5.9in (150mm) guns in six twin turrets, and a tertiary battery of sixteen 4.1in (105mm) anti-aircraft guns in eight twin turrets complemented by large numbers of 37mm and 20mm cannon wherever deck space could be found; but the basic obsolescence of the hull was evident in the poor protection provided for the rudders and associated steering gear, the location of the main armoured deck toward the bottom edge of the armoured belt at a time when other countries, drawing on experience in the destruction of older battleships, had moved this to a position farther up the belt to provide better protection for communications and data-transmission systems. Both of these faults played a decisive part in the eventual loss of the *Bismarck*. Three other weak points were the provision of separate low-angle secondary and high-angle tertiary gun batteries, making extensive demands on deck area and displacement as a result of Germany's failure to keep abreast of the latest developments in dual-purpose ship's armament, the indifferent quality of the armour that was designed to be proof against penetration by 15in fire in its key areas but was in fact penetrated by 8in (203mm) fire, and the poor quality of the 15in shells, which often failed to detonate. All these factors notwithstanding, the two 'Bismarck' class battleships were magnificent vessels that exercised a horrible fascination on the British, who retained powerful forces in home waters to meet the threat of these two battleships.

The slightly later British contemporaries of the 'Bismarck' class were the five ships of the 'King George V' class, which were originally designed within the constraints of the Washington Naval Treaty with a primary armament of nine 15in (381mm) guns in three triple turrets, a secondary armament of 6in (152mm) guns, and only modest speed. Revision of the

47

core design in 1934 resulted in the replacement of the 6in weapons with 4.7in (120mm) guns, but the final selection was the excellent 5.25in (133mm) dual-purpose gun mounting introduced on the 'Dido' class of light cruisers. Finally, the 15in main guns were replaced by 14in (356mm) weapons ordained as the maximum by the London Naval Treaty: the British felt that Japan might not ratify the treaty, thereby opening the probability that other countries would opt for the 16in (406mm) weapons then allowed by the treaty, but as British plans were based on the possibility of war with Germany by 1940, which was the earliest date in which guns and turrets ordered in 1936 could be delivered, the British opted for the smaller calibre of main gun in combination with armour designed to provide survivability against 16in fire.

The plan was now to install twelve 14in guns in two pairs of superfiring triple turrets, but the need to provide additional horizontal armour meant the sacrifice of two guns to produce a final disposition of ten 14in guns installed in two quadruple turrets and one twin superfiring turret. The 'all or nothing' protection was based on armour up to 15in (381mm) thick, and the propulsion arrangement allowed for the delivery of 110,000hp (82,015kW) to four shafts by four sets of steam turbines for a speed of 29.25 knots.

At much the same time, France was planning a class of four battleships offering greater capabilities than the two units of the 'Dunkerque' class and thus providing the French navy with a counter to the German 'Bismarck' and Italian 'Vittorio Veneto' class battleships. These were the 'Richelieu' class battleships, of which only one was completed in World War II and another in the period immediately after the end of the war. The type retained the basic configuration of the 'Dunkerque' class ships, with the primary armament grouped in the forward part of the ship, although in this instance the main armament was eight 15in (381mm) guns in two quadruple turrets. The secondary armament comprised nine 6in (152mm) guns in three triple turrets in the after part of the ship, and the tertiary armament was twelve 3.9in (100mm) anti-aircraft guns in six twin turrets clustered round the 'mack'.

The blast pattern on the surface of the water is telling evidence of the power generated by the 16in (406mm) main guns of the 'Iowa' class, seen here in the form of the *New Jersey* shelling Palestinian positions near Beirut in Lebanon during 1984. Such a capability in the shore bombardment role is no longer available to any navy in the world.

Protection was adequate, and a speed of 32 knots was possible on the 155,000hp (115,570kW) delivered to four shafts by four sets of steam turbines.

The only other countries to complete new classes of battleship in this period were Japan and the USA. The Japanese offering was the extraordinary 'Yamato' class, of which two were completed during World War II as the largest, most strongly defended and most powerfully armed battleships ever placed in service. The result of an evolutionary process that had seen the creation of 23 designs in the period between 1934 and 1937, the 'Yamato' class design resulted in ships of magnificent appearance with a full-load displacement of 71,660 tons, armour up to a maximum of 25.6in (650mm) thick on the turrets and 16.1in (410mm) thick on the belt, a propulsion arrangement in which steam turbines delivered 150,000hp (111,840kW) to four shafts for a speed of 27 knots, and a comprehensive armament fit that included a main battery of nine 18.1in (460mm) guns in three triple turrets (including a superfiring pair forward), a secondary battery of twelve 6.1in (155mm) guns in three triple turrets clustered round the superstructure, and a tertiary battery of twelve 5in dual-purpose guns in twin mountings. The two 6.1in turrets in the 'wing positions' were later replaced by an additional twelve 5in guns for increased anti-aircraft protection at a time when American land-based and carrierborne warplanes were rampant in the Pacific, and by the end of her life in 1945 the *Yamato* had a specialised anti-aircraft armament of no fewer than 150 25mm cannon. There can be no denial of the fact that the two completed ships were obsolete by the time of their service debuts, and saw little effective use in the face of overwhelming American air power superiority. Both ships were in fact lost to air attack, the strength of their construction being attested by the fact that the *Musashi* absorbed between 11 and 19 torpedo hits and at least 17 bomb strikes before succumbing, while the *Yamato* took between 11 and 15 torpedo hits and seven bomb strikes before sinking.

The last American battleships were the two ships of the 'North Carolina' class, the four ships of the 'South Dakota' class, and the four ships of the

The *Long Beach* was the first nuclear-powered surface combatant to enter service anywhere in the world, an event that took place in September 1961. The ship was also the first cruiser to be designed in the USA after World War II, and was also the world's first warship with a primary armament of guided missiles, in this instance surface-to-air missiles for the defence of American carrier battle groups. In its present form, the ship has a full-load displacement of 17,525 tons, length of 721ft 3in (219.9m), armament of two 5in (127mm) dual-purpose guns in a twin turret, two 20mm Vulcan six-barrel cannon in two Phalanx close-in weapon system mountings, two twin launchers for 120 Standard Missile SAMs, two quadruple launchers for eight Tomahawk cruise missiles, two quadruple launchers for eight Harpoon anti-ship missiles, one ASROC octuple launcher for anti-submarine rockets and six 12.75in (324mm) tubes in two triple mountings for lightweight anti-submarine torpedoes, propulsion in the form of nuclear-powered geared steam turbines delivering 80,000hp (59,650kW) to two shafts for a speed of 30 knots, and complement of 960.

The *Leahy* is the lead ship of the US Navy's nine-strong 'Leahy' class of conventionally powered escort cruisers, all delivered in the period between 1962 and 1962 and now typified by a standard that includes a full-load displacement of 8,200 tons, length of 533ft 0in (162.5m), armament of two 20mm Vulcan six-barrel cannon in two Phalanx close-in weapon system mountings, two twin launchers for 80 Standard Missile SAMs, two quadruple launchers for eight Harpoon anti-ship missiles, one ASROC octuple launcher for anti-submarine rockets and six 12.75in (324mm) tubes in two triple mountings for lightweight anti-submarine torpedoes, propulsion in the form of geared steam turbines delivering 85,000hp (63,375kW) to two shafts for a speed of 32.7 knots, and complement of 425.

'Iowa' class. The 'North Carolina' class was the first American battleship type built after the end of the Washington Naval Treaty limitations, but was originally planned round the London Naval Treaty armament of twelve 14in (356mm) guns in two pairs of superfiring turrets. When the Japanese refused to ratify the treaty, the Americans recast the 'North Carolina' class ships with a primary armament of nine 16in (406mm) guns in three triple turrets, and this arrangement, with a superfiring pair of turrets forward and a single turret aft, became standard in the two succeeding classes: this gun fired a 2,700lb (1,225kg) shell to a range of 36,900yds (33,740m) at an elevation of 45 degrees, and was a notably successful weapon. The secondary armament comprised twenty 5in (127mm) guns around the superstructure. 'All or nothing' protection was based on armour up to 16in (406mm) thick, and a speed of 28 knots was provided by four shafts receiving 121,000hp (90,220kW) from four sets of steam turbines.

The four ships of the 'South Dakota' class were built to what was a basically improved version of the 'South Carolina' class design with reduced habitability, an increased level of blast interference from the 5in guns, and a hull shortened by 50ft (15.2m) to allow the incorporation of much-improved horizontal and underwater protection.

The four ships of the 'Iowa' class were the last American battleships to be completed, and were designed as successors to the 'South Dakota' class with a longer and finer hull whose additional volume and displacement were used for increased protection and power rather than greater armament. This resulted in a type possessing basically the same primary and secondary armaments as carried by the two preceding classes, but armoured to a maximum of 19.7in (495mm) and capable of 33 knots on the 212,000hp (158,065kW) delivered to four shafts by four sets of steam turbines.

The 'Iowa' class battleships were in every respect superb fighting ships, but the obsolescence of the type as 'the' capital ship had been highlighted by World War II operations, including the Japanese air attack on the US Pacific Fleet in Pearl Harbor during December 1941. The American battleships of World War II were generally not used in the effort to bring Japanese battleships to decisive action; the older ships were used to provide gunfire support for amphibious operations, while the more modern ships typically operated as force flagships and/or escorts for aircraft carrier task forces. Most of the American battleships were retired shortly after the end of World War II, but the four 'Iowa' class ships were recalled to active service in the Korean War (1950-53) and during the Vietnam War (American involvement between 1961 and 1973), and were later upgraded with offensive and defensive missile capability for continued service into the early 1990s in the gunfire support and flagship roles.

It is also worth noting two other capital ship types. The British Vanguard, completed in 1946 and little used in any meaningful fashion as the day of the battleship was past, was a singleton type resulting from the survival of the four 15in (381mm) twin turrets removed from the Courageous and Glorious after World War I. These turrets were installed in superfiring pairs on a hull that was basically an improved version of that designed for the 'King George V' class. Finally, there are the four units of the 'Kirov' class completed by the USSR (and succeeding Commonwealth of Independent States) between 1980 and the early 1990s. These are attractive and highly capable major surface combatants often dubbed battle-cruisers. With a full-load displacement of 23,400 tons, the ships have a hybrid propulsion arrangement in which the steam from two pressurised water-cooled nuclear reactors is superheated by two oil-fired burners to power two sets of steam turbines delivering 150,000hp (111,840kW) to two shafts for a speed of 30 knots. The ships are armoured, although the basis of this armour has not been revealed, and the primary armament is missiles rather than the guns that had been used in all previous capital ship designs: this armament comprises twenty SS-N-19 'Shipwreck' anti-ship missiles with a conventional or nuclear warhead, and is complemented by three types of surface-to-air missile, a hybrid surface-to-air missile/30mm cannon system for close-in defence against aircraft and missiles, a twin launcher for SS-N-14 'Silex' anti-submarine missiles, and a gun armament comprising two main guns (3.9in/100mm or 5.1in/130mm depending on ship) and eight 30mm 'Gatling' cannon for close-in defence.

The Soviet 'Kynda' class of four anti-ship cruisers was designed in the late 1950s as the world's first surface combatant designed with a primary armament of large anti-ship missiles.

The Cruiser

IN its original form as a sailing ship, the cruiser (often spelt cruizer at the time), was a fourth-rate ship or large frigate detached from the main fleet to sail independently in search of the enemy, whose position was then reported back to the fleet so that engagement could be brought about. The term was also employed for frigates and smaller vessels operated independently against the enemy's maritime lines of communication in the *guerre de course* role. In both these tasks, the essential requirement of any successful cruiser was a sailing ability superior to that of the enemy, especially in terms of speed and ability to point high into the wind.

All this changed with the advent of steam propulsion and iron (later steel) protection in the first half of the nineteenth century, when the cruiser ceased to be a generic name for any warship acting independently of the main fleet and became a type of warship in its own right. The cruiser was evolved in the middle and later years of the nineteenth century in four basic types, namely the armoured cruiser with a displacement of up to 14,600 tons and comprehensive protection matched by powerful guns, and the protected cruiser that was built in three subclasses with horizontal deck armour but no vertical belt armour and additional protection and survivability provided by the arrangement of the coal bunkers on the sides of the ship along the waterline and the compartmentalisation of the hull's interior spaces: in descending order of displacement, these three subclasses were the first-, second- and third-class protected cruisers with maximum displacements of 14,200, 6,000 and 3,000 tons.

The British built a total of 136 cruisers of these 'pre-dreadnought' types in the form of 35 armoured, 21 first-class protected, 51 second-class

The 8,800-ton *Deutschland*, launched in 1874 and completed in 1875, was the second unit of the two-strong 'Kaiser' class of central battery ironclads that paved the way for the armoured cruiser in German service. The two ships were built in the UK, and were in fact the last German major warships built outside Germany. As completed, the ships had a full sail rig, steel armour over a teak backing, and an armament of one 8.25in gun and eight 10.25in (260mm) guns. In 1882 the single 8.25in (210mm) weapon was replaced by seven 5.9in (150mm) guns complemented by four 3.15in (80mm) and six 37mm guns, and in the 1880s the two ships were rebuilt in Germany to cruiser standard, as illustrated in this 1898 photograph, with two military masts and the revised armament of eight 10.25in, eight 5.8in (150mm) and eight 3.4in (88mm) guns together with five 21in (533mm) torpedo tubes. Both ships became harbour vessels in the first decade of the twentieth century, the Deutschland being renamed Jupiter and then used as a target ship before being broken up in 1909.

protected and 29 third-class protected cruisers. The armoured cruisers were intended to provide a scouting capability within sight of the Royal Navy fleets to which they were attached, and also to serve as the flagships of overseas squadrons that did not need a battleship, while the task of the three subclasses of protected cruiser was the protection of British mercantile trade, the escort of troopship convoys to and from various parts of the British empire, and the provision of a 'naval outpost' capability in less advanced parts of the world. By the outbreak of World War I, 51 of these ships had already been deleted or reduced to non-combatant status, and another seven converted into minelayers. There were also 10 small cruisers with a displacement of up to 1,850 tons.

The evolution of the cruiser through the second half of the 19th century paralleled that of the battleship, starting as wooden vessels to which were added a layer of protective armour and steam machinery to supplement the three-masted ship rig with its full complement of sails, progressing through interim stages in which iron and then steel became the primary structural medium and the steam propulsion system gradually superseded the sailed arrangement, to reach the point at which the masts disappeared (except in vestigial form to provide the means of hoisting flags and carrying control tops) and the main armament was a mixed assortment of breech-loading weapons in which the largest-calibre guns were carried in trainable turrets and the intermediate-calibre guns were installed in casemates. The three main weapons carried by British cruisers were the 9.2in (234mm) gun firing a 380lb (172kg) shell, the 7.5in (190mm) gun firing a 200lb (91kg) shell, and the 6in (152mm) gun firing a 100lb (45kg) shell.

Typical of the British cruiser types before the advent of the 'dreadnought' era in 1906 were the first-class cruisers of the 'Warrior' armoured and 'Diadem' protected classes, the 'Challenger' second-class cruisers, and the 'Pelorus' third-class cruisers. The 'Warrior' class, of which four were launched in 1905, had a full-load displacement of 13,550 tons, an armament of six 9.2in guns, four 7.5in and twenty-three 3pdr quick-firing guns, armour protection up to a maximum thickness of 6in (152mm), and a speed of 23 knots on the 23,000hp (17,150kW) provided to two shafts by triple-expansion steam engines. The 'Diadem' class, of which eight were launched between 1896 and 1898, had a full-load displacement of 11,000 tons, an armament of sixteen 6in, fourteen 12pdr and three 3pdr quick-firing guns,

Completed in 1914, the two German light cruisers of the 'Regensburg' class, including the *Regensburg* illustrated, were basically improved versions of the 'Karlsruhe' class of three ships. As completed, the ships had a displacement of 5,500 tons, length of 468ft 0in (142.6m), armament of twelve 4.1in (105mm) guns in single mountings and four 19.7in (500mm) torpedo tubes, protection in the form of a 2.5in (65mm) belt and 0.75in (20mm) deck, propulsion in the form of steam turbines delivering 32,000hp (23,860kW) to two shafts for a speed of 27.25 knots, and complement of 420. During World War I, the armament was altered to seven 5.9in (150mm) guns in single mountings, two 3.4in (88mm) anti-aircraft guns in single mountings and up to 120 mines, and after the war the ships were handed over to France and Italy as war reparations, the *Regensburg* becoming the French *Strasbourg* and the *Graudenz* becoming the Italian *Ancona*.

armour protection up to a maximum thickness of 4.5in (114mm), and a speed of 20.25 knots on the 16,500hp (12,300kW) provided to two shafts by triple-expansion steam engines. The 'Challenger' class, of which five were launched in two subclasses between 1898 and 1902, had a full-load displacement of 5,880 tons, an armament of eleven 6in, nine 12pdr and six 3pdr quick-firing guns, armour protection up to a maximum thickness of 3in (76mm), and a speed of 21 knots on the 12,500hp (9,320kW) provided to two shafts by triple-expansion steam engines. The 'Pelorus' class, of which 11 were launched between 1896 and 1900, had a full-load displacement of 2,135 tons, an armament of eight 4in (102mm) and eight 3pdr quick-firing guns, armour protection up to a maximum thickness of 3in (76mm) on very limited areas, and a speed of twenty knots on the 7,000hp (5,220kW) provided to two shafts by triple-expansion steam engines.

These ships were rendered obsolete by the development of the 'dreadnought' and the comparable development of improved warships in smaller classes, but were still in extensive service on the outbreak of World War I. The armoured cruisers were generally retained for service in home waters until their losses up to and including the Battle of Jutland in May 1916 revealed their fateful weakness against more powerfully armed opponents, but the protected cruisers served a useful function in overseas waters in the pursuit and destruction of Germany's merchant raiding force, and were also used for the convoy escort role in the North Atlantic.

A major turning point in the design of cruisers came in 1904-05 with the advent of the 'River' class of light warships, in which the torpedo boat and torpedo boat destroyer had come of age as a unified type offering genuine ocean-going rather than merely coastal or at best sea-going capability. The new ocean-going destroyer was a far greater threat to major surface forces than the earlier sea-going torpedo boat, and the commanders of major surface forces now had to take into consideration the possibility of massed attacks by torpedo-firing ships using their speed and agility to evade destruction. The threat of the destroyer in the early 1900s therefore called for the development of a new type of light cruiser

The *Novara* was one of the three-strong 'Improved Spaun' class of light cruisers delivered to the Austro-Hungarian navy in 1914 to a specification that included a displacement of 3,445 tons, length of 428ft 6in (130.6m), armament of eight 3.9in (100mm) guns in single mountings and six 17.7in (450mm) torpedo tubes in three twin mountings, protection in the form of a 2.5in (65mm) belt and 0.75in (20mm) deck, propulsion in the form of steam turbines delivering 25,000hp (18,640kW) to four shafts for a speed of 27 knots, and complement of 320.

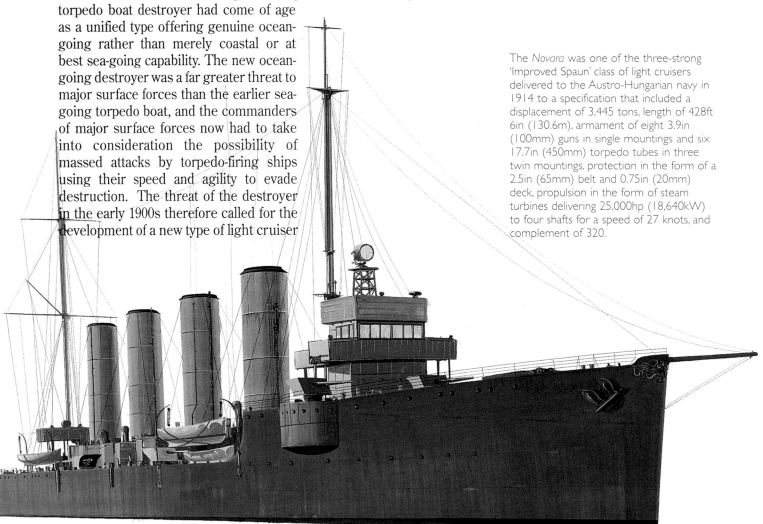

Lead ship of a three-strong class of German light cruisers completed in 1908, the *Stettin* survived World War I and was assigned to the UK as part of Germany's war reparations and was later scrapped. The details of this ship, which fought at Jutland in 1916, included a displacement of 3,550 tons, length of 385ft 0in (117.3m), armament of ten 4.1in (105mm) guns in single mountings and two 17.7in (450mm) torpedo tubes, protection in the form of a 2in (51mm) deck, propulsion in the form of triple-expansion steam engines delivering 21,000hp (15,660kW) to two shafts for a speed of 25.5 knots, and complement of 350.

that was fast enough to work with destroyer flotillas, for which it provided a command capability, and also fast enough and sufficiently well armed with quick-firing guns to provide a defensive screen against attacks by the enemy's destroyer flotillas.

The first results of this new requirement were the 15 ships of the 'Scout' classes that were built between 1904 and 1912 with a displacement in the order of 2,700 to 3,500 tons, and the 21 ships of the 'Town' classes that were built between 1909 and 1915 with a displacement in the order of 4,800 to 5,500 tons with a much greater endurance and the ability to operate semi-independently from remote bases. There were six classes of 'Scout' type light cruisers, of which the last was the three-strong 'Active' class with a displacement of 3,440 tons, an armament of ten 4in (102mm) guns and two 21in (533mm) torpedo tubes, no protection, and a propulsion arrangement of steam turbines delivering 18,000hp (13,420kW) to two shafts for a speed of 26 knots. There were five classes of the 'Town' type light cruisers, of which the last was the two-strong 'Birkenhead' class with a displacement of 5,200 tons, an armament of ten 5.5in (140mm) guns and two 21in torpedo tubes, protection in the form of a 3in (76mm) belt, and a propulsion arrangement of steam turbines delivering 31,000hp (23,115kW) to four shafts for a speed of 26.5 knots.

Early experience with the 'Scout' and 'Town' types of light cruiser indicated that they were useful types of warship, but that a hybrid type would be best suited to the requirements of working with major surface forces in the North Sea, which was the area in which the Grand Fleet intended to secure a climactic victory over the German High Seas Fleet in the event of an outbreak of war. This hybrid type combined features of the 'Scout' and 'Town' types with a more potent propulsion arrangement for the higher speed required for effective use in collaboration with the Grand Fleet and its fast destroyer flotillas. The first of the new classes, which eventually totalled nine including the five ships of the 'Delhi' class completed after the end of the war, was the 'Arethusa' class of eight ships that started to enter service just before the outbreak of World War I. As built, the ships had a displacement of 3,512 tons, an armament of two 6in (152mm) and six 4in (102mm) guns as well as eight 21in (533mm) torpedo tubes, protection in the form of a 3in (76mm) belt and 1in (25mm) deck, and a speed of 30 knots on the 40,000hp (29,825kW) provided to four shafts by four sets of steam turbines. Wartime changes included a revision of the gun armament to three 6in and four 4in guns as well as one 4in or two 3in (76mm) anti-aircraft guns, and the original pole foremast was replaced by a tripod foremast. The ships

55

were somewhat cramped but, soon proving themselves admirably well suited to their task, were used as the basis for steadily improved successor classes whose main changes were a larger number of 6in guns in replacement of 4in weapons. The details of the 'Delhi' class included a displacement of 4,650 tons, an armament of six 6in guns and two 3in anti-aircraft guns as well as twelve 21in torpedo tubes, protection in the form of a 3in (76mm) belt and 1in (25mm) deck, and a speed of 29 knots on the 40,000hp (29,825kW) provided to four shafts by four sets of steam turbines.

As the leading maritime power in the world during the last years of the nineteenth century, the UK was generally followed in terms of naval developments although rivals such as Germany sought to offset British numerical superiority with qualitative superiority in matters such as firepower and speed. At the beginning of World War I, the German navy had six armoured cruisers, of which the most advanced were the two ships of the 'Scharnhorst' class with a displacement of 11,600 tons, an armament of eight 8.2in (210mm), six 5.9in (150mm) and twenty 3.4in (88mm) guns as well as four 17.7in (450mm) torpedo tubes, protection in the form of a 6in (152mm) belt and 2in (51mm) deck, and a speed of 22.5 knots on the 26,000hp (19,385kW) provided to three shafts by triple-expansion steam engines.

It is also worth noting that Germany produced just one example of a heavy armoured cruiser, the *Blücher*, that was designed to provide a capability comparable to that of the 'Invincible' class, which were the Royal Navy's first battle-cruisers and originally described (for disinformation purposes) as being armed with 9.2in (234mm) guns. The Germans therefore responded with a design based on that of the 'Westfalen' class of 'dreadnought' battleships but scaled down and fitted with a primary armament of 8.2in guns. This resulted in a vessel characterised by a displacement of 15,500 tons, an armament of twelve 8.2in, eight 5.9in and sixteen 3.4in guns as well as four 17.7in torpedo tubes, protection in the form of a 6.75in (170mm) belt and turrets, and a speed of 26 knots on the 44,000hp (32,805kW) provided to three shafts by triple-expansion steam engines. Inevitably the *Blücher* was too lightly armed and armoured to be a real battle-cruiser, and paid the penalty at the Battle of the Dogger Bank in 1915, when she fought alongside the German battle-cruisers and was completely overwhelmed.

Germany also operated 17 protected cruisers, approximating in overall capabilities to the British second-class protected cruisers, and of these it was the 10 ships of the closely related 'Gazelle', 'Nymphe' and 'Frauenlob' classes

Second of the two-strong 'Karlsruhe' class of German light cruisers completed in 1913, the *Rostock* was sunk at Jutland in 1916. The details of the ship included a displacement of 5,500 tons, length of 468ft 0in (142.6m), armament of twelve 4.1in (105mm) guns in single mountings and four 17.7in (450mm) torpedo tubes, protection in the form of a 2.5in (65mm) belt and 0.75in (20mm) deck, propulsion in the form of steam turbines delivering 32,000hp (23,860kW) to two shafts for a speed of 27.25 knots, and complement of 420.

that were the most modern, all having been completed between 1899 and 1903 with a displacement of between 2,645 and 2,715 tons, a primary armament of ten 4.1in (105mm) guns and two 17.7in torpedo tubes, protection in the form of a 2in (50mm) deck, and a speed of 21.5 knots on the 8,500hp (6,340kW) delivered to two shafts by triple-expansion steam engines.

Like the UK, Germany came to appreciate in the first years of the twentieth century that the protected cruiser was obsolete in conceptual terms and that the immediate future lay with the light cruiser, of which the country built 14 classes in the period up to the end of World War I. The first of these, completed in 1904, was the 'Bremen' class of five ships with a displacement of 3,250 tons, an armament of ten 4.1in guns and two 17.7in torpedo tubes, protection in the form of a 2in (50mm) deck, and a speed of 23 knots on the 11,000hp (8,200kW) delivered to two shafts by triple-expansion steam engines. The last, completed in 1918, was the second 'Dresden' class of two ships with a displacement of 6,150 tons, an armament of eight 5.9in guns, two or three 3.4in anti-aircraft guns, and four 19.7in (500mm) torpedo tubes, protection in the form of a 2.5in (65mm) belt and a

The french World War II cruiser *Montcalm*, photographed in 1935.

0.75in (20mm) deck, and a speed of 28.5 knots on the 45,000hp (33,550kW) delivered to two shafts by steam turbines. The remarkable thing about these two classes, and this is a fact that was also evident in comparable British classes, was their conceptual similarity: the later class was larger, more heavily armed and armoured, and possessed a higher speed as a result of a more powerful propulsion arrangement based on steam turbines rather than triple-expansion engines, but in overall terms was merely a scaling-up of the earlier class with the incorporation of a number of operational improvements.

France, Italy and Russia followed basically the same course of development at slightly later dates and to smaller overall numbers of ships. The same was true of the US Navy, which entered the twentieth century with just two armoured cruisers, 15 protected cruisers and three unprotected cruisers, but then began a major programme of cruiser development and construction that saw the delivery of more advanced ships at an increasing rate. On the outbreak of World War I, when the USA remained neutral, the most modern type of armoured cruiser was the 'Tennessee' class of four ships launched between 1904 and 1906 with a

displacement of 14,500 tons, an armament of four 10in (254mm) guns in two twin turrets, sixteen 6in (152mm) guns in casemated mountings, twenty-two 3in (76mm) guns, twelve 3pdr guns and four 21in (533mm) torpedo tubes, protection in the form of a 5in (127mm) belt and 9in (229mm) turrets, and a speed of 22 knots on the 23,000hp (17,150kW) delivered to two shafts by triple-expansion steam engines. Dating from the same period was the 'St Louis' class of three protected cruisers with a displacement of 9,700 tons, an armament of fourteen 6in and eighteen 3in guns, protection in the form of a 4in (102mm) belt and 5in (127mm) conning tower, and a speed of 22 knots on the 21,000hp (15,660kW) delivered to two shafts by triple-expansion steam engines.

The only unprotected cruisers were three wholly obsolete ships of the 'Montgomery' class launched in 1891 and 1892, and the American cruiser force was completed by the three scout cruisers of the 'Chester' class launched in 1907 with a displacement of 3,750 tons, an armament of two 5in guns, six 3in guns and two 21in torpedo tubes, no protection, and a speed of 24 knots on the 16,000hp (11,930kW) delivered to two shafts by steam turbines.

Japanese developments reflected those of the Western powers, the last armoured cruisers being the two ships of the 'Kasuga' class ordered from an Italian yard by Argentina, which sold the two units to Japan in 1903. The ships had a displacement of some 7,650 tons, an armament of one 10in and two 8in or four 8in guns in one single and one twin or two twin turrets, fourteen 6in guns, ten 3in guns, six 3pdr guns and four 18in torpedo tubes, protection in the form of a 5.9in (150mm) belt, barbettes and conning tower, and a speed of twenty knots on the 13,500hp (10,065kW) delivered to two shafts by triple-expansion steam engines. The equivalent protected cruiser type was the 'Chikuma' class of three ships completed in 1912 with a displacement of 4,400 tons, an armament of six 6in guns, eight 12pdr guns and four 21in torpedo tubes, protection in the form of a 3in (76mm) deck and 4in (102mm) conning tower, and a speed of 26 knots on the 22,500hp (16,775kW) provided to two shafts by steam turbines. During World War I Japan kept a close watch on British warship developments, and in 1916 felt sufficiently confident in the utility of the new light cruiser concept to order an initial class of two 'Tenryu' class light cruisers modelled closely on the British 'C' type (the closely related 'Caroline', 'Cambrian', 'Centaur',

The Italian navy's heavy cruiser *Zara* was a classic ship of its type reflecting the Italians' realisation that French heavy cruisers offered superior all-round capabilities as a result of sacrificing a small measure of speed for significantly improved protection. The four ships of the 'Zara' class were launched in 1930 and 1931 for subsequent completion to a standard that included a full-load displacement of 14,600 tons, length of 599ft 5in (182.7m), armament of eight 8in (203mm) guns in four twin turrets, sixteen 3.9in (100mm) dual-purpose guns in eight twin turrets, eight 37mm anti-aircraft guns and two aircraft, protection in the form of 5.9in (150mm) belt and barbettes, 5.5in (140mm) turrets and 2.75in (70mm) deck, propulsion in the form of geared steam turbines delivering 108,000hp (80,535kW) to two shafts for a speed of 32 knots, and complement of 830. In March 1941 the *Zara*, *Fiume* and *Pola* were caught unawares at night off Cape Matapan by a powerful force of British ships including battleships that used radar direction to shatter and sink the Italian cruisers at very short range with 15in (381mm) shell fire.

A typical member of the 18-strong 'Baltimore' class of American heavy cruisers completed during the closing stages of and immediately after the end of World War II, the *St Paul* remained on the active list to 1971 and was scrapped in 1973. The details of the class included a full-load displacement of 17,070 tons, length of 675ft 0in (205.75m), armament of nine 8in (203mm) guns in three triple turrets, twelve 5in (127mm) dual-purpose guns in six twin turrets, forty-eight 40mm anti-aircraft guns in 11 quadruple and two twin mountings, twenty-two 20mm cannon in single mountings and four aircraft launched with the aid of two catapults, protection in the form of 6in (152mm) belt, barbettes and turrets, 8in (203mm) conning tower and 3in (76mm) deck, propulsion in the form of geared steam turbines delivering 120,000hp (89,470kW) to four shafts for a speed of 33 knots, and complement of 1,700.

'Caledon', 'Ceres' and 'Carlisle' classes). These two ships were completed only after the end of World War II, but paved the way for future Japanese light cruiser developments.

So far as the cruiser was concerned, the main lesson of World War I was that the naval reconnaissance role was better effected by aircraft than by the cruiser, which was thereafter operated mainly in alternative roles such as escort of major convoys, commerce protection and raiding, and gunfire support of amphibious operations.

This fact had become evident to the British in the later stages of World War I, when they had started to build cruisers somewhat larger than the otherwise standard cruisers that had proved so effective in the part of the war. Many of the latter were still comparatively new ships and were retained in service during the 1920s and 1930s, increasingly for second-line tasks such as the protection of trade routes. The oldest classes to survive into World War II were the 'Caledon', 'Carlisle' and 'Ceres' classes numbering three, five and five ships respectively. The 'Caledon' class ships were little altered in real terms from the standard in which they fought in World War I, but three of the 'Ceres' and all of the 'Carlisle' classes were considerably altered in overall capability by conversion to anti-aircraft cruisers. The *Coventry* and *Curlew* were prototype conversions with a primary armament of ten 4in (102mm) anti-aircraft guns in single mountings and sixteen 2pdr anti-aircraft guns in two octuple mountings, but the definitive standard adopted for the other six ships was eight 4in anti-aircraft guns in four twin turrets and four 2pdr anti-aircraft guns in a quadruple mounting.

Four of the five 'Improved Birmingham' class cruisers survived for limited service in World War II, and these larger and more capable ships were characterised by a displacement in the order of 9,700 tons, an armament of seven or five 7.5in (190mm) guns in single mountings and four or five 4in anti-aircraft guns in single mountings and, reflecting the increased threat posed by aircraft in World War II, eight 2pdr anti-aircraft guns in two quadruple mountings and ten 20mm anti-aircraft cannon, protection in the form of a 3in (76mm) belt and 1.5in (38mm) deck, and a speed of 30.5 knots on the 65,000hp (48,465kW) delivered to four shafts by steam turbines.

Another survivor from World War I and its immediate aftermath was the

'D' class of eight light cruisers originally built in the 'Danae' and 'Delhi' classes, and the two cruisers of the 'E' class completed in the early 1920s with a displacement of some 7,550 tons, an armament of seven 6in and three 4in anti-aircraft guns, protection in the form of a 2.5in (64mm) belt and 1in (25mm) deck, and a speed of 33 knots on the 80,000hp (59,650kW) delivered to four shafts by steam turbines.

These ships pre-dated the limitation treaties of the 1920s and 1930s, which did not in fact place any limit on the numbers of cruisers that could be built. Instead qualitative and later total tonnage restrictions were imposed, and replacement of over-age ships was also permitted. These conditions led to the general evolution of the cruiser into two species differentiated mainly by gun calibre: the light cruiser was generally a smaller type with guns of up to 6in calibre and indifferent armour protection, while the heavy cruiser was a larger type with guns of up to 8in calibre and relatively more effective armour protection.

The first of these modern cruiser classes in British service was the 'Kent' class of seven ships (including two for the Royal Australian Navy) with a displacement in the order of 9,800 tons, an armament of eight 8in guns in four twin turrets, eight 4in anti-aircraft guns in four twin turrets, eight 2pdr anti-aircraft guns in two quadruple mountings, and eight 21in (533mm) torpedo tubes, protection in the form of a 5in (127mm) belt and 4in (102mm) turrets, and a speed of 31.5 knots on the 80,000hp (59,650kW) supplied to four shafts by steam turbines. The same basic pattern of armament was followed in the 'London' class of three heavy cruisers and the 'Norfolk' class of two heavy cruisers, but the number of 8in main guns was reduced to six in three twin mountings in the two smaller heavy cruisers of the 'York' class that followed in the late 1920s.

Construction during the 1920s gave the Royal Navy a strong force of heavy cruisers, and in the 1930s attention switched to the replacement of the light cruiser types surviving from World War I with more advanced ships designed to complement the heavy cruisers. The first result of this effort was the 'Leander' class of light cruisers of which five were built for the UK and three for Australia. The British ships had a displacement in the order of 7,200 tons, an armament of eight 6in guns in four twin turrets, eight 4in anti-aircraft guns in four twin turrets, eight 2pdr anti-aircraft guns in two quadruple mountings, and eight 21in torpedo tubes, protection in the form of a 4in (102mm) belt and 2in (51mm) deck, and a speed of 32.5 knots on the

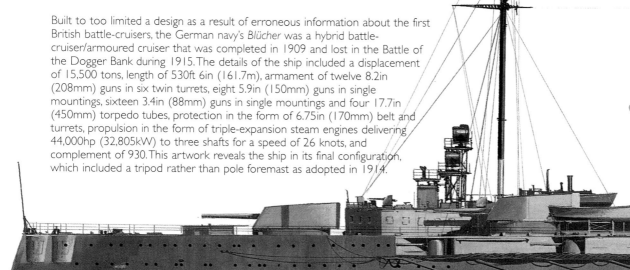

Built to too limited a design as a result of erroneous information about the first British battle-cruisers, the German navy's *Blücher* was a hybrid battle-cruiser/armoured cruiser that was completed in 1909 and lost in the Battle of the Dogger Bank during 1915. The details of the ship included a displacement of 15,500 tons, length of 530ft 6in (161.7m), armament of twelve 8.2in (208mm) guns in six twin turrets, eight 5.9in (150mm) guns in single mountings, sixteen 3.4in (88mm) guns in single mountings and four 17.7in (450mm) torpedo tubes, protection in the form of 6.75in (170mm) belt and turrets, propulsion in the form of triple-expansion steam engines delivering 44,000hp (32,805kW) to three shafts for a speed of 26 knots, and complement of 930. This artwork reveals the ship in its final configuration, which included a tripod rather than pole foremast as adopted in 1914.

72,000hp (53,685kW) delivered to four shafts by steam turbines. The three Australian ships differed in their displacement of some 6,900 tons and lack of 2pdr 'pom-pom' anti-aircraft guns. The following 'Arethusa' class of four ships was somewhat smaller with a displacement of some 5,250 tons, an armament of six 6in guns in three triple turrets, eight 4in anti-aircraft guns in four twin turrets, eight 2pdr anti-aircraft guns in two quadruple mountings and six 21in torpedo tubes, protection in the form of a 2in (51mm) belt and deck, and a speed of 32.25 knots on the 64,000hp (47,720kW) delivered to four shafts by steam turbines.

The next class of British ships was a hybrid type combining the size and most of the protection of the heavy cruiser with an augmented light cruiser armament. This was the 'Southampton' class built in three subclasses totalling five, three and two ships respectively. The first two subclasses had displacements of 9,100 and 9,400 tons respectively, an armament of twelve 6in guns in four triple turrets, eight 4in anti-aircraft guns in four twin turrets, eight 2pdr anti-aircraft guns in two quadruple mountings and six 21in torpedo tubes, protection in the form of a 4in (102mm) belt and 2in (51mm) deck and turrets, and a speed of 32 and 32.5 knots on the 75,000 or 82,500hp (55,920 or 61,510kW) respectively delivered to four shafts by steam turbines. The ships of the last subclass had a displacement of 10,000 tons, an armament of twelve 6in guns in four triple turrets, twelve 4in anti-aircraft guns in six twin turrets, sixteen 2pdr anti-aircraft guns in two octuple mountings and six 21in torpedo tubes, improved protection in the form of a 4.5in (114mm) belt and 2in (51mm) deck, and a speed of 32 knots on the 80,000hp (59,650kW) delivered to four shafts by steam turbines. The ships proved to be remarkably resilient, and saw very extensive service.

By the time the ships of the 'Southampton' class had been laid down in the mid-1930s, it had become clear that the warplane was rapidly becoming one of the most significant menaces faced by naval forces, and the British responded to this increasing threat with a classic class of dedicated anti-aircraft cruisers, the 'Dido' class of which 16 units were completed in 11- and five-ship subclasses with a displacement of 5,450 and 5,770 tons respectively and an armament in the first subclass of ten 5.25in (133mm) dual-purpose guns in five twin turrets, eight 2pdr anti-aircraft guns in two quadruple mountings and six 21in torpedo tubes, or in the second subclass of eight 5.25in dual-purpose guns in four twin turrets, twelve 2pdr anti-aircraft guns in three quadruple mountings and six 21in torpedo tubes. Features common to both subclasses were protection in the form of a 3in (76mm) belt and 2in (51mm) deck, and a speed of 33 knots on the 62,000hp (46,225kW) delivered to four shafts by steam turbines.

The next British cruiser type was the 'Fiji' class that reverted to the standard light cruiser concept, and these 11 ships were completed in eight- and three-ship subclasses whose common features included protection in the form of a 3.25in (83mm) belt and 2in (51mm) deck, and a speed of 33 knots on the 72,500hp (54,055kW) delivered to four shafts by steam

The light cruiser *Dresden* was the only major German ship to avoid destruction in the Battle of the Falkland Islands in 1914, but was severely damaged and was later scuttled off Juan Fernandez to avoid capture. The details of the ship, sister of the *Emden* that was a celebrated commerce raider brought to action and sunk off the Cocos Islands in 1914 by the Australian cruiser *Sydney*, included a displacement of 3,650 tons, length of 388ft 0in (118.25m), armament of ten 4.1in (105mm) guns and two 17.7in (450mm) torpedo tubes, protection in the form of a 2in (51mm) deck, propulsion in the form of steam turbines delivering 14,000hp (10,440kW) to four shafts for a speed of 24.5 knots, and complement of 360.

turbines: the first subclass had a displacement of 8,000 tons and an armament of twelve 6in guns in four triple turrets, eight 4in anti-aircraft guns in four twin turrets, nine 2pdr anti-aircraft guns in one single and two quadruple mountings and six 21in torpedo tubes, while the second subclass had a displacement of 8,800 tons, and an armament of nine 6in guns in three triple turrets, twenty 2pdr anti-aircraft guns in five quadruple mountings and twenty 20mm anti-aircraft cannon in ten twin mountings.

The final British cruiser class of the World War II period was the 'Minotaur' class, of which six were completed in three-ship subclasses during or immediately after the war to a design modelled on that of the second subclass of the 'Fiji' class. The principal common features were the hull and the protection, the latter in the form of a 3.5in (89mm) belt and 2in (51mm) deck and turrets. The first subclass had a displacement of 8,800 tons, an armament of nine 6in guns in three triple turrets, ten 4in anti-aircraft guns in five twin turrets, sixteen 2pdr anti-aircraft guns in four quadruple mountings, eight 40mm anti-aircraft guns in eight single mountings and six 21in torpedo tubes, and a speed of 32.5 knots on the 72,500hp (54,055kW) delivered to four shafts by steam turbines. The second subclass, which comprised the ships completed some time after the war, at whose termination construction had been suspended, had a displacement of 9,550 tons, an armament of four 6in dual-purpose guns in two twin turrets and six 3in anti-aircraft guns in three twin turrets, and a speed of 31.5 knots on the 80,000hp (59,650kW) delivered to four shafts by steam turbines. The

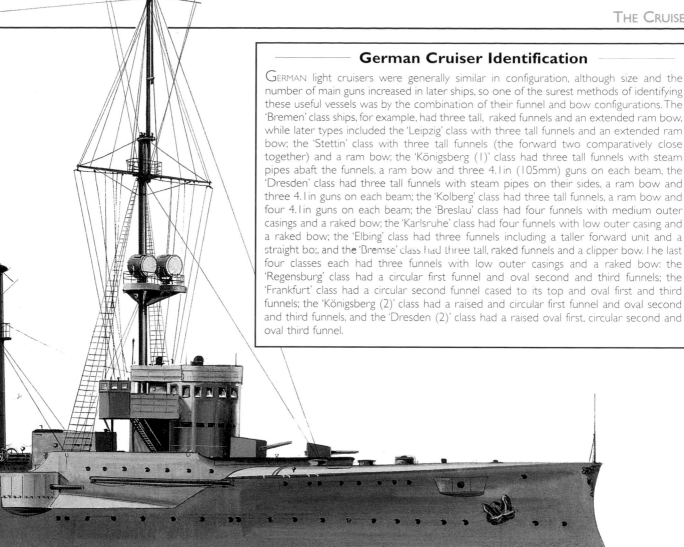

reduction in the number of guns in the second subclass was more than counterbalanced by the incorporation of the latest fire-control methods, which included extensive radar equipment.

During the course of the war, existing ships were extensively modified as they underwent refits or heavy repairs. The major part of this improvement effort was devoted to an upgrading of the ships' anti-aircraft capability by the addition of 20mm cannon in place of the original machine guns, the later replacement of these 20mm cannon by 40mm weapons, the supplementing of optical fire-control systems with radar fire-control systems, the removal of aircraft (between one and three depending on class) together with their associated hangar and catapult facilities (as long-range warning of ships and aircraft was increasingly and more reliably provided by radar), and in many ships the removal of one of the after main gun turrets to provide additional deck area for anti-aircraft weapons and radar equipment.

The US Navy disposed of most of its World War I cruisers during the 1920s and 1930s, but at the time of the USA's entry into World War II in December 1941 it had a total of 37 cruisers (18 heavy and 19 light). The size of this total was fortunate, for after the Japanese attack on Pearl Harbor and the loss, permanent or temporary, of many of its battleships, the US Navy was forced to rely on its cruiser force as its primary surface warfare capability as the surviving battleships were used for the escort of vital troop convoys. The intensity of this surface warfare in the period up to the middle of 1943 is attested by the fact that all of the pre-war cruisers involved in the protracted Solomons campaign were either sunk or damaged, and after the middle of 1943 the surviving cruisers were generally used for the gunfire support of amphibious landing and for the escort of carrier task forces. In common with their British counterparts, every protracted stay in port, either for refit or repair, was used to enhance the fighting capabilities of these very useful warships: radar was fitted and the anti-aircraft fit was considerably enhanced by the adoption of both specialised fire-control systems and additional weapons. The latter were of the lighter type designed to provide a high volume of fire for protection at shorter ranges against mass attacks, and may be typified by the enhancement of the 'Northampton' class ships, which each received sixteen 40mm guns in four quadruple mountings and nearly thirty 20mm cannon in single mountings.

Some of the ships suffered a fairly severe loss of stability as a result of the additional topweight, but even so the ships retained a remarkable tolerance to battle damage as a result of their construction, which was sturdy in the extreme although there were a number of structural failures as a result of poor welding: the *Pittsburgh*, for example, lost 90ft (27.4m) of her bows in a typhoon after a poor weld separated.

The two types of cruiser standardised in the US Navy during the 1920s were the heavy cruiser with an armament of 8in (203mm) guns and moderately thick armour, and the light cruiser with an armament of 6in (152mm) guns and comparatively thin armour.

The oldest heavy cruiser type in service during World War II was the 'Pensacola' class, of which the two units were launched in 1929. These were built in accordance with the dictates of the Washington Naval Treaty and were flushdecked ships with a low freeboard. The USA was the last of the treaty signatories to start on the construction of new heavy cruisers, and was therefore able to capitalise on the lessons that were discernible in the heavy cruisers that had already been built by other signatories: the French and Italians had opted for high speed at the expense of protection in the 'Duquesne' and 'Trento' class ships respectively, the Japanese had been influenced by initial reports of very heavy gun armament on the proposed American ships and had therefore adopted an additional main gun turret as well as good protection and a high turn of speed in the 'Myoko' class that in fact exceeded the treaty displacement limit by some 1,000 tons, and the British had opted in the 'Kent' class for a design that was altogether lighter than its contemporaries in firepower, protection and speed but which, as events were to prove, was robustly built and was an excellent seaboat. After assessing these other classes, the Americans opted for an approach similar to that of the Japanese with a main armament of ten 8in (203mm) guns located not in five twin turrets, as in the Japanese ships, but in superfiring pairs of triple and twin turrets. This primary armament was complemented by eight 5in (127mm) dual-purpose guns in single mountings, and other details of these ships included a full-load displacement of 12,050 tons, protection in the form of a 3in (76mm) belt and 2in (51mm) deck, and a speed of 32.5 knots on the 107,000hp (79,780kW) delivered to four shafts by steam turbines. A notable feature of the design was the considerable extent of weight saving that was effected in the design and construction of these fine ships, which emerged at a displacement some 900 tons below the Treaty standard displacement limit of 10,000 tons and were therefore considerably better value than the heavier Japanese ships.

The 'Pensacola' class set the pattern for the following heavy cruiser classes, which began with the six ships of the 'Northampton' class launched in 1929 and 1930. This was in effect a development of the 'Pensacola' class with a raised forecastle for improved seaworthiness and reduced wetness

Seen here behind its torpedo net defences in a Norwegian fjord during World War II, the *Lützow* was the pocket battleship *Deutschland*, which had been renamed in November 1939 in response to fears that the destruction of a ship named after the Fatherland would be a blow to morale. In 1940 the ship was reclassified as a heavy cruiser, but thereafter played only an undistinguished part in the war.

forward, and with further weight saving effected by the replacement of the ten 8in guns in a four-turret arrangement in the 'Pensacola' class with nine 8in guns in a three-turret arrangement. The ships were at first subject to a heavy rolling tendency, but this was cured by the installation of deeper bilge keels, and their primary details including a full-load displacement of some 12,250 tons, an armament of nine 8in guns and eight 5in dual-purpose guns, protection in the form of a 3in (76mm) belt and 2in (51mm) deck, and a speed of 32.5 knots on the 107,000hp (79,780kW) delivered to four shafts by steam turbines.

By the time the 'Northampton' class was under construction, the other signatories of the Washington Naval Treaty had produced their second generation of heavy cruiser, and the Americans were yet again able to profit from a survey of these vessels: the primary lesson learned was that the French and Italians had decided that their first-generation heavy cruisers had sacrificed too much protection in an effort to secure the highest possible speed, and the new 'Suffren' and 'Zara' classes, together with the 'Canarias' class designed for Spain in the UK, were notable for improved protection at a modest sacrifice in speed. The British and Japanese did not follow the same course as they had already opted for a better balance of protection and speed, and the Americans felt that this was the best option to be followed in the 'Indianapolis' class of two ships, which were very similar to the preceding 'Northampton' class except for a redistribution of the armour to provide additional protection amidships. The details of the ships, which were launched in 1931 and 1932, included a full-load displacement of 12,575 tons, an armament of nine 8in guns and eight 5in dual-purpose guns, protection in the form of a 4in (102mm) belt and 2in (51mm) deck, and a speed of 32.75 knots on the 107,000hp (79,780kW) delivered to four shafts by steam turbines.

The final American heavy cruisers built to Washington Naval Treaty limitations were the seven ships of the 'Astoria' class, which were in every way superlative ships matched in overall combat capability only by the single ship of the French 'Algérie' class and the three ships of the German 'Admiral Hipper' class. The principal changes from the 'Indianapolis' class were a lengthening of the forecastle to the rear for improved seaworthiness, pole rather than tripod masts, and improved protection in the form of a longer belt and thicker armour for the decks, turrets and conning tower. The details of the ships, which were launched between 1933 and 1936, therefore included a full-load displacement of 13,500 tons, an armament of nine 8in (203mm) guns, eight 5in (127mm) dual-purpose guns and sixteen 1.1in anti-aircraft guns, protection in the form of a 5in (127mm) belt and 3in (76mm) deck, and a speed of 32.75 knots on the 107,000hp (79,780kW) delivered to four shafts by steam turbines.

Launched in 1937, the single ship of the 'Wichita' class had been planned as the eighth ship of the 'Astoria' class but was completed to a standard resembling the 'Brooklyn' class of light cruiser except in its armament details. The ship had a full-load displacement of 13,700 tons, an armament of nine 8in (203mm) guns and eight 5in (127mm) dual-purpose guns, protection in the form of a 5in (127mm) belt and 3in (76mm) deck, and a speed of 32.5 knots on the 100,000hp (74,560kW) delivered to four shafts by steam turbines.

This similarity to the 'Brooklyn' class provides striking evidence of the gradual merging of American heavy and light cruiser design concepts, the heavy cruiser generally having slightly greater length and the light cruiser having five turrets each carrying three 6in (152mm) guns rather than the heavy cruiser's fit of three turrets each carrying three 8in guns. The Japanese also followed this concept, although not to so standardised a level, and were therefore able to upgrade the 'Mogami' class light cruisers to heavy cruiser standard by the replacement of the triple 6.1in (155m) turrets by twin 8in turrets.

The tendency towards the use of a conceptually similar design for light and heavy cruisers became fully evident with the 'Baltimore' class of 17 ships launched between 1942 and 1945 with an eighteenth following in 1951, although only 14 of these were completed in World War II. The design was based on that of the 'Cleveland' class of light cruisers with the hull lengthened

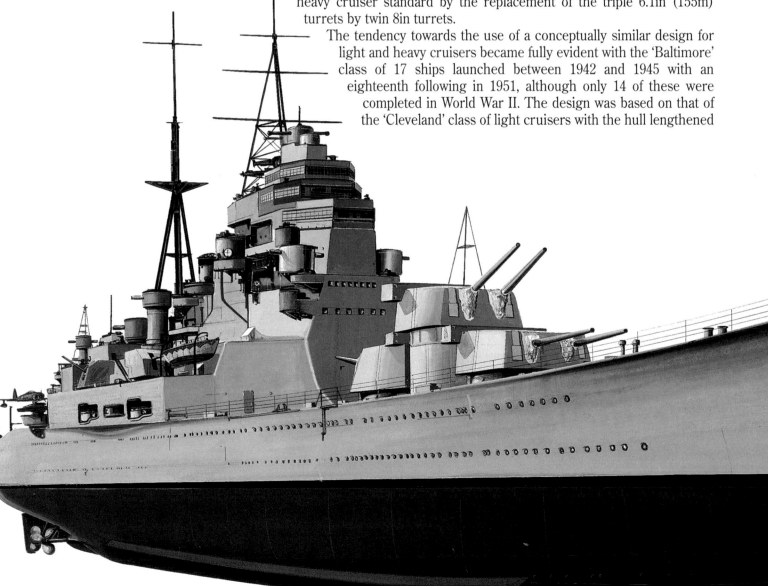

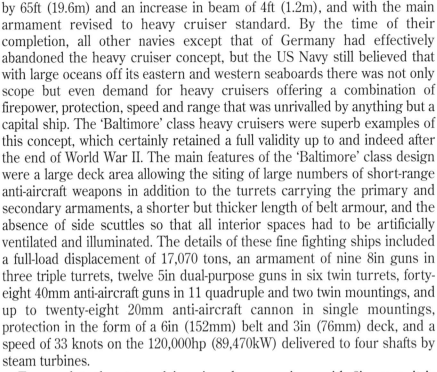

A notably potent heavy cruiser of the Imperial Japanese navy, the *Chokai* was a unit of the four-strong 'Takao' class and was completed in the early 1930s to a standard that included a full-load displacement of 13,160 tons, length of 661ft 6in (201.6m), armament of ten 8in (203mm) guns in five twin turrets (three forward and two aft), four 4.7in (120mm) anti-aircraft guns in single mountings, eight 24in (610mm) torpedo tubes in four twin mountings and two aircraft, protection in the form of a 4in (102mm) belt and 1.5in (38mm) turrets and decks, propulsion in the form of geared steam turbines delivering 135,000hp (100,655kW) to four shafts for a speed of 35.5 knots, and complement of 775. After suffering major damage from aircraft-launched torpedoes, the Chokai was scuttled off the Philippines in October 1944.

by 65ft (19.6m) and an increase in beam of 4ft (1.2m), and with the main armament revised to heavy cruiser standard. By the time of their completion, all other navies except that of Germany had effectively abandoned the heavy cruiser concept, but the US Navy still believed that with large oceans off its eastern and western seaboards there was not only scope but even demand for heavy cruisers offering a combination of firepower, protection, speed and range that was unrivalled by anything but a capital ship. The 'Baltimore' class heavy cruisers were superb examples of this concept, which certainly retained a full validity up to and indeed after the end of World War II. The main features of the 'Baltimore' class design were a large deck area allowing the siting of large numbers of short-range anti-aircraft weapons in addition to the turrets carrying the primary and secondary armaments, a shorter but thicker length of belt armour, and the absence of side scuttles so that all interior spaces had to be artificially ventilated and illuminated. The details of these fine fighting ships included a full-load displacement of 17,070 tons, an armament of nine 8in guns in three triple turrets, twelve 5in dual-purpose guns in six twin turrets, forty-eight 40mm anti-aircraft guns in 11 quadruple and two twin mountings, and up to twenty-eight 20mm anti-aircraft cannon in single mountings, protection in the form of a 6in (152mm) belt and 3in (76mm) deck, and a speed of 33 knots on the 120,000hp (89,470kW) delivered to four shafts by steam turbines.

To complete the story of American heavy cruisers with 8in guns, it is necessary to mention two classes that were designed during World War II but completed after the end of hostilities and then only in small numbers and in different forms. The 'Oregon City' class was planned as eight ships of which only four were completed to an improved 'Baltimore' class design with a single funnel rather than twin funnels to give the guns improved arcs of fire, and the 'Des Moines' class was planned as 12 ships of which only three were completed to an improved 'Oregon City' class design with automatic 8in guns, a tertiary battery of twenty-four 3in (76mm) anti-aircraft guns in 12 twin turrets to replace the 40mm guns of the preceding classes, and a longer and thicker belt of waterline armour.

Mention should also be made of the supremely elegant 'Alaska' class of large heavy cruisers, often but erroneously called battle-cruisers. The origins of the class are to be found in the pre-war report that Japan was emulating the German lead and building a class of 'pocket battleships', and to this report the US Navy responded with the 'Alaska' class projected as six large heavy cruisers of which only three were laid down and two actually completed to what was basically an enlarged version of the 'Baltimore' class design, with a primary armament of nine 12in (305mm) rather than 8in guns and the protection scaled up to approximately the same extent. With a full-load displacement of 34,250 tons and a length of 808ft 6in (246.43m), the 'Alaska' class large heavy cruiser carried a primary armament of nine 12in guns in three triple turrets including a superfiring pair forward, a secondary armament of twelve 5in dual-purpose guns in six twin turrets, and a tertiary armament of fifty-six 40mm guns in 14 quadruple mountings and thirty-four 20mm anti-aircraft cannon in single mountings. The ships were protected by extensive but only moderately thick armour that included an 8in (203mm) belt and 3.75in (95mm) deck, and the highly impressive sustained speed of 33 knots was attained on the 150,000hp (111,840kW) delivered to four shafts by steam turbines.

The oldest class of light cruisers still in service with the US Navy at the time of the American entry into World War II was the 'Omaha' class of 10 ships, planned in the aftermath of World War I as the first light cruisers designed in the USA for more than 10 years. The light cruiser had fully proved its worth in World War I, and as the starting point for its new type the US Navy took the British 'Danae' and 'Delhi' classes as well as the German 'Dresden' class. These classes had a speed of 29 and 28.5 knots respectively for the British and German types, which also had a main armament of six 6in and seven 5.9in (150mm) guns, so the US Navy proposed that its new class should have a speed of 35 knots and an armament of eight 6in guns on a displacement of 7,100 tons. The guns were in casemated installations fore and aft, and included four guns that could bear on either beam: it was therefore decided to add four more 6in guns in two twin turrets located fore and aft, although this meant an increase of 400 tons in displacement, a 9in (0.23m) increase in draught, a 1 knot decrease in speed, and the trimming of the belt to a length on each beam alongside the machinery spaces. It was then decided that the originally planned torpedo armament of two submerged tubes should be replaced by 10 tubes above the waterline and that two catapults and aircraft should be added, so the further increase in weight resulted in the omission of the after 6in casemated guns in half of the class, for improved stability. The ships were launched between 1920 and 1924, and during World War II were generally used in the South Atlantic and in a few secondary actions in the Pacific as well as for the gunfire support role in a number of secondary amphibious landings. As completed, the ships had a full-load displacement of 9,150 tons, an armament of twelve or ten 6in guns including four in twin turrets, eight 3in anti-aircraft guns in single mountings and ten 21in (533mm) torpedo tubes, protection in the form of a 3in (76mm) belt and 1.5in (38mm) deck, and a speed of 33.5 knots on the 90,000hp (67,105kW) delivered to four shafts by steam turbines.

With their four tall funnels in two pairs, the 'Omaha' class light cruisers were not visually attractive, but the same cannot be said of the 'Brooklyn' class that followed the last 'Omaha' class ships after an interval of more than 10 years. The spur for the development of this classic class was the Japanese 'Mogami' class of large light cruisers that began to appear in 1935 after Japan's completion of its quota of 12 heavy cruisers permitted under the restrictions of the Washington Naval Treaty. The 'Mogami' class was planned as a light cruiser type able to offer heavy cruiser capabilities through the combination of a large hull with an armament of no fewer than fifteen 6.1in (155mm) guns in five centreline turrets (three forward,

The *Diadem* was completed in 1943 as one of the five-strong second group of the 'Dido' class of British light cruisers optimised for the air defence role with a specification that included a displacement of 5,770 tons, length of 512ft 0in (156.1m), armament of eight 5.25in (133mm) dual-purpose guns in four twin turrets, twelve 2pdr anti-aircraft guns in three quadruple mountings, twelve 20mm cannon in six twin mountings and six 21in (533mm) torpedo tubes in two triple mountings, protection in the form of a 3in (76mm) belt, 2in (51mm) turrets and deck and 1in (25mm) conning tower, propulsion in the form of geared steam turbines delivering 62,000hp (46,225kW) to four shafts for a speed of 33 knots, and complement of 535. The ship survived the war and remained in British service up to 1956, when it was sold to Pakistan for further service as the Babur.

including one superfiring pair, and two aft in a superfiring pair): in the days before radar, when the maximum effective firing range was limited by visibility, the advantage in nocturnal and poor weather operations lay with the ships that could deliver the highest volume of aimed fire, and here the advantage would generally rest with the 'Mogami' class light cruisers even in engagements with heavy cruisers.

The American response to the threat of the 'Mogami' class ships was a type of similar concept but with a greater displacement, thicker armour (to the same basic levels as the 'Astoria' class of heavy cruisers with the exception of a slightly thinner but longer belt) and shorter overall length: the hull was of the flushdecked type, and the main armament of fifteen 6in guns was carried in five triple turrets arranged in the same manner as those of the Japanese ships with the exception that in the American ships it was 'B' rather than 'C' turret that was the superfiring unit of the forward trio.

The nine ships of the 'Brooklyn' class were launched between 1936 and 1938, and their details included a full-load displacement of some 12,700 tons, an armament of fifteen 6in guns in three triple turrets, eight 5in dual-purpose guns in eight single mountings or, in the last two units, four twin turrets, and sixteen 1.1in anti-aircraft guns in four quadruple mountings, protection in the form of a 5in (127mm) belt and 3in (76mm) deck, and a speed of 32.5 knots on the 100,000hp (74,560kW) delivered to four shafts by steam turbines. Wartime alterations included a strengthening of the anti-aircraft armament by sixteen 40mm guns in four quadruple mountings and between twenty and twenty-four 20mm cannon in single mountings. The ships saw very extensive and successful service in World War II, in which only one of the vessels was lost, and in the early 1950s six of the ships were passed in pairs to three US allies in South America, where some of the ships are still operational.

The next class of American light cruisers was completely different from the 'Brooklyn' class and, indeed, from any other type of American light cruiser as it was an anti-aircraft and flotilla leader type inspired by the British 'Dido' class of anti-aircraft cruisers. Although the 'Atlanta' class of four ships, launched in 1941, mirrored the role of the 'Dido' class, it was wholly American in its interpretation of how this role should be achieved to maximum effect. The type had the right armament (including two banks of torpedo tubes) and the high speed required for use with destroyer flotillas operating round the edges of a carrier task force, but was really too large for this role: wartime experience revealed that more success might have been achieved by a reduction in the number of main-calibre guns to allow the incorporation of more than just two high-angle directors, which limited each ship's ability to the engagement of only two aircraft at any one time. As completed, the ships had a full-load displacement of 8,100 tons, an armament of sixteen 5in dual-purpose guns in eight twin turrets, twelve or sixteen 1.1in anti-aircraft guns in three or four quadruple mountings, eight 20mm cannon in single mountings and eight 21in torpedo tubes, protection in the form of a 3.5in (89mm) belt and 2in (51mm) deck, and a speed of 33 knots on the 75,000hp (55,920kW) delivered to four shafts by steam turbines.

The following class comprised the 27 light cruisers of the 'Cleveland' class, which was to have numbered 39 including three ships that were cancelled and nine that were converted into aircraft carriers. This class was an enhanced version of the 'Brooklyn' class with one 6in triple turret sacrificed to make space for a much improved anti-aircraft armament. Launched between 1941 and 1944, the ships had a full-load displacement of 13,755 tons, an armament of twelve 6in guns in four triple turrets, twelve 5in dual-purpose guns in six twin turrets, between eight and twenty-eight 40mm

British Cruiser Operations in the Mediterranean

THE 'Substance' operation was undertaken between 21 and 27 July 1941, intended for the relief of the beleaguered garrison on the island of Malta. At this time Malta's garrison was in sore need of reinforcements and supplies, but as no convoy could be passed westward through the Mediterranean from Alexandria, it was decided to try an eastward convoy from Gibraltar. The British plan was that the troopship *Leinster* and six storeships should be passed to Malta while the auxiliary *Breconshire* and six empty merchantmen escaped from the island to Gibraltar. The convoy departed the River Clyde on 11 July and reached Gibraltar on 19 July, allowing the operation proper to begin on 21 July. The British plan was for Admiral Sir Andrew Cunningham's Mediterranean Fleet to sortie from Alexandria in order to deal with the Italian fleet if this should sail from Taranto, Palermo or Messina; for a patrol group of eight submarines to lurk on the likely approach routes of any Italian surface forces, and for the convoy to head east under escort of the reinforced Force H (two battleships, one aircraft carrier, five cruisers and 18 destroyers), which would turn back in the Sicilian Narrows, leaving the convoy to proceed to Malta, as the ships from Malta escaped westwards. The operation proceeded without undue incident until 23 July, when the convoy was south of Sardinia and came under heavy air attack. Despite the efforts of the fighters flown off the carrier *Ark Royal*, the first casualties were the *Manchester*, which was so heavily damaged by a torpedo that it had to return to Gibraltar, and the destroyer *Fearless*, which had eventually to be sunk by the British. The vital storeships were undamaged, however, and reached the Skerki Channel for the final dash to Malta. Air attacks on the convoy continued, but the only casualty was a warship, this time the destroyer *Firedrake*, which was detached to Gibraltar. Early on 24 July, one of the storeships was torpedoed and damaged by a Pantellaria-based torpedo craft, but managed to get through to Malta. At daybreak the cruisers headed independently for Malta (as there was now chance of interception by Italian heavy warships), unloaded their troops and stores, and made off to Gibraltar late on 24 July. Later on the same day the storeships and their destroyer escort arrived safely as the empty ships that had broken out from the island headed for Gibraltar, all arriving despite the attentions of the Axis air forces.

anti-aircraft guns in four twin or four quadruple and six twin mountings, and between ten and twenty-one 20mm cannon in single mountings, protection in the form of a 5in (127mm) belt and 2in (51mm) deck, and a speed of 33 knots on the 100,000hp (74,560kW) delivered to four shafts by steam turbines.

Next came seven anti-aircraft light cruisers of the 'Oakland' class that were completed in two groups of four ships launched between 1942 and 1944, and three ships launched between 1945 and 1946. The type was a further development of the 'Atlanta' class with a full-load displacement of 8,200 tons, armour protection in the form of a 3.75in (95mm) belt and 2in (51mm) deck, and a speed of 33 knots on the 75,000hp (55,920kW) delivered to four shafts by steam turbines. The two groups differed principally in their armament: the four ships of the first group had twelve 5in dual-purpose guns in six twin turrets, sixteen 40mm anti-aircraft guns in eight twin mountings, sixteen 20mm cannon in single mountings, and eight 21in torpedo tubes; while the three ships of the second group had twelve 5in dual-purpose guns in six twin mountings, thirty-two 40mm anti-aircraft guns in six quadruple and four twin mountings and twenty 20mm cannon in single mountings.

The 'Fargo' class of only two out of a planned 13 units, was a further development of the 'Cleveland' class with changes to improve the efficiency of their guns' fire: these changes included a more compact superstructure and the two uptakes trunked into a single funnel to give the guns larger arcs of fire. The details of the two ships, which were launched in 1945, included a full-load displacement of 13,755 tons, an armament of twelve 6in guns in four triple turrets, twelve 5in dual-purpose guns in six twin turrets, twenty-eight 40mm anti-aircraft guns in six quadruple and two twin mountings, and twenty-eight 20mm cannon in 14 twin mountings, protection in the form of a 5in (127mm) belt and 3in (76mm) deck, and a speed of 33 knots on the 100,000hp (74,560kW) delivered to four shafts by steam turbines.

The last American light cruiser design created during World War II was the 'Worcester' class of which only two out of a planned 10 units were completed, and then only well after the end of the war. The design was basically a development of the 'Oakland' class design with fully automatic 6in twin turrets replacing the manually operated 5in twin turrets, resulting in a longer hull and a larger displacement. The details of the class included a full-load displacement of 18,000 tons, an armament of twelve 6in dual-purpose guns in six twin turrets and twenty-four 3in dual-purpose guns in 11 twin and two single turrets, protection in the form of a 6in (152mm) belt and 3in (76mm) deck, and a speed of 32.75 knots on the 120,000hp (89,470kW) delivered to four shafts by steam turbines.

The other two naval powers involved in World War II on the Allied side were France and the USSR, neither of which played a major part in naval hostilities. The French cruiser force included the three light cruisers of the 'Duguay Trouin' class launched in 1923 and 1924 with a full-load displacement of 9,350 tons and a main armament of eight 6.1in (155mm) guns in four twin turrets; the two heavy cruisers of the 'Duquesne' class launched in 1925 and 1926 with a full-load displacement of 12,200 tons and a main armament of eight 8in (203m) guns in four twin turrets; the four heavy cruisers of the 'Suffren' class launched between 1927 and 1930 with a full-load displacement of 12,780 tons and a main armament of eight 8in (203mm) guns in four twin turrets; the single but outstanding heavy cruiser of the 'Algérie' class launched in 1932 with a full-load displacement of 13,900 tons and a main armament of eight 8in guns in four twin turrets; the single light cruiser of the 'Emile Bertin' class launched in 1933 with a full-load displacement of 8,480 tons and a main armament of nine 6in (152mm) guns in three triple turrets; and the six excellent light cruisers of the 'La

Galissonnière' class launched between 1933 and 1935 with a full-load displacement of 9,100 tons and a main armament of nine 6in guns in three triple turrets. The USSR operated a number of obsolete and obsolescent cruisers in the 1920s and 1930s, and the only truly modern type available in World War II was the 'Kirov' class, of which six were completed before and during the war with a full-load displacement of 11,500 tons and a main armament of nine 7.1in (180mm) guns in three triple turrets.

On the other side of the naval front line in World War II were Germany, Italy and Japan. Germany planned a class of five 'Admiral Hipper' class heavy cruisers from the early 1930s, and these were orthodox but large ships of their type. Launched in the second half of the 1930s, only three of the ships were completed. The main armament was limited to eight 8in guns in four twin turrets located as superfiring pairs forward and aft, and this allowed a considerable proportion of the displacement to be devoted to a sturdy structure and very good protection. One of the ships was sunk by Norwegian shore batteries in April 1940, but the other two survived the war after playing a distinguished part in its first phases. The basic details of these impressive ships included a full-load displacement of 18,400 tons, an armament of eight 8in guns in four twin turrets, twelve 4.1in (105mm) dual-purpose guns in six twin turrets, twelve 37mm anti aircraft guns in six twin mountings, twenty-four 20mm cannon and twelve 21in (533mm) torpedo tubes, protection in the form of a 3.1in (80mm) belt and 2in (51mm) deck, and a speed of 33.4 knots on the 132,000hp (98,430kW) delivered to three shafts by steam turbines.

The other major element of Germany's cruiser strength was provided by the six light cruisers of the 'Köln' class, which were relatively modern ships but not particularly notable with their armament of nine 5.9in (150mm) guns and six 3.4in (88mm) anti-aircraft guns.

Italy was a firm believer in the cruiser concept, which it saw as tactically efficient for the support of its battle force in the central Mediterranean and also as a cost-effective means of providing powerful warships suited for the command and support of flotilla operations in more confined waters such as those of the Aegean. In the years after World War I the Italian navy lacked the financial resources to undertake the construction of many new ships, and for this reason retained a number of obsolescent types such as the two 'San Giorgio' class armoured cruisers, the single 'Libia' and 'Campania' class protected cruisers, and the one 'Quarto', two 'Bixio', three 'Poerio', three 'Mirabello', four 'Aquila' and three 'Leone' class scout cruisers. During the 1920s, however, relations between France and Italy began to worsen, and when the French started work on the two 'Duquesne' class heavy cruisers to the limits imposed by the Washington Naval Treaty, Italy responded with the 'Trento' class offering firepower and speed comparable with those of the French class but with somewhat better protection. The 'Trento' class ships were still under construction when France replied with its four 'Suffren' class heavy cruisers in which a measure of speed was sacrificed to greater protection. Italy did not immediately respond to these impressive ships, largely as a result of financial and industrial limitations, and this gave the Italian navy the time to digest the nuances of the 'Suffren' class design before proceeding three years later with the four ships of the 'Zara' class. This class sacrificed some performance, the propulsion arrangement being reduced to 108,000hp (80,535kW) delivered to two shafts by steam turbines for a speed of 32 knots, so that better protection could be worked into the design: this protection took the form of a 5.9in (150mm) belt and 2.75in (70mm) deck, and the firepower of these impressive heavy cruisers was provided by a main battery of eight 8in guns in two pairs of superfiring

An overhead view of the US Navy's nuclear-powered cruiser Long Beach reveals some of the salient features of this important ship's layout. From bow to stern, these include the two twin launchers for surface-to-air missiles, the forward pair of SPG-55 fire-control radars, the forward superstructure flanked by two Mk 32 triple mountings for anti-submarine torpedoes and carrying the air and surface search radars as well as two more SPG-55 fire-control radars, the ASROC launcher and 5in (127mm) gun turret, the after superstructure carrying the long-range air search radar as well as the two quadruple launchers for Harpoon anti-ship missiles and the two Phalanx close-in weapon system mountings for last-ditch defence against attack aircraft and anti-ship missiles, and the two quadruple launchers for Tomahawk cruise missiles.

turrets, a secondary battery of sixteen 3.9in (100mm) dual-purpose guns in eight twin mountings, and a tertiary battery of eight 37mm anti-aircraft guns.

So far as light cruisers were concerned, the Italians also responded to French initiatives. Thus the construction of the three 'Duguay Trouin' light cruisers spurred the laying down from 1928 of the first four of an eventual 12 light cruisers of the 'Condotierri' type produced in five subclasses as four 'Bande Nere', two 'Diaz', two 'Montecuccoli', two 'Aosta' and two 'Garibaldi' class ships. Like their French counterparts, the 'Bande Nere' class ships carried a primary armament of eight 6in guns in two pairs of superfiring twin turrets and carried armour protection that can only be described as vestigial, but they were very fast. The four later subclasses of the 'Condotierri' type were a response to the French light cruisers of the 'La Galissonnière' class with improved protection, and successive subclasses introduced greater size and displacement to permit the incorporation of better protection and a more potent propulsion arrangement so that speed did not suffer. The last pair of ships, launched in 1933, were the 'Garibaldi' class with a further enlargement in beam and draught to allow the incorporation of two additional main-calibre guns. The details of these ships included a full-load displacement of 11,260 tons, an armament of ten 6in guns in superfiring pairs of triple and twin turrets, eight 3.9in anti-aircraft guns, eight 37mm anti-aircraft guns, ten 20mm anti-aircraft cannon and six 21in torpedo tubes, protection in the form of a 5.1in (130mm) belt and 1.6in (40mm) deck, and a speed of 32 knots on the 102,000hp (76,060kW) delivered to two shafts by steam turbines.

Although the concept of the small scout cruiser had generally lapsed after the end of World War I except in Japan, where a number of such ships were built in the 1920s, the French reverted to such a type in the mid-1930s with the 'Mogador' class of ships (officially rated as large destroyers but which were in fact scout cruisers), with a full-load displacement of 4,010 tons, a main armament of eight 5.5in (140mm) guns in two superfiring pairs of twin turrets and complemented by four 37mm anti-aircraft guns in two twin mountings and ten 21.7in (550mm) torpedo tubes, and the remarkable speed of 39 knots on the 92,000hp (68,630kW) delivered to two shafts by

The *Yorktown* was completed as the second unit of the 'Ticonderoga' class of guided missile cruisers, numerically the most important type of cruiser for the defence of US Navy major surface forces. The details of this and other early units, before the introduction of the vertical-launch missile system in the sixth ship, include a full-load displacement of 9,410 tons, length of 567ft 0in (172.8m), armament of two 5in (127mm) dual-purpose guns in single turrets, two 20mm Vulcan six-barrel cannon in two Phalanx close-in weapon system mountings, two twin launchers for up to 68 weapons (Standard Missile surface-to-air missiles and up to 20 ASROC anti-submarine rockets), two quadruple launchers for eight Harpoon anti-ship missiles and six 12.75in (324mm) tubes in two triple mountings for lightweight anti-submarine torpedoes, propulsion in the form of gas turbines delivering 80,000hp (59,650kW) to two shafts for a speed of 30 or more knots, and complement of 360.

steam turbines. The capability of these destroyers, of which only two were built to a standard that effectively outgunned the British 'Dido' class light cruisers, was seen by the Italians as a major threat that was countered by the 'Capitani Romani' class of fast light cruisers: 12 ships were laid down, but only four of these were completed. The key to the design was a long and relatively beamy hull able to accommodate a sizeable propulsion arrangement: the machinery of the Italian ships was capable of generating 125,000hp (92,310kW), which was about the same as that of the four times heavier 'Des Moines' class heavy cruisers, and this was delivered to two shafts for the astonishing speed of 43 knots. However, the ships carried virtually no protection, and the armament comprised eight 5.3in (135mm) guns in two superfiring pairs of twin turrets, eight 37mm anti-aircraft guns, eight 20mm anti-aircraft cannon and eight 21in torpedo tubes.

Like the Italians, the Japanese viewed the cruiser as an ideal weapon for a country that lacked a large industrial base and indigenous raw materials, especially iron ore: the cruiser offered the possibility of striking at larger and potentially more threatening warships by using its speed and agility, in combination with daring Japanese tactics, to close to effective torpedo range. The first result of this philosophy, which had seen the laying down of the two 'Tenryu' class light cruisers in the closing stages of World War I, was the five-strong 'Kuma' class of light cruisers with a displacement of 5,100 tons, an armament of seven 5.5in (140mm) guns in a single mounting and eight 21in torpedo tubes, protection in the form of a 2in (51mm) belt and 1.5in (37mm) deck, and a speed of 36 knots on the 90,000hp (67,105kW) delivered to four shafts by steam turbines. Two of the vessels, it is worth noting, were adapted in 1941 into the ultimate torpedo-armed cruisers after the introduction of the 24in (610mm) 'Long Lance' long-range/high-speed torpedo with liquid oxygen propellant: the *Kitakami* and *Oi* were altered by the revision of the gun armament to four 5.5in weapons in two twin mountings and up to thirty-six 25mm anti-aircraft guns in six triple and 18 single mountings: the deck was extended on each beam with sponsons to carry a total of 10 quadruple mountings for the 'Long Lance' torpedo.

After World War I, Japan planned a programme of major military and naval expansion designed to turn the country into the decisive military power in the western half of the Pacific Ocean and in eastern and south-eastern Asia. An early decision was that the Japanese navy was lacking in balance, for construction in the period before and during World War I had been concentrated on capital ships and destroyers. With a major capability in the western half of the Pacific now envisaged, there was clearly demand for larger numbers of more capable cruisers in the scouting and ambush roles. The first result of this was the 'Natori' class of six light cruisers completed in the period between 1922 and 1925. These were unexceptional ships based on the 'Nagara' class with a displacement of 5,170 tons, an armament of seven 5.5in guns in seven single turrets and eight 24in torpedo tubes, protection in the form of a 2in (51mm) belt and 1.5in (37mm) deck, and a speed of 36 knots on the 90,000hp (67,105kW) delivered to four shafts by steam turbines.

The same philosophy was maintained in the following 'Sendai' class of six light cruisers, of which only three were completed. This class had the same basic dimensions, armament and protection as the two preceding classes, although a change was made in the propulsion arrangement that now included 11 oil- and one mixed-burning boilers by comparison with the eight oil- and four coal-burning boilers of the 'Nagara' class and the 10 oil- and two mixed-burning boilers of the 'Kuma' class.

As the 'Sendai' class was being planned and laid down, the final negotiations of the Washington Naval Conference were being undertaken

Cruiser Battles off Guadalcanal

THE land campaign that started the American fight-back after Japan's series of runaway victories between December 1941 and mid-1942 was that for the island of Guadalcanal toward the south-eastern tip of the Solomon Islands. This started with the landing of the US 1st Marine Division in Operation 'Watchtower' on 7 August 1942, and continued with increasing fury until the final Japanese evacuation of the island by 7 February 1943. In the course of this campaign, which was entirely reliant on maritime support for the delivery of men and equipment, seven major naval engagements took place, four of them involving mainly cruisers and destroyers. These were the nocturnal Battle of Savo Island on 8/9 August 1942 in which a Japanese force of seven cruisers under Vice Admiral Mikawa inflicted a severe reverse on the American and Australian force of six cruisers under the command of Rear Admiral Crutchley, who lost four of his major vessels but foiled the Japanese attempt to reinforce Guadalcanal; the nocturnal Battle of Cape Esperance on 11/12 October 1942 in which a Japanese force including four cruisers under the command of Rear Admiral Goto fought a tactically inconclusive action with an American force under Rear Admiral Scott and including five cruisers; and the actions of 12 November and 30/31 November 1942 in 'Ironbottom Sound' between Guadalcanal and Tulagi Islands. The first resulted in a modest American victory when a force under the command of Rear Admiral Callaghan (five cruisers and eight destroyers) saw off a Japanese force under Vice Admiral Abe (two battleships, two cruisers and 14 destroyers), in the process sinking two cruisers and damaging all of the other Japanese ships for the loss of two cruisers and four destroyers. The second was a Japanese victory when Rear Admiral Tanaka's force of eight destroyers encountered Rear Admiral Wright's force of five cruisers and seven destroyers, sinking one cruiser and damaging three others for the loss of only one destroyer.

and the probability of new types of cruiser persuaded the Japanese navy to build the single 'Yubari' class light cruiser as an experimental type offering the same broadside weight as its predecessors on a displacement of only 2,900 tons. This was achieved by limiting the protection to a 2in (50mm) belt, trunking the two uptakes into a single funnel, limiting the torpedo armament to four 24in (610mm) tubes, locating the main armament of six 5.5in (140mm) guns on the centreline in two twin and two single turrets with the twin turrets in superfiring positions, and revising the propulsion arrangement for a speed of 35.5 knots on the 57,900hp (43,170kW) delivered to three shafts by steam turbines. The ship was a considerable success at the technical level, and paved the way for the design and construction of both light and heavy cruisers within the constraints of the Washington Naval Treaty.

The first result of this process was the 'Kako' class of two heavy cruisers completed in 1926. These were impressive ships, well within the treaty limits for the new class of heavy cruisers with 8in (203mm) guns and a maximum displacement of 10,000 tons, as they were armed with six 7.9in (200mm) guns in single turrets (three forward and three aft) and had a displacement of 8,100 tons. Their other primary details included a secondary armament of four 3in (76mm) anti-aircraft guns in single mountings and twelve 24in (610mm) torpedo tubes, protection in the form of a 3in (76mm) belt and 1.5in (37mm) deck, and a speed of 34.5 knots on the 102,000hp (76,050kW) delivered to three shafts by steam turbines. The overall capabilities of the class were improved in the late 1930s, when the original six single gun turrets were replaced by three twin turrets (a superfiring pair forward and a singleton aft) carrying 8in weapons.

The following two ships of the 'Aoba' class were generally similar with the exception of having their six 7.9in guns, later replaced by 8in weapons, in three twin turrets and the strengthened anti-aircraft armament of four 4.7in guns in single mountings. With a displacement of 8,300 tons and protection in the form of a 3in (76mm) belt and 1.5in (37mm) deck, the 'Aoba' class cruiser attained a speed of 34.5 knots on the 102,000hp (76,050kW) delivered to four shafts by steam turbines.

Further development of the concept embodied in these first two classes of Japanese heavy cruiser resulted in the mid-1920s in the considerably improved 'Myoko' class of four ships completed in 1928 and 1929 with a displacement of 10,940 tons, an armament of ten 7.9in guns, later replaced by 8in weapons, in five twin turrets (three forward and two aft), six 4.7in anti-aircraft guns in single mountings, twelve 24in torpedo tubes, protection in the form of a 4in (102mm) belt and 5in (127mm) deck, and a speed of 35.5 knots on the 130,000hp (96,930kW) delivered to four shafts by steam turbines. The most important features of the additional size and displacement introduced with this class were the significantly heavier main armament, carried as a triplet forward with the central unit as the superfiring turret and as a superfiring pair aft, and the considerably thicker armour that made these vessels particularly resistant to terminal battle damage.

The following four ships of the 'Takao' class were to an improved 'Myoko' class design with a more 'piled' superstructure of streamlined design, extensive use of welding rather than riveting and the use of light alloy in place of steel wherever possible to keep weight to a minimum, an increase in the armour protection for the magazines, and a primary armament of 8in guns. The details of the ships therefore included a displacement of 11,350 tons, an armament of ten 8in guns in five twin turrets (three forward and two aft), four 4.7in anti-aircraft guns in single mountings and eight 24in torpedo tubes, protection in the form of a 4in (102mm) belt and 1.5in (37mm) deck, and a speed of 35.5 knots on the 130,000hp (96,930kW) delivered to four shafts by steam turbines.

The Battle of Midway

OPERATION 'MI' was the Japanese operation between 25 May and 5 June 1942 for the capture of Midway Island, and led to the Battle of Midway that was one of the decisive battles of World War II resulting, as it did, in the reversal of Japan's expansion south and east into the Pacific, already checked in the Battle of the Coral Sea, and the removal of the strategic initiative from the Japanese in favour of the Americans. Approval of Admiral Isoroku Yamamoto's plan was given when the navy provided assurances that the occupation of Midway (together with the launching of Operation 'AL' against the Aleutians as a strategic diversion) was only a lure to draw out the Pacific Fleet for the decisive battle. The scheme devised by Yamamoto was essentially simple in concept (though complex in detail) and strategically sound, and used virtually the whole strength of the Imperial Japanese navy's surface fleet. The plan was predicated on the assumption that of the four aircraft carriers available in May to Admiral Chester W. Nimitz, US Commander-in-Chief Pacific Fleet, at least one (*Lexington*) had been sunk in the Battle of the Coral Sea, another (*Yorktown*) had sunk after the battle or was too severely damaged to be operational, and the other two (*Enterprise* and *Hornet*) were absent in the South-West Pacific Area. In fact Nimitz had three carriers available for Rear Admiral Frank J. Fletcher as the *Enterprise* and *Hornet* had reached Pearl Harbor to join the *Yorktown*, which had been repaired with extraordinary rapidity (repairs that had been estimated to need 90 days of work were completed between 27 and 30 May by 1,400 men working 24 hours per day).

Yamamoto attached great importance to the distraction of American attention by the activities associated with 'AL', which was to be undertaken just before 'MI' by Vice Admiral Boshiro Hosogawa's 5th Fleet. The main weight of Yamamoto's plan was in the south, however, and here Vice Admiral Chuichi Nagumo's 1st Mobile Force sortied from Hashirajima in Japan on 27 May with the fleet carriers *Akagi*, *Kaga*, *Soryu* and *Hiryu* (with a total of 72 dive-bombers, 90 attack aircraft and 72 fighters) escorted by the battleships *Haruna* and *Kirishima*, the heavy cruisers *Tone* and *Chikuma*, the light cruiser *Nagara*, 12 destroyers and a fleet train of eight tankers. This was to provide cover and support for Rear Admiral Raizo Tanaka's 2nd Fleet Escort Force, which sailed from Saipan in the Mariana Islands on 28 May with one light cruiser and 10 destroyers as escort for the Midway Occupation Force of 5,000 troops in 15 transports, together with a mine-sweeping group, these being supported by Rear Admiral Takeo Kurita's 2nd Fleet Occupation Support Force (the heavy cruisers *Kumano*, *Mogami*, *Mikuma* and *Suzuya*, two seaplane tenders and three destroyers) from Guam. The basic plan was for these forces to close in Midway from the north-west and west in order to attack Midway at dawn on 4 June unless US Navy forces were detected in the area, in which case Nagumo's carrier aircraft would attack these before neutralising Midway's defences so that the troops could land; to the west lurked a powerful reserve in case US opposition (at sea or on Midway) was stronger than expected. This reserve was Vice Admiral Nobutake Kondo's 2nd Fleet Strike Force (the light carrier *Zuiho* with 24 aircraft, the battleships *Hiei* and *Kongo*, the heavy cruisers *Atago*, *Chokai*, *Myoko* and *Haguro*, the light cruiser *Yura* and eight destroyers supported by four tankers), which was to crush US Navy forces in the region or to shatter the defences of Midway with gunfire. Yamamoto expected that all these operations would finally compel Nimitz to commit all naval forces available at Pearl Harbor, which would then be totally destroyed by the 2nd Fleet in conjunction with his own 1st Fleet Main Body (the light carrier *Hosho* with 19 aircraft, the battleships *Yamato*, *Nagato* and *Mutsu*, the light cruiser *Sendai* and nine destroyers) from Japan.

Intrinsic to the success of this complex operation, involving as it did some 71 major units of the Imperial Japanese navy, were security (already breached by the US Navy breaking of the Japanese JN-25 code), good and timely communications (impossible as everything had to be routed through Yamamoto) and accurate reconnaissance to upgrade the current intelligence picture. This last factor was denied the Japanese by the fact that operation 'K' had been cancelled, so removing Japan's capability for the aerial reconnaissance of Pearl Harbor, and that the screen of 13 submarines on picket duties between Pearl Harbor and Midway arrived only after the US carrier force had passed to the east; the result was that the Japanese forces did not know of the presence of US naval units near Midway, a situation exacerbated by the fact that neither Nagumo nor Kondo had been informed of the cancellation of 'K', and thus did not think to put up significant aerial reconnaissance patrols; thanks to the breaking of JN-25, Nimitz knew what was afoot, and Midway was

Continued on page 77

By 1931, Japan had completed the maximum of 12 heavy cruisers permitted under the terms of the Washington Naval Treaty, so further construction had to be limited to light cruisers carrying guns with a calibre of no more than 6.1in (155mm). The Japanese answer to this dilemma was the creation of the four-strong 'Mogami' class of cruisers with the prodigious armament of fifteen 6.1in guns in five triple turrets, and it was the threat of these ships that persuaded the Americans and British into the design and construction of the 'Brooklyn' and 'Southampton' classes respectively. Displacement was clearly going to be a critical problem with so many turrets, so the use of welding and light alloys, already pioneered in the 'Takao' class, was taken to a greater extreme. This was not without its problems, however, and sea trials with the first two ships were hampered by excessive top weight and structural problems due to poor welding, which resulted in hull deformations that prevented the main turrets from being trained over their full arcs. The two ships were therefore rebuilt with a wider hull carrying external bulges, and this provided greater structural strength as well as improving stability. The latter pair of ships were completed to this revised standard, and in 1939 all four ships were revised to full heavy cruiser standard with their fifteen 6.1in guns in triple turrets replaced by ten 8in guns in twin turrets. As completed to definitive initial standard, the ships had a displacement of 11,200 tons, an armament of fifteen 6.1in guns in five triple turrets, eight 5in anti-aircraft guns in four twin turrets, four 40mm anti-aircraft guns in single mountings and twelve 24in torpedo tubes, protection in the form of a 4in (102mm) belt and 1.5in (37mm) deck, and a speed of 35 knots on the 152,000hp (113,330kW) delivered to four shafts by steam turbines.

The final type of Japanese heavy cruiser was the 'Tone' class of two ships completed in 1938 and 1939. The design was an improved version of that developed in the 'Mogami' class with the main armament reduced to twelve 6.1in guns in four triple turrets all located forward with one unit in a superfiring position. This arrangement was adopted as the ships were intended specifically for the scouting role associated with Combined Fleets operations deep in the Pacific, and allowed the after part of the ship to be dedicated to the floatplane complement of five aircraft (as opposed to the three and two aircraft carried respectively by the preceding two classes) and two beam catapults. The details of the 'Tone' class included a displacement of 11,215 tons, an armament of eight 8in guns in four twin turrets, eight 5in anti-aircraft guns in four twin turrets, twelve 25mm anti-aircraft guns in six twin mounting, and twelve 24in torpedo tubes, protection in the form of a 4in (102mm) belt and 2.5in (63mm) deck, and a speed of 35 knots on the 152,200hp (113,480kW) delivered to four shafts by steam turbines.

In the late 1930s the Japanese navy decided that the time was ripe for the replacement of its older light cruisers built in the early 1920s with a main armament of 5.5in (140mm) guns. The first result of this decision was the completion between 1942 and 1944 of the four ships of the 'Agano' class with a full-load displacement of 8,535 tons, an armament of six 5.9in (150mm) guns in three twin turrets (a superfiring pair forward and a singleton unit aft), four 3in (76mm) anti-aircraft guns in two twin turrets, up to fifty-nine 25mm anti-aircraft guns in ten triple and 29 single mountings and eight 24in torpedo tubes, protection in the form of a 2.25in (57mm) belt and 0.75in (19mm) deck, and a speed of 35 knots on the 110,000hp (82,015kW) delivered to four shafts by steam turbines.

The final cruiser to be completed by the Japanese in World War II was the single light cruiser of the 'Oyodo' class, which was based on the 'Agano' class design but with revisions suiting it to the somewhat different role of commanding a scouting and hunting group of aircraft and submarines. The

primary gun armament of six 6.1in guns was therefore located forward of the superstructure in a superfiring pair of triple turrets, and this left the after part of the ship clear for the floatplane installation, which comprised two aircraft launched from a single centreline catapult but recovered from the sea at the end of their missions by a pair of beam cranes. The other details of this ship, which was completed early in 1943, included a displacement of 8,165 tons, a secondary armament of eight 3.9in anti-aircraft guns in four twin mountings and twelve 25mm anti-aircraft guns in four triple mountings, protection in the form of a 2in (51mm) belt and 2in deck, and a speed of 35 knots on the 110,000hp (82,015kW) delivered to four shafts by steam turbines.

All these Japanese cruisers were extensively used in World War II, and in general proved to be excellent and sturdy warships well able to undertake the tasks asked of them. Wartime modification was extensive as the ships were refitted and repaired, most of the modification efforts being concerned with the improvement of the ships' short-range anti-aircraft defences in an effort to provide them with a counter to the overwhelming air superiority that the Americans were able to bring to bear from a time late in 1942. Virtually every spare part of deck area was used for single or multiple anti-aircraft mountings, and the need for such enhancement often meant the removal of some or all of the aircraft capability, and also some of the torpedo capability.

The end of World War II signalled the end of the gun-armed cruiser as an effective naval weapon at a time when the guided missile soon came to replace the gun as the primary weapon carried by major warships. The more modern ships were maintained in service to provide an interim capability, but the way forward was revealed by the USA in the first half of the 1950s, when two heavy cruisers of the 'Baltimore' class were converted as guided missile cruisers for the fleet escort role: the after end of each ship was remodelled with two twin-arm launchers (for a total of 144 RIM-2 Terrier medium-range surface-to-air missiles) and their associated surveillance, target acquisition and missile guidance radars together with the fire-control systems. The success of the two conversions, which were recommissioned in 1955 and 1956, paved the way for a conversion of six 'Cleveland' class light cruisers, whose after ends were similarly cleared and adapted for the carriage of one twin-arm launcher for 120 Terrier SAMs and their associated radar and fire-control system. These ships were recommissioned between 1958 and 1960, and were followed between 1962 and 1964 by the most elaborate of the conversions. These were three more 'Baltimore' class ships that were stripped of all their main gun armament turrets to permit their modification into two-ended missile ships with two twin-arm launchers for a total of 104 RIM-8 Talos long-range SAMs complemented by two twin-arm launchers abreast of the forward superstructure for 84 Terrier SAMs. These launchers were complemented by the associated radar and fire-control systems, the provision of four target-tracking/missile-guidance radars allowing the simultaneous engagement of four targets rather than the maximum of two that was possible with the earlier conversions.

The success of these ships paved the way for the creation of purpose-designed guided missile cruisers optimised for the defence of the carrier battle groups that had become the most important surface assets operated

Lead ship of a nine-strong class that was delivered between 1964 and 1967 as one of the most potent escort elements for American surface battle groups, the cruiser *Belknap* had a full-load displacement of 8,200 tons, length of 547ft 0in (166.7m), armament of one 5in (127mm) dual-purpose gun, two 20mm Vulcan six-barrel cannon in two Phalanx close-in weapon system mountings, one twin launcher for 40 Standard Missile surface-to-air missiles and 20 ASROC anti-submarine rockets, two quadruple launchers for eight Harpoon anti-ship missiles, six 12.75in (324mm) tubes in two triple mountings for lightweight anti-submarine torpedoes, and one helicopter; propulsion in the form of geared steam turbines delivering 85,000hp (63,375kW) to two shafts for a speed of 32.5 knots, and complement of 480. The ship therefore had a good blend of anti-aircraft, anti-submarine and anti-ship armament, its principal limitation being its inability to undertake the simultaneous engagement of more than two aircraft targets.

by the US Navy. The first of these new missile cruisers carried the same missiles as their predecessors, but these were replaced in due course by the superb RIM-66 and RIM-67 medium- and long-range versions of the Standard Missile. The missile cruisers were built in two basic forms with conventional or nuclear propulsion, the latter being designed for the support of nuclear-powered aircraft carriers on extended-duration deployments, but financial considerations have dictated that production of nuclear-powered missile cruisers has lagged behind the totals required for protection of the nuclear-powered aircraft carriers, which therefore operate with a mix of conventional- and nuclear-powered cruisers.

The current force of such cruisers operated by the US Navy includes the single nuclear-powered ship of the 'Long Beach' class completed in 1961; the nine conventionally powered ships of the 'Leahy' class completed between 1962 and 1964; the single ship of the 'Bainbridge' class completed in 1962 as a nuclear-powered version of the 'Leahy' class design; the one conventionally powered ship of the 'Belknap' class completed between 1963 and 1965; the single ship of the 'Truxtun' class completed in 1964 as a nuclear-powered version of the 'Belknap' class design; the two nuclear-powered ships of the 'California' class completed in 1974 and 1975; the four nuclear-powered ships of the 'Virginia' class completed between 1976 and 1980; and the planned 27 units of the 'Ticonderoga' class completed from 1983 with the extraordinarily complex and capable AEGIS mission system based on the SPY-1A electronically scanned planar-array radar system.

The *Long Beach* is the largest of these ships with a full-load displacement of 16,600 tons, an armament of two twin-arm launchers for 120 Standard Missiles, one octuple launcher for eight RUR-5 ASROC anti-submarine weapons, one octuple launcher for eight BGM-109 Tomahawk cruise missiles, two quadruple launchers for eight RGM-84 Harpoon anti-ship missiles, two 5in (127mm) dual-purpose guns in single turrets, two 20mm Vulcan six-barrel cannon in two Phalanx close-in weapon system mountings, and two triple tubes for 12.75in (324mm) anti-submarine torpedoes; the vessel has a speed of 30 knots on the 80,000hp (59,650kW) delivered to two shafts by steam turbines powered by two Westinghouse C1W pressurised water-cooled reactors. In all, this represents a prodigious capability against targets ranging from aircraft to pinpoint land objectives via submarines, ships and other surface targets on both sea and land.

The later nuclear-powered ships are somewhat smaller and have reduced, although still formidable, capabilities, but the most modern of the cruiser classes currently in service is the large 'Ticonderoga' class. This is based on a development of the hull designed for the 'Spruance' class destroyer, and its details include a full-load displacement of 9,450 tons, an armament of two twin-arm or, in later ships, two vertical-launch systems for a total of 68 or 122 weapons respectively in the form of various mixes of Standard Missile, up to 20 RUR-5 ASROC anti-submarine and 20 BGM-109 Tomahawk cruise missiles, two quadruple launchers for eight BGM-84 Harpoon anti-ship missiles, two 5in dual-purpose guns in single turrets, two 20mm Vulcan six-barrel cannon in Phalanx close-in weapon system mountings and two triple tubes for six 12.75in anti-submarine torpedoes; ships of the class are capable of a speed of 30 or more knots on the 80,000hp (59,650kW) delivered to two shafts by four General Electric LM2500 gas turbines.

Other Western countries that have built cruisers since the end of World War II include France with the single 'de Grasse' class light cruiser with a main armament of sixteen 5in (127mm) dual-purpose guns in eight twin turrets grouped in superfiring quadruplets forward and aft, and the single 'Colbert' class light cruiser with a similar main armament but later rebuilt as

reinforced to some 3,000 men under the command of the 6th Marine Defense Battalion, extra aircraft were flown in (bringing the island's air strength to 109), and reconnaissance patrols were flown in a great fan from the north-west to the south-west of the island; the naval support for these measures was the dispatch from Pearl Harbor of Fletcher's forces, consisting of Fletcher's Task Force 17 (the fleet carrier *Yorktown* with 13 torpedo bombers, 37 dive-bombers and 25 fighters, the heavy cruisers *Astoria* and *Portland*, and six destroyers) and Rear Admiral Raymond A. Spruance's Task Force 16 (the fleet carriers *Enterprise* and *Hornet* with a total of 29 torpedo bombers, 75 dive-bombers and 54 fighters, the heavy cruisers *New Orleans*, *Minneapolis*, *Vincennes*, *Northampton* and *Pensacola*, the light cruiser *Atlanta* and 11 destroyers). Other forces involved on the US side were Task Group 7.3 (a patrol of four submarines guarding the approaches to Oahu) and Task Group 7.1 (a patrol of 12 submarines in the western approaches to Midway). As the Japanese forces approached Midway, TFs 16 and 17 were ready to the north-north-east of the island, and the Japanese were first sighted at 09.00 on 3 June.

Operations began at 04.30 on 4 June, when Nagumo launched a first strike against Midway; the second wave of aircraft on board the Japanese carriers were armed with armour-piercing bombs or torpedoes in anticipation of an American naval counterattack. US aircraft took off from Midway to engage the incoming raid and to attack the carriers, but were generally knocked about by the superior Japanese aircraft and pilots; however, the leader of the Japanese strike called for another raid against the Midway defences, and at 07.00, Nagumo ordered his carrier crews to begin the lengthy task of replacing the second wave's anti-ship weapons with conventional bombs. Work had just begun when Nagumo was informed at 07.28 that a Japanese scout aircraft had spotted 10 US ships some 200 miles (320km) to the north-east; the report made no mention of this force's composition, but at 07.58 came another report that the US ships were five cruisers and five destroyers; thus work could proceed with the rearming of the second strike, although at this time the carriers' remaining fighters had to be scrambled to intercept an attack by Midway-based aircraft; then at 08.20 came yet another scout report, this time to the effect that the US naval force included one carrier.

Continued on page 79

a guided missile cruiser with an armament of one twin-arm launcher for Masurca SAMs aft and two 3.9in (100mm) guns in a pair of superfiring single turrets forward; Italy with the two 'Andrea Doria' class helicopter cruisers with an armament of one twin-arm launcher for Terrier (later Standard Missile) SAMs forward, eight 3in (76mm) dual-purpose guns in single turrets, and up to four anti-submarine helicopters aft; and the single 'Vittorio Veneto' class helicopter cruiser with an armament of one twin-arm launcher for Terrier (later Standard Missile) SAMs forward, eight 3in dual-purpose guns in single turrets, and up to nine anti-submarine helicopters aft; the Netherlands with two 'de Ruyter' class light cruisers with an armament of eight 6in (152mm) guns in two pairs of superfiring twin turrets; and the UK with three 'Tiger' class cruisers with an armament of two 6in guns in one twin turret, two launchers for Sea Cat SAMs, and up to four anti-submarine helicopters.

On the other side of the politico-military divide that emerged in the period after World War II, the only country to have built cruisers in the Warsaw Pact bloc was the USSR. This country had a strength of 15 cruisers in 1947, comprising two Russian ships from World War I, one American 'Omaha' class ship, one ex-German 'Nürnberg' class ship, one ex-Italian 'Aosta' class ship, two 'Kirov' class ships, four 'Maksim Gorky' class ships and four 'Chapayev' class ships. The USSR's next cruiser type was the 'Sverdlov' class: 24 of these were ordered, 20 were laid down, 17 were launched and only 14 were completed between 1951 and 1955 to a standard that included a full-load displacement of 17,200 tons, an armament of twelve 6in guns in two pairs of superfiring triple turrets, twelve 3.9in dual-purpose guns in six twin turrets, sixteen 37mm anti-aircraft guns in eight twin mountings and ten 21in (533mm) torpedo tubes, protection in the form of a 4.9in (125mm) belt and 3in (76mm) deck, and a speed of 32.5 knots on the 110,000hp (82,015kW) delivered to two shafts by steam turbines. These

The *Jeanne d'Arc* is the French navy's primary training ship, and in this task had accommodation and facilities for 140 cadets. The vessel is in fact a cruiser-sized helicopter carrier that in time of war would be used for the carriage of a 700-man commando battalion that would be landed by the eight helicopters carried on the large flightdeck abaft the superstructure/funnel assembly. The details of this interesting ship include a full-load displacement of 12,365 tons, length of 597ft 1in (182.0m), armament of four 3.9in (100mm) dual-purpose guns in single turrets, two triple launchers for six MM.38 Exocet anti-ship missiles, and four helicopters, propulsion in the form of geared steam turbines delivering 40,000hp (29,825kW) to two shafts for a speed of 26.5 knots, and complement of 625.

ships were obsolete even as they were being built, but in the later 1950s the USSR started to create considerably more powerful cruisers of two new types within the context of the Soviet ambition to create a navy with genuine blue-water capability. This might not have been able to wrest command of the seas from the US Navy, but was schemed to create the strength that could inflict major casualties on any American force attempting an amphibious invasion of the USSR.

The first of the new types was intended specifically for the engagement and destruction of American aircraft carriers and their supporting warships in operationally vital carrier battle groups, and its first example was the 'Kynda' class of four ships completed between 1962 and 1965 with a full-load displacement of 5,600 tons, an armament of two quadruple launchers for sixteen SS-N-3 'Shaddock' nuclear-tipped anti-ship missiles, one launcher for 24 SA-N-1 SAMs, four 3in dual-purpose guns in two twin turrets, two 12-tube anti-submarine rocket launchers, and six 21in torpedo tubes, and a speed of 34 knots on the 100,000hp (74,560kW) delivered to two shafts by steam turbines.

The 'Kynda' class ships provided a very useful initial capability against the American aircraft carrier force, but were complemented in 1967 and 1968 by the four 'Kresta I' class cruisers that still provided a major offensive punch but were better able to provide their own protection against aircraft and submarine attack. The ships therefore had a full-load displacement of 7,500 tons, an armament of two twin launchers for just four SS-N-3 'Shaddock' anti-ship missiles, two twin-arm launchers for 44 SA-N-1 SAMs, four 57mm anti-aircraft guns in two twin mountings, two 12-tube and two six-tube anti-submarine rocket launchers, ten 21in torpedo tubes, and one anti-submarine and/or missile-guidance helicopter, and a speed of 34 knots on the 100,000hp (74,560kW) delivered to two shafts by steam turbines.

At this time the nuclear-powered ballistic missile submarine was beginning to come to the fore as a decisive strategic weapon, and the threat of the USA's growing force of such boats was reflected in the construction of the 'Kresta II' class of ten cruisers adapted from thc 'Kresta I' class design for the specialised task of hunting and killing American nuclear-powered submarines. In this task the primary sensor was an advanced sonar system located in the forefoot of the lengthened bow section, and the primary weapon, the SS-N-14 'Silex' missile, was used to deliver a homing torpedo or nuclear depth charge to the area pinpointed by the sonar (either shipborne or helicopter-carried) as the location of the target submarine.

From 1971 the 'Kresta II' class cruisers were complemented by seven 'Kara' class anti-submarine cruisers, which were the first full-size cruisers to enter service with the Soviet navy after the 'Sverdlov' class ships. With a full-load displacement of 9,900 tons, the ships of this class carry an armament of two quadruple launchers for eight SS-N-14 'Silex' anti-submarine weapons, two twin-arm launchers for 72 SA-N-3 'Goblet' SAMs, two twin-arm launchers for 40 SA-N-4 'Gecko' SAMs, four 3in dual-purpose guns in two twin turrets, four 30mm six-barrel anti-aircraft cannon in single mountings, up to ten 21in torpedo tubes, and two 12- and two six-tube anti-submarine rocket launchers. Propulsion is based on the delivery of 134,000hp (91,710kW) to two shafts by a combined gas turbine or gas turbine (COGOG) arrangement of four large and two small gas turbines for a speed of 34 knots.

The 'Kara' class ships seem to have persuaded the Soviets of the advantage of a full-size cruiser hull for good ocean-going and weapon-carrying capability, and the most recent Soviet class comprises the four ships of the 'Slava' class optimised for the dual-role anti-ship and anti-submarine task with a full-load displacement of 11,200 tons for the carriage of a weapons fit that includes eight twin launchers for SS-N-12 anti-ship

Nagumo's position was now impossible, for the scrambled fighters needed refuelling, the first Midway attack wave was due back, and the second wave was in no position to attempt either sort of attack; while still dithering, Nagumo turned north-east at 09.18 to attack the US forces.

Now it was Fletcher's turn, and he launched a first strike at 07.52 from the *Enterprise* and *Hornet*, following with a strike from the *Yorktown* at 09.00 as she was farther to the north. At 09.30 the US torpedo bombers found the Japanese carriers and attacked. The aircraft were obsolete Douglas Devastators and were destroyed, in the process convincing Nagumo that the Americans' first strike had been beaten, giving the Japanese time to complete the arming of his aircraft for an anti-ship strike. Thus the decks of the Japanese carriers were packed with aircraft as the Douglas Dauntless dive-bombers of Fletcher's first strike arrived overhead and screamed down at 10.25, within five minutes devastating the *Akagi*, *Kaga* and *Soryu*. Between 19.00 and 19.30 the *Soryu* and *Kaga* sank, and the *Akagi* was finished off with torpedoes on the following day. It was a devastating blow from which only the *Hiryu*, cruising separately, escaped. Thus the sole Japanese carrier launched two strikes, and these found and struck the *Yorktown* between 12.05 and 12.15, and at 14.30. The US carrier was abandoned at 15.00 and later sunk by submarine attack while under tow. Now it was the turn of the *Hiryu*, which was devastated by aircraft from the *Enterprise* at 17.00 and scuttled at 05.10 on the following day, being finished off later by Japanese torpedoes. This was a disaster from which the Japanese could not really recover, though Yamamoto tried desperately to entice the US forces into combat with his battleship forces. Fletcher made the right tactical and strategic decision, and thus withdrew.

The Americans had lost 307 dead and 147 aircraft, as well as one carrier and one destroyer; on the other side the Japanese had lost some 3,500 dead (including highly trained and irreplaceable aircrews) and 332 aircraft, as well as four carriers. The Japanese heavy cruisers *Mogami* and *Mikuma* were also damaged in a collision, both ships then being damaged further by air attacks and the *Mikuma* later sinking. The Japanese had suffered a blow of mortal proportions, and Yamamoto had no option but to call off the rest of 'MI', which can justly claim to have cost the Japanese the war; the Battle of Midway was thus one of history's truly decisive battles.

The key to the genuine anti-aircraft capability of most US Navy modern surface warships and those of the USA's allies is the General Dynamics Standard Missile. This was an evolutionary development of the RIM-2 Terrier and RIM-24 Tartar weapons, and is currently operated in four forms as the single-stage RIM-66A/B Standard Missile 1 MR in the medium-range role, the two-stage RIM-67A Standard Missile 1 ER in the long-range role, the single-stage RIM-66C Standard Missile 2 MR in the medium-range role and the two-stage RIM-67B Standard Missile 2 ER in the long-range role. The Standard Missile 2 series had an improved guidance package by comparison with the Standard Missile 1, allowing a considerable increase in range through optimisation of the missiles' trajectories. Seen here is a RIM-66A/B being fired from the type of single-arm launcher typical of American frigates. The missile weighs either 1,276lb (579kg) for the RIM-66A or 1,342lb (609kg) for the RIM-66B, is either 14ft 8in (4.47m) or 15ft 6in (4.724m) long for the RIM-66A and RIM-66B respectively with a diameter of 1ft 1.5in (0.343m) and a span of 3ft 0in (0.914m), and its data include a speed of more than Mach 2, a range of 28.75 or 41.6 miles (46.25 or 67km) and an upper altitude limit of 50,000 or 62,500ft (15,240 or 19,050m) for the RIM-66A and RIM-66B respectively.

missiles, eight octuple launchers for 64 SA-N-6 'Grumble' SAMs, two twin-arm launchers for 40 SA-N-4 'Gecko' SAMs, two 5.1in (130mm) dual-purpose guns in a twin turret, six 30mm six-barrel anti-aircraft guns in single mountings, ten 21in torpedo tubes, two 12-tube anti-submarine rocket launchers, and one anti-submarine/missile update helicopter. Propulsion is based on the delivery of 120,000hp (89,470kW) to two shafts by four gas turbines for a speed of 34 knots.

The Soviet cruiser force was completed by the two hybrid helicopter cruisers of the 'Moskva' class that were commissioned in 1967 and 1968 with a full-load displacement of 19,300 tons, an armament of two twin-arm launchers for 48 SA-N-3 'Goblet' SAMs, one SUW-N-1 twin launcher for 18 FRAS-1 anti-submarine weapons, two 12-tube anti-submarine rocket launchers, four 57mm anti-aircraft guns in two twin turrets, and 14 anti-submarine helicopters.

Further development of the cruiser is in abeyance as the CIS lacks the need and financial resources for further such ships, and in these circumstances the USA is well equipped with its current types.

Destroyers and Escorts

The *Manchester* is the lead ship of the four-strong 'Type 42 Batch 3' subclass of the 'Type 42' class of guided missile destroyers operated by the Royal Navy since the commissioning of all 12 of the ships between 1976 and 1985. The 'Type 42 Batch 3' subclass has greater length and beam than the other two subclasses for improved seaworthiness and an enlarged missile capacity, and the details of these four ships include a full-load displacement of 5,350 tons, length of 462ft 10in (141.1m), armament of one 4.5in (114mm) dual-purpose gun, two 20mm Vulcan six-barrel cannon in two Phalanx close-in weapon system mountings, four 20mm cannon in single mountings, one twin launcher for 40 Sea Dart surface-to-air missiles, six 12.75in (324mm) tubes in two triple mountings for lightweight anti-submarine torpedoes and one helicopter, propulsion in the form of a COGOG arrangement with two gas turbines delivering 50,000hp (37,280kW) or two gas turbines delivering 9,700hp (7,230kW) to two shafts for a speed of 30 or 18 knots respectively, and complement of 300.

With the advent of the locomotive torpedo as a viable weapon from 1868, most navies began to expend considerable effort on flotillas of fast torpedo-armed vessels intended mainly for the coast defence role by threatening the battle fleets of any potential invader. So great was the threat of the torpedo boat in the minds of most admirals, who feared for the survival of their fleets of battleships that were several nations' most important military assets, that considerable effort was soon put into the creation of ships to catch and destroy torpedo boats. This demanded a speed comparable with that of the torpedo boat as well as a primary armament of quick-firing guns and a small complement of torpedo tubes, which could be replaced by additional quick-firing guns, so that the type could also be used as a torpedo boat. The first of these torpedo boat catchers, soon to be known

The six large destroyers of the 'L'Audacieux' class were launched in 1933 and 1934 for service with the French navy, and the last units were not scrapped until the early 1980s. In their heyday these were superb destroyers offering considerable firepower and very high speed that could be maintained under all conditions. The ship illustrated here is *Le Fantasque* that was scrapped in 1957, and the details of this important class include a full-load displacement of 3,400 tons, length of 434ft 6in (132.4m), armament of five 5.5in (140mm) guns in single turrets, four 37mm anti-aircraft guns in single mountings and nine 21.7in (550mm) torpedo tubes in three triple mountings, propulsion in the form of geared steam turbines delivering 74,000hp (55,365kW) to two shafts for a speed of 37 knots, and complement of 210.

as torpedo boat destroyers, were launched in the UK in 1886. These lacked the speed to catch their prey, however, and it was only in 1892 that the Admiralty took the plunge in a decisive way, ordering no fewer than 42 'turtleback' torpedo boat destroyers from a number of yards that were given considerable discretion about the manner in which they fulfilled the Admiralty's basic requirement for a given armament, triple-expansion steam engines and a speed of 27 knots. The first of these generally successful 'A' class torpedo boat destroyers were ordered from Yarrow as the *Havock* and *Hornet* with triple-expansion steam engines powering two shafts for a speed of 26 knots with an armament that comprised one 12pdr and three 6pdr guns as well as three 18in (457mm) torpedo tubes that could be replaced by two more 6pdr guns.

The two vessels and their successors quickly displayed so marked an ascendancy over the torpedo boat that the earlier type was soon discontinued in favour of rapid development and construction of the torpedo boat destroyer (soon to be called the destroyer) as a dual-purpose type for torpedo attacks on the enemy's fleet and protection of its own fleet against enemy torpedo attack. These early destroyers were capable of speeds in the order of 26 or 27 knots, although a lengthening of the hull and the installation of more powerful engines soon allowed the creation of improved destroyers with a speed of 30 knots, and 60 of these improved torpedo boat destroyers were ordered for later allocation to the 'B', 'C' and 'D' classes depending on their use of four, three and two funnels respectively. The decisive moment in the development of the early destroyer came in 1897, however, when the Hon.

The Indian navy's three 'Blackwood' class frigates, here exemplified by the *Kuthar*, were built in the UK during the mid-1950s to a standard that included a full-load displacement of 1,535 tons, length of 310ft 0in (94.5m), armament of three 40mm anti-aircraft guns in single mountings, two three-barrel Limbo Mk 10 anti-submarine mortars and four 21in (533mm) torpedo tubes in two twin mountings, propulsion in the form of geared steam turbines delivering 15,000hp (11,185kW) to one shaft for a speed of 27 knots, and complement of 140. The class, which included 12 British ships, was intended as a cheaper successor to the 'Whitby' class frigates with the same anti-submarine capability but with only half the power.

The Brazilian navy's destroyer *Para* was originally the US Navy's Guest of the 'Fletcher' class. Brazil acquired the ship in December 1959, and discarded the vessel as wholly obsolete in 1978, when the cost of refurbishment would have been prohibitive. The armament of the ship in its latter days was five 5in (127mm) dual-purpose guns in single turrets, ten 40mm anti-aircraft guns in two twin and two single mountings, one 'Hedgehog' anti-submarine projector, and depth charge racks.

Charles Parsons produced his *Turbinia* to prove the capabilities of his steam turbine propulsion arrangement. So impressive was the performance of this privately funded experimental type that the Royal Navy switched to the steam turbine for its latest destroyers, starting with the *Viper* that was completed in 1900 with a speed of 33.75 knots on a light displacement of 344 tons with a four-shaft steam turbine propulsion arrangement.

These and other early destroyers, powered by triple-expansion or later by turbine engines, were capable of reaching their legend speed only under ideal conditions, however, and anything but a smooth sea made the vessels very wet and rendered the forward guns all but unworkable. By the early 1900s, therefore, the British and other navies had decided that greater size was not just inevitable but also desirable: this would allow the introduction of more powerful engines so that a high speed could be maintained under adverse conditions, and also make possible the introduction of the raised forecastle that would reduce wetness and allow the forward guns to be fought under most operational conditions. The way was paved by the German 'S90' class in which a raised forecastle replaced the turtledeck for improved seaworthiness, and the British responded with the 34 units of the 'River' or 'E' class with considerably greater displacement and a far more seaworthy basic design matched by a more powerful propulsion arrangement and greater bunkerage for improved seaworthiness and greater range. The ships were built in a large number of subvariants by different yards and to a standard that included a full-load displacement of some 620 tons, a propulsion arrangement of triple-expansion steam engines delivering 7,000hp (5,220kW) for a sustained speed of 25.5 knots, and with the same armament as the smaller 30-knot vessels, although from 1906 this was increased to four 12pdr guns and two 18in (457mm) torpedo tubes.

It is with these 'River' class vessels that the era of the true destroyer may be said to have started in a meaningful way, for all that was now needed to create the 'modern destroyer' was the combination of the improved size and seaworthiness of the 'River' class with turbine propulsion and oil- rather than coal-fired boilers.

The first move in this direction came in the period between 1907 and 1909, when the twelve units of the 'Tribal' or 'F' class were completed in two major subclasses as five and seven ships as what may be regarded as the destroyer equivalents of the 'dreadnought' battleship with a virtual doubling of the displacement, a primary armament of 4in (102mm) guns, and a propulsion arrangement that combined oil-fired boilers and steam turbines. The ships were the first genuinely ocean-going rather than sea-going destroyers, and while the earlier vessels had a displacement of between 865 and 890 tons, a length of between 250 and 270ft (76.2 and 82.3m) and a speed of between 33 and 36 knots with a propulsion arrangement in which steam turbines delivered 14,500hp (10,815kW) to three shafts, the later vessels had a displacement of between 970 and 1,090 tons, a length of 280ft (85.3m) and a speed of between 33 and 36 knots with a propulsion arrangement in which steam turbines delivered 15,500hp (11,555kW) to three shafts.

A portent of things to come was the *Swift*, which was completed in 1907 as a flotilla leader with a displacement of 1,850 tons, an armament of four 4in guns and one 2pdr gun as well as two 18in torpedo tubes, and a speed of 39 knots on the 50,000hp (37,280kW) delivered to four shafts by steam turbines.

All these early destroyers had provided both builders and the Royal Navy with considerable experience in the design and operation of destroyers, and the sensible decision was now taken to concentrate on the introduction of homogeneous classes of ships at the rate of between 16 and 24 units per year. The first of these groups was the 16-strong 'Basilisk' or 'G' class completed in 1909 and 1910 with a displacement of between 885 and 965 tons, an armament of one 4in and three 12pdr guns as well as two 18in torpedo tubes, and a speed of some 28 knots on the 12,500hp (9,320kW) delivered to three shafts by steam turbines supplied from coal-fired boilers, which were adopted as there were fears that oil might be in short supply in the event of war. The speed of this class was on the low side, but the ships were very seaworthy. The following 'Acorn' or 'H' class, of which 20 were completed in 1910 and 1911, was somewhat smaller with a displacement of 780 tons, but was capable of a speed between 27 and 30 knots on the 13,500hp (10,065kW) delivered to three shafts by steam turbines supplied from oil-fired boilers, which now became a standard feature of British destroyers. The armament comprised two 4in guns and, for the first time in British destroyers, two 21in (533mm) torpedo tubes. The ships were each built in an average time of 18 months, a rate considerably faster than earlier types as a result of claims by the Germans that they were building large numbers of destroyers in a time of between twelve and 15 months.

The 'Acheron' or 'I' class that followed in 1911 and 1912 totalled 20 ships

The US Navy's force of destroyers built in the 1930s, many of them to a design with the uptakes from two boiler rooms trunked into a single funnel, provided invaluable fleet capability in the early years of the US involvement in World War II, after which they were phased into less taxing service as they were supplemented and then replaced by more modern destroyers of the 'Fletcher', 'Gearing' and 'Allen M. Sumner' classes.

that comprised 14 to a standard pattern and six slightly different ships with a more powerful propulsion arrangement and a number of innovatory features. The standard type had a displacement of between 750 and 780 tons, an armament of two 4in and two 12pdr guns as well as two 21in torpedo tubes, and a speed of between 27 and 30 knots on the 13,500hp (10,065kW) delivered to three shafts by steam turbines, while the more powerfully engined type had a speed of between 29 and 31 knots on the 15,000–16,500hp (11,185 – 12,300kW) delivered to three shafts by steam turbines. Another six ships were delivered to the Royal Australian Navy, three of them from original British contracts which were replaced by another three ships built by Yarrow to an improved standard with a displacement of 790 tons and a speed of between 32 and 35 knots on the 20,000hp (14,910kW) delivered to three shafts by steam turbines. The last three ships were in effect the prototypes for the later Yarrow variants of the Admiralty standard destroyer design.

The final two destroyer classes introduced before World War I were the 'Acasta' or 'K' class and the 'L' class, which introduced a new British system of nomenclature in which all the ships of a given class had names beginning with the same letter. The 'Acasta' class completed in 1912 and 1913 comprised 12 standard ships, six ships with a different armament disposition and with two rather than three shafts, and two prototypes for the two- and three-funnel versions of the following 'L' class. The standard version had a displacement of 780 tons, an armament of two 4in guns and two 21in torpedo tubes, and a speed of between 27 and 30 knots on the 13,500hp (10,065kW) delivered to three shafts by steam turbines.

The 'L' class was the definitive version of the British destroyer in the period leading up to World War I, and totalled six two-funnel and sixteen three-funnel ships that introduced a raked rather than vertical stem, twin torpedo tube mountings and a 'bandstand' mounting for the amidships gun. The ships each possessed a displacement of between 965 and 1,070 tons, an armament of three 4in guns and one 2pdr gun as well as four 21in torpedo tubes, and a speed of between 29 and 31 knots on the 22,500 – 24,500hp (16,775 – 18,265kW) delivered to two shafts by steam turbines.

Not surprisingly, Japanese destroyers of the World War II period revealed a number of conceptual similarities to the same navy's light cruisers. The ships were generally notable for their armament of 5in (127mm) guns in twin turrets, and multiple banks of 24in (610mm) tubes for the exceptionally potent 'Long Lance' anti-ship torpedo, a weapon in which the Japanese navy placed great reliance and which proved very successful up to the middle of 1943, when the US Navy had perfected the radar-directed tactics that negated the favourite Japanese tactic of night destroyer attacks.

As the war broke out in August 1914, the first of the new 'M' class destroyers were coming into service as improved versions of the 'L' class ships, with a displacement in the order of 994 – 1,042 tons, an armament of three 4in guns and one 2pdr gun as well as four 21in torpedo tubes, and a speed of 34 knots (often exceeded by a considerable margin) on the 25,000hp (18,640kW) delivered to three shafts by steam turbines. The 'M' class was built to a total of 112 ships, which was so great that the Admiralty ran out of suitable names and therefore gave many of the ships 'N', 'O', 'P' and even 'R' and 'T' names.

The 'M' class ships were followed by 49 'R' class ships with 'R', 'S', 'T' and 'U' names to a standard that differed from that of the 'M' class mostly in their 'bandstand' mounting for the after 4in gun and their propulsion arrangement of 27,000hp (20,130kW) delivered to three shafts by geared steam turbines for a speed of 36 knots. The final class of 1,000-ton British destroyers comprised the 67 units of the 'S' class with 'S' and 'T' names, a displacement of 1,075 tons, an armament of three 4in guns and one 2pdr gun as well as four 21in and two 14in (356mm) torpedo tubes (which were later removed), and a speed of 36 knots on the 27,000hp (20,130kW) delivered to two shafts by geared steam turbines.

By the middle of World War I, it was clear that further improvement of the destroyer called for a larger hull with a greater displacement, and this led to the development of the 'VW' class with 'V' and 'W' names, a longer and beamier hull, a displacement of between 1,272 and 1,339 tons, and a speed of 34 knots on the 27,000hp (20,130kW) delivered to two shafts by geared steam turbines. The ships fell into two subclasses: the 'V' subclass had an armament of four 4in guns and one 3in anti-aircraft gun as well as four 21in torpedo tubes, while the 'W' subclass had an armament of three 4in guns and one 3in anti-aircraft gun as well as six 21in torpedo tubes in two triple mountings.

The Royal Navy appreciated that effective control of destroyer flotillas demanded leaders with the additional size to carry a flotilla commander and his staff, but had only the *Swift* at the beginning of the war. The service was fortunate, however, that four strong flotilla leader class were under construction in British yards for Chile and Turkey, and these were taken over as the 'Botha' and 'Talisman' classes for completion in 1914-15 and 1916 respectively. The first new leaders built specifically to British specification appeared in 1916, and these were the seven and six units of the 'Marksman' and 'Later Marksman' classes supplemented in 1917 and 1918 respectively by the three ships of the 'Shakespeare' class and the eight ships of the 'Scott' class that were alternatively known as the 'Thornycroft' and 'Admiralty' types.

The British generally led the world in the design and construction of destroyers in this period. Germany's most advanced destroyer class at the beginning of World War I was the 'S30' class of six ships completed in 1914 and 1915 with a

Opposite top: Although they often lack the technical skills and the financial resources to operate and maintain the advanced ships they sometimes feel compelled to buy for reasons of national prestige, many Third-World countries make effective use of less advanced vessels. Into this latter category falls the *Otobo*, the Vosper Thornycroft Mk 3 corvette of the Nigerian navy. Commissioned in 1972, this vessel has a full-load displacement of 660 tons, length of 202ft 0in (61.6m), armament of one 3in (76mm) dual-purpose gun in a single turret and two 40mm anti-aircraft guns in a twin turret, propulsion in the form of diesel engines delivering 8,000hp (5,965kW) to two shafts for a speed of 22 knots, and complement of 70. Such ships allow the development of greater naval skills in the tactical and technical senses, and in the shorter term provide a useful capability for the patrol of the country's coastal waters.

Opposite centre: The *Herstal* of the Belgian navy, which originally had 16 of the class, is a good example of the type of inshore minesweeper required to keep clear the approaches to a port such as Antwerp.

Opposite bottom: Among the many lesser known but still important types of ships are mine warfare vessels, here epitomised by the French navy's *Circé*, lead ship of a class of five minehunters commissioned in the early 1970s. The ships have only the lightest of conventional armament, namely one 20mm cannon, but carry sophisticated sonar for the detection and localisation of sea-bed mines that are then investigated and, if required, destroyed with the aid of the PAP electrically powered and remotely controlled underwater vehicle that carries a TV camera and a 220lb (100kg) explosive charge that can be laid close to the mine and then detonated by remote control.

displacement of 970 tons, an armament of three 3.4in (88mm) guns and six 19.7in (500mm) torpedo tubes, and a speed of between 33 and 36 knots on the 23,500 – 25,000hp (17,520 – 18,650kW) delivered to two shafts by steam turbines. After 1916, Germany's priority was submarines rather than surface warships, and this meant that only 22 more destroyers were completed in the period up to the end of the war. The last of these were the three ships of the 'H145' class of which two were commissioned in 1918 and the third only in 1920 for the French navy as part of Germany's war reparations. These ships had a displacement of 1,147 tons, an armament of three 4.1in (105mm) guns and six 19.7in (500mm) torpedo tubes, and a speed of between 34 and 37 knots on the 23,500 – 25,500hp (17,520 – 19,010kW) delivered to two shafts by steam turbines.

Advanced destroyers were also built in this period by France, Italy, Japan and the USA, and less advanced ships were constructed by countries such as Austria-Hungary and Russia.

After World War I, all the British destroyers up to and including the 'M' class were soon discarded, and further development was based on the 'VW' and 'Marksman' classes. Throughout the 1920s and 1930s, the older destroyers were gradually replaced by newer vessels and, on the outbreak of World War II, the only earlier destroyers still in service were one 'R' class ship, 11 'S' class ships used mainly in the minelaying role, most of the 'VW' class ships used mostly in the escort role, and eight leaders.

With large numbers of comparatively new ships on strength, the Royal Navy ordered no new destroyers in the period between 1918 and 1924, and then made the sensible decision to give Thornycroft and Yarrow, the two

The Royal Navy's frigate *Seymour* of the 'Captain' class was a destroyer escort built in the USA during World War II with a displacement of 1,300 tons, length of 306ft 0in (93.3m), armament of three 3in (76mm) anti-aircraft guns in three single mountings, two 30mm anti-aircraft guns in single mountings and eight or ten 20mm cannon in single mountings, propulsion in the form of a turbo-electric drive delivering 12,000hp (8,945kW) to two shafts for a speed of 26 knots, and complement of 200.

premier builders of British destroyers, a relatively free hand in the creation of two prototypes (*Amazon* and *Ambuscade*) to provide the basis of a new standard type offering improvements over the 'VW' class in terms of greater speed, improved habitability and greater range. Both ships were launched in 1926, and from them were evolved for the Royal Navy and Royal Canadian Navy the 11 ships of the 'A' class with an armament of four or five 4.7in (120mm) guns and quadruple mountings for their eight 21in (533mm) torpedo tubes, nine generally improved ships of the 'B' class, 14 ships of the 'C/D' class with a single 3in (76mm) anti-aircraft gun in place of the earlier ships' two 2pdr anti-aircraft guns, 18 ships of the 'E/F' class with provision for rapid conversion to the minelaying task, 18 generally improved ships of the 'G/H' class, and nine ships of the 'I' class with a tripod rather than pole main mast and quintuple rather than quadruple torpedo tube mountings.

The 'I' class destroyers were launched in 1936 and 1937, and at this stage the British halted further development along this course to produce the 'Tribal' class of an eventual 27 destroyers for the Royal Navy, Royal Australian Navy and Royal Canadian Navy. These ships reflected British concerns that their destroyers were being outstripped technically and operationally by the large destroyers being built in a number of other countries. The result was a highly capable although expensive destroyer with a doubled gun armament, a halved torpedo armament, and much enhanced anti-aircraft and anti-submarine armaments. The 'Tribal' class destroyers possessed a displacement between 1,870 and 1,925 tons, an armament in their baseline British form of eight 4.7in guns in four twin turrets, four 2pdr anti-aircraft guns in a quadruple mounting and four 21in torpedo tubes, and a speed of 36 knots on the 44,000hp (32,805kW) delivered to two shafts by geared steam turbines.

The expense of the 'Tribal' class was too high for its capabilities to be repeated in later classes, which therefore dropped one 4.7in twin turret, reintroduced two quintuple mountings for 21in torpedoes, and reduced the number of boilers to just two so that a single funnel could be used. This scheme resulted in the nine and eight ships of the generally similar 'J' and 'K' classes launched in 1938 and 1939. The sixteen ships of the equally sized 'L' and 'M' classes differed mainly in having dual-purpose guns in fully enclosed twin turrets, but the additional expense of this arrangement resulted in the eight ships of the 'N' class reverting to the earlier and simpler arrangement.

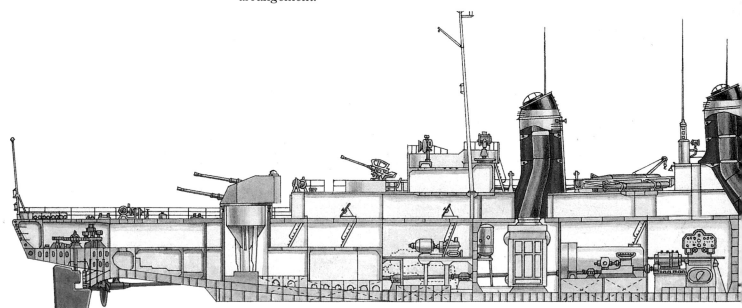

By the time that the 'N' class destroyers were under construction, the UK had accepted the inevitability of war with Germany and, reminded by its merchant shipping losses to submarine attack in World War I, had decided to waste no time in the introduction of a convoy system as soon as war did finally break out. This raised the need for a large number of specialised escort vessels if the Royal Navy's force of fleet destroyers was not to be stripped to the point that it could not support major surface forces. The result was a series of dual-role and escort destroyer classes optimised for the escort role with the same basic hull construction and boiler arrangement as the latest fleet destroyers but with an armament of main guns in single mountings, improved anti-submarine weapons, and enhanced anti-aircraft weapons in which the standard arrangement of four 2pdr guns in a quadruple mounting was supplemented by four single (later twin) mountings for 20mm cannon, replaced later in the war by 40mm weapons in single mountings.

The dual-role destroyer classes comprised the eight ships of the 'O' class fitted for minelaying and with 4in (102mm) rather than 4.7in guns in four of the vessels; the eight ships of the generally similar 'P' class with 4in rather than 4.7in guns and in four of the vessels one 4in anti-aircraft gun in place of one of the two quintuple mountings for 21in (533mm) torpedoes; the eight ships of the 'Q' class with the light anti-aircraft armament increased from four to six 20mm cannon; the eight ships of the 'R' class with eight 20mm cannon and surface warning radar; the eight ships of the 'S' class that introduced the 4.5in (114mm) dual-purpose gun in one ship, had eight 20mm cannon in all ships, and in some ships replaced the 2pdr quadruple mounting with two 40mm guns or four 20mm cannon, the eight ships of the 'T' class with ten and later twelve 20mm cannon; the eight ships of the 'U' class with lattice masts and a diverse arrangement of anti-aircraft guns; the eight ships of the 'V' class with a light anti-aircraft armament of two 40mm guns in a twin mounting or four 2pdr guns in a quadruple mounting and eight 20mm cannon in four twin mountings; the eight ships of the 'W' class with a light anti-aircraft armament of two 40mm guns in a twin mounting and eight 20mm cannon in four twin mountings or, in some ships, four or five 40mm guns in single mountings; and the eight ships of the 'Z' class with the 4.5in dual-purpose gun and a light anti-aircraft armament of two 40mm guns in a twin mounting and six 20mm cannon in two twin and two single mountings.

Finally in the first series of this family of dual-role ships came the 32 destroyers of the 'C' class in four equal 'CA', 'CH', 'CO' and 'CR' subclasses with a displacement of some 1,720 tons, an armament of four 4.5in dual-purpose guns in single mountings, four 40mm anti-aircraft guns in one twin and two single mountings, four 20mm anti-aircraft cannon in two twin mountings and four 21in torpedo tubes in a quadruple mounting, and a speed of 36.75 knots on the 40,000hp (29,825kW) delivered to two shafts by geared steam turbines.

Late in the war, with the defeat of Germany certain and greater emphasis now placed on longer-range operations in the Pacific against the Japanese, the British designed a new destroyer type as the 'Battle' class on the basis of a larger hull to provide greater seaworthiness, a longer range, enhanced self-sufficiency in the course of protracted operations away from a major base, and a much heavier anti-aircraft armament for the protection not only of itself but of the larger warships (especially the aircraft carriers) it was supporting. Some 44 of the class, including two

The *Centauro* was completed in 1957 as one of the Italian navy's four 'Canopo' class frigates designed for the destroyer escort rather than conventional frigate role, and was based on a scaled-down version of the hull of the 'Impetuoso' class destroyer. The details of this small but nicely planned type included a full-load displacement of 2,250 tons, length of 338ft 4in (103.1m), armament of four 3in (76mm) dual-purpose guns in two twin turrets, four 40mm anti-aircraft guns in two twin mountings, one three-barrel Menon anti-submarine mortar in a turreted installation and two 21in (533mm) torpedo tubes (later altered to three 3in/76mm dual-purpose guns in single turrets, one Menon mortar and six 12.75in/324mm tubes in two triple mountings for lightweight anti-submarine torpedoes), propulsion in the form of geared steam turbines delivering 22,000hp (16,405kW) to two shafts for a speed of 26 knots, and complement of 210.

for the Royal Australian Navy, were ordered but only 28 were completed as sixteen units of the second group were cancelled. The ships had a displacement of some 2,325 tons and a speed of 35.75 knots on the 50,000hp (37,280kW) delivered to two shafts by geared steam turbines, and two types of armament: in the first group this comprised four 4.5in dual-purpose guns in two twin turrets, one 4in anti-aircraft gun, fourteen 40mm anti-aircraft guns in four twin and six single mountings or alternatively twelve 40mm anti-aircraft guns in three twin and six single mountings, and eight or ten 21in torpedo tubes; the second group had five 4.5in dual-purpose guns in two twin and one single turrets, eight 40mm anti-aircraft guns in three twin and two single mountings, and ten 21in torpedo tubes.

Another type ordered only slightly later and completed to the extent of only two ships was the 'Weapon' class, optimised for the anti-aircraft and anti-submarine roles with anti-ship capability offered only by the low-angle fire of its six 4in dual-purpose guns, which were installed in three twin turrets, and its ten 21in torpedo tubes.

The standard type of escort destroyer built by the British was the 'Hunt' class of which 86 units were completed in four subclasses including the 'Hunt Type IV' class of only two ships. These ships were essentially small and simple, and the three main subclasses were the 'Hunt Type I' class of 20 ships (generally used in home waters) with a displacement of 907 tons, an armament of four 4in anti-aircraft guns in two twin turrets, four or five 2pdr anti-aircraft guns in one quadruple and one single mounting and two 20mm cannon, and a speed of 26 knots on the 19,000hp (14,165kW) delivered to two shafts by geared steam turbines; the 'Hunt Type II' class of 36 ships (common in home and Mediterranean waters) with a displacement of 1,050 tons, an armament of six or four 4in anti-aircraft guns in three or two twin turrets, four or five 2pdr anti-aircraft guns in one quadruple and one single mounting, and two or three 20mm cannon in single mountings, and a speed of 25 knots on the 19,000hp (14,165kW) delivered to two shafts by geared steam turbines; and the 'Hunt Type III' class of 28 ships (also used in home and Mediterranean waters) with a displacement of 1,085 tons, an armament of four 4in anti-aircraft guns in two twin turrets, four or five 2pdr anti-aircraft guns in one quadruple and one single mounting, two or three 20mm cannon in single mountings and two 21in torpedo tubes, and a speed of 25 knots on the 19,000hp (14,165kW) delivered to two shafts by geared steam turbines.

In World War I the Royal Navy ordered the construction of an eventual 72 ships of the 'Flower' class, generally known as the 'herbaceous borders' and officially designated as fleet minesweeping sloops. These were built in three

Name ship of an 18-strong class of destroyers built in the late 1930s and operated with great success by the Imperial Japanese navy in the early part of World War II, the *Kagero* was built to an improved 'Asashio' class design and proved so good that all later Japanese destroyer classes in World War II were merely developments of the 'Kagero' class. The details of this excellent destroyer included a displacement of 2,033 tons, length of 388ft 6in (118.4m), armament of six 5in (127mm) dual-purpose guns in three twin turrets, four 25mm anti-aircraft guns in two twin mountings and eight 24in (610mm) torpedo tubes in two quadruple mountings, propulsion in the form of geared steam turbines delivering 52,000hp (38,770kW) to two shafts for a speed of 35 knots, and complement of 240. The Kagero was badly damaged by a mine in May 1943 and then finished off by US Navy aircraft off Rendova Island in the Solomons chain, but sister ships that survived to 1943 and 1944 generally had the 5in gun turret in the X position replaced by six 25mm anti-aircraft guns in two triple mountings, thereby raising the number of such weapons to fourteen as four 25mm guns had already been added to the original fit, and from 1944 seven of the ships were further improved in anti-aircraft capability by an increase to between 18 and twenty-eight 25mm guns.

subclasses as the 'Acacia', 'Azalea' and 'Arabis' types, and although intended mainly for the fleet minesweeping role soon proved themselves very versatile and were therefore adapted for other roles such as escort or, in the case of 39 more ships, completed as Q ships with hidden armament that was designed for the destruction of submarines lured to the surface by the apparently innocuous appearance of these 'merchant' ships. A further 24 ships were built in the '24' class of general-purpose sloops with a central funnel, a dummy bridge aft, and a straight stem and stern to present a double-ended appearance that made it difficult to detect the way the ships were moving at slow speed, especially as effective dazzle painting was employed. These two classes of sloop provided most of the Royal Navy's coastal escort strength in the second half of World War I, and remained in service through the 1920s and 1930s.

In the later 1930s, the apparent inevitability of war with Germany, and with it the renewed threat of submarine attack on the UK merchant navy fleet, persuaded the Admiralty to reconsider its escort capabilities, a process that resulted in the ordering of 20 fast escorts, the ordering of 56 whale-catcher type vessels for the coastal escort role, the conversion of old destroyers to the escort task, and the construction of a new class of oceanic escort as the 'Black Swan' class of sloops. This last class appeared from mid-1939, and eventually totalled 37 ships including four for the Royal Indian Navy, with the final five (including another two Indian ships) cancelled in the closing stages of the war. The ships were built in two forms: as the 'Black Swan' class with a displacement of 1,250 tons, an armament of six 4in anti-aircraft guns in three twin turrets, four 2pdr guns in a quadruple mounting, and four 0.5in (12.7mm) machine guns in a quadruple mounting or twelve 20mm cannon in six twin mountings, and a speed of 19.25 knots on the 3,600hp (2,685kW) delivered to two shafts by geared steam turbines; and as the 'Modified Black Swan' class with a displacement of 1,350 tons, an armament of six 4in anti-aircraft guns in three twin turrets and twelve 20mm cannon in six twin mountings, and a speed of 20 knots on the 4,300hp (3,205kW) delivered to two shafts by geared steam turbines.

The 'Black Swan' and 'Modified Black Swan' classes offered very useful escort capabilities, but they were fairly large vessels built to full warship standards with a geared steam turbine propulsion arrangement, and this made for considerable cost and slow production. The Admiralty had already appreciated this fact and in 1939 ordered the 'Flower' class of escort corvette, of which an eventual 270 were completed in the UK and Canada for service with the navies of the British empire as well as a number of Allied navies. The type, based on a whale-catcher design, was designed for construction to mercantile (and therefore cheaper and quicker) standards with a triple-expansion steam propulsion arrangement, and was produced in two forms. The basic 'Flower' class had a displacement of 950 tons, an armament of one 4in gun, one 2pdr anti-aircraft gun or four 0.5in machine guns in a quadruple mounting and four 0.303in (7.7mm) machine guns in two twin mountings, and a speed of 16 knots on the 2,750hp (2,050kW) delivered to one shaft by a triple-expansion steam engine; the 'Modified Flower' class had a displacement of 980 tons, an armament of one 4in gun, one 2pdr anti-aircraft gun, six 20mm cannon in single mountings, and one 'Hedgehog' anti-submarine projector, and a speed of sixteen knots on the 2,880hp (2,145kW) delivered to one shaft by a triple-expansion steam engine.

The importance of the two 'Flower' classes to the eventual Allied victory over Germany cannot be overestimated, but from an early date the Admiralty realised that the hull was slightly too small for the oceanic escort role and therefore complemented the 'Flower' classes with the larger and faster 'River' class of frigates, which were built to mercantile standards and had a two-shaft propulsion arrangement powered by triple-expansion steam engines. Some 139 of this class were completed in the UK, Australia and Canada for service with the navies of the British empire as well as several Allied navies. The type had a displacement of 1,370 tons, a varied armament of anti-ship and anti-aircraft weapons as well as a Hedgehog anti-submarine projector, and a speed of 20 knots on the 5,500hp (4,100kW) delivered to two shafts by triple-expansion steam engines.

Economical to build and capable in operational terms, the 'River' class was a highly effective type, but its length precluded its construction in many of the yards that had been able to build the 'Flower' classes of corvette. The Admiralty therefore tapped this production source with the 'Castle' class of corvettes, which was built from 1943 and totalled 44 units with a large number of others cancelled at the end of the war. The details of this excellent class included a displacement of 1,010 tons, an armament of one 4in gun, ten 20mm cannon in two twin and six single mountings and one 'Squid' anti-submarine projector, and a speed of 16.5 knots on the 2,880hp (2,145kW) delivered to one shaft by a triple-expansion steam engine.

The 'River' class was followed into production by the 'Loch' and 'Bay' classes of general escort and anti-aircraft frigates, which were built from prefabricated elements to speed production. Some 56 of the two classes were completed, with another 54 cancelled late in the war, and the details of the 'Loch' class included a displacement of 1,435 tons, an armament of one 4in gun, four 2pdr anti-aircraft guns in a single mounting, six 20mm cannon in two twin and two single mountings, and two Squid anti-submarine projectors, and a speed of 20 knots on the 6,500hp (4,845kW) delivered to two shafts by geared steam turbines or 5,500hp (4,100kW) delivered to two shafts by triple-expansion steam engines; the details of the 'Bay' class included a displacement of 1,580 tons,

The *Parramatta* was the second of four (originally to have been six) 'River' class frigates commissioned into the Royal Australian Navy in the early 1960s after construction in Australia to a slightly modified British 'Whitby' class design with a full-load displacement of 1,560 tons, length of 370ft 0in (112.7m), armament of two 4.5in (114m) dual-purpose guns in a twin turret, two 40mm anti-aircraft guns in a twin mounting, twelve 21in (533mm) torpedo tubes in two twin and eight single mountings and two Limbo Mk 10 three-barrel anti-submarine mortars, propulsion in the form of geared steam turbines delivering 30,000hp (22,370kW) to two shafts for a speed of 29 knots, and complement of 230.

Lead ship of a three-strong class of Australian guided missile destroyers modelled closely on the American 'Charles F. Adams' class and delivered from an American yard in the mid-1960s, the *Perth* has a full-load displacement of 4,525 tons, length of 437ft 0in (133.2m), armament of two 5in (127mm) dual-purpose guns in single turrets, one twin launcher for Standard Missile surface-to-air missiles, two Ikara launchers for anti-submarine rockets and six 12.75in (324mm) tubes in two triple mountings for lightweight anti-submarine torpedoes, propulsion in the form of geared steam turbines delivering 70,000hp (52,190kW) to two shafts for a speed of 33 knots, and complement of 350.

Built as a light cruiser in World War II, the *Oklahoma City* was recommissioned into the US Navy in 1960 as one of six such cruisers converted to the fleet escort role with a completely revised armament and associated electronic fit. The ships remained in service into the period 1970-79, and their revised standard included a full-load displacement of 15,150 tons, length of 610ft 0in (186.0m), armament of three 6in (152mm) guns in a triple turret, two 5in (127mm) dual-purpose guns in a twin turret and one twin launcher for 46 RIM-8 Talos surface-to-air missiles, propulsion in the form of geared steam turbines delivering 100,000hp (74,560kW) to four shafts for a speed of 32 knots, and complement of 1,380.

an armament of four 4in anti-aircraft guns in two twin turrets, four 40mm anti-aircraft guns in two twin mountings, four 20mm cannon in two twin mountings and one Hedgehog anti-submarine projector, and a speed of 20 knots on the 6,500hp (4,845kW) delivered to two shafts by geared steam turbines or 5,500hp (4,100kW) delivered to two shafts by triple-expansion steam engines.

At the time of its involvement in World War II in December 1941, the US Navy had 171 operational destroyers, including 71 of the two related 'flushdeck' types that had been built to the extent of 272 destroyers in World War I. Some 31 of these were of the 'Wickes' class with a displacement of 1,090 tons, an armament of four 4in guns in single mountings, one 3in anti-aircraft gun and twelve 21in torpedo tubes, and a speed of 35 knots on the 26,000hp (19,410kW) delivered to two shafts by geared steam turbines. The other 40 of the 'flushdeck' destroyers were units of the 'Clemson' class with a displacement of 1,190 tons, with similar armament, speed and propulsion arrangement.

Construction of destroyers was halted in the USA until the early 1930s, when destroyer developments in other parts of the world finally persuaded the Americans to undertake the construction of a more advanced type in the form of the 'Farragut' class of seven ships with a displacement of 1,395 tons, an armament of five 5in guns in single mountings and eight 21in torpedo tubes in two quadruple mountings, and a speed of 36.5 knots on the 42,800hp (31,910kW) delivered to two shafts by geared steam turbines. In the period leading up to World War II, the US Navy developed the conceptual design of the 'Farragut' class via the 'Mahan' class of 18 ships with twelve 21in torpedo tubes in three quadruple mountings to the 'Craven' class of 22 ships with an armament of four 5in guns in single mountings, four 1.1in anti-aircraft guns in single mountings and sixteen 21in torpedo tubes in four quadruple mountings.

A parallel course of evolution produced the eight and five ships of the 'Porter' and 'Somers' classes respectively for the squadron leader task. The basic design of the 'Porter' class included a displacement of 1,850 tons, an armament of eight 5in guns in four twin mountings and eight 21in torpedo tubes in two quadruple mountings, and a speed of 37 knots on the 50,000hp (37,280kW) delivered to two shafts by geared steam turbines, and the 'Somers' class differed mainly in its uprated propulsion arrangement with 52,500hp (39,145kW) for a speed of 37.5 knots.

Further development of the basic fleet destroyer concept in the late 1930s led to the 'Sims' class of twelve ships that proved to be top-heavy, so one of their five 5in guns and one of their three quadruple 21in torpedo tube mountings were soon removed. The same fate befell the early units of the 'Benson' class, which was an improved version of the 'Sims' class, and itself later upgraded as the 'Livermore' class: construction of the 'Benson' and 'Livermore' classes totalled 32 and 64 ships respectively.

Experience with these classes paved the way for the 'Fletcher' class destroyer that was the US Navy's most important ship of its type in the first part of the war. Built to the extent of 178 ships that were delivered from 1942 with a beamier, flushdecked hull, an increased displacement of 2,050 tons, an armament of five 5in guns in single mountings, between six and ten 40mm and 20mm anti-aircraft guns and ten 21in torpedo tubes in two quintuple mountings, and a speed of 37 knots on the 60,000hp (44,870kW) delivered to two shafts by geared steam turbines.

The 'Fletcher' class destroyers were complemented from 1944 by the 'Allen M. Sumner' and 'Gearing' class destroyers, which were bigger and more heavily armed vessels well suited to the demands of long-range operations in the western Pacific, where they were often exposed to

93

intensive Japanese air attack by *kamikaze* as well as conventional aircraft. The 58 'Allen M. Sumner' class ships were completed to a standard that included a displacement of 2,200 tons, an armament of six 5in dual-purpose guns in three twin turrets, twelve 40mm anti-aircraft guns and ten 21in torpedo tubes in two quintuple mountings, and a speed of 36.5 knots on the 60,000hp (44,870kW) delivered to two shafts by geared steam turbines, and the 99 ships of the 'Gearing' class, completed during and after the closing stages of the war as a development of the 'Allen M. Sumner' class with a lengthened hull, had a displacement of 2,425 tons, an armament of six 5in dual-purpose guns in three twin turrets, twelve or sixteen 40mm anti-aircraft guns and ten 21in torpedo tubes in two quintuple mountings (except in ships with 40mm guns), and a speed of 35 knots on the 60,000hp delivered to two shafts by geared steam turbines.

The US Navy had not initially appreciated the need for dedicated destroyer escorts, and the type was originally ordered in 1941 by the UK, which contracted with American yards for an initial 50 destroyer escorts, or escort destroyers as they were called by the British, before increasing this total to 250 in the following year. After entering the war, the USA soon appreciated the unglamorous but nonetheless vital important of the destroyer escort for the protection of troop and equipment convoys in the Pacific, where their faster and more heavily armed destroyer half-brothers were better employed for the protection of carrier and amphibious task forces. Thus only 55 of these American ships were finally transferred to the British, and of the orders placed by 1943 for 1,005 destroyer escorts, 508 were completed – 452 as destroyer escorts (29 of them for transfer to Allies other than the UK) and the other 56 as high-speed transports.

The ships were completed with two types of hull. The original group of 61 ships comprised the 'Evarts' class with an overall length of 283ft 4in (86.36m), while the others had a hull with an overall length of 306ft 0in (93.27m) and were the 'Buckley', 'Rudderow', 'Cannon', 'Edsall' and 'John C. Butler' classes. The 'Evarts' class had a displacement of 1,140 tons, an armament of three 3in guns in single mountings, four 40mm anti-aircraft guns and five 20mm cannon, and a speed of 21 knots on the 6,000hp

The *Zaal* is one of four 'Saam' or 'Vosper Thornycroft Mk 5' class frigates launched in the UK for the Iranian navy in the late 1960s with a full-load displacement of 1,400 tons, length of 310ft 0in (94.5m), armament of one 4.5in (114mm) dual-purpose gun in a single turret, two 35mm anti-aircraft guns in a single turret, one quintuple launcher for five Sea Killer Mk 2 anti-ship missiles, one triple launcher for nine Seacat surface-to-air missiles and one Limbo Mk 10 three-barrel anti-submarine mortar, propulsion in the form of a CODOG arrangement with gas turbines delivering 46,000hp (34,300kW) and diesels delivering 3,800hp (2,835kW) to two shafts for a speed of 40 or 17.5 knots respectively, and complement of 135.

(4,475kW) delivered to two shafts by a diesel-electric propulsion arrangement. The ships of the 'Buckley' class had a displacement of 1,400 tons, an armament of three 3in guns in single mountings, six 40mm anti-aircraft guns and three 21in torpedo tubes, and a speed of 23.5 knots on the 12,000hp (8,950kW) delivered to two shafts by a turbo-electric propulsion arrangement. The following 'Rudderow' class had a displacement of 1,450 tons, an armament of two 5in guns in single mountings, ten 40mm anti-aircraft guns and three 21in torpedo tubes, and a speed of 24 knots on the 12,000hp (8,950kW) delivered to two shafts by a turbo-electric propulsion arrangement. However, in the 'Cannon' class a diesel-electric propulsion arrangement had to be adopted, as in the 'Buckley' class, because of shortages of turbo-electric equipment, and this resulted in a displacement of 1,240 tons, an armament of three 3in guns in single mountings, six 40mm anti-aircraft guns and three 21in torpedo tubes, and a speed of 21 knots on the 6,000hp (4,475kW) delivered to two shafts by a diesel-electric propulsion arrangement. The 'Edsall' class was similar, and its details included a displacement of 1,200 tons, an armament of three 3in guns in single mountings, eight 40mm anti-aircraft guns and three 21in torpedo tubes, and a speed of 21 knots on the 6,000hp (4,475kW) delivered to two shafts by a diesel-electric propulsion arrangement. The final 'John C. Butler' class was somewhat different, and its details included a displacement of 1,350 tons, an armament of two 5in guns in single mountings, ten 40mm anti-aircraft guns and three 21in torpedo tubes, and a speed of 24 knots on the 12,000hp (8,950kW) delivered to two shafts by geared steam turbines.

Of the other Allied powers in World War II, only France operated a large navy to any effect, and then only to June 1940 in any strategically meaningful manner. The French destroyer force, in order of design, included the six large destroyers of the 'Jaguar' class launched in 1923 and 1924 before completion with a full-load displacement of 3,050 tons and a primary armament of five 5.1in (130mm) guns in single mountings; the 24 medium destroyers of the 'Simoun' class launched in two groups between 1924 and 1929 before completion with a full-load displacement of 2,000 tons and a main armament of four 5.1in guns in single mountings; the 18 large destroyers of the 'Guépard' class launched in four groups between 1928 and 1932 before completion with a full-load displacement of 3,400 tons and a primary armament of five 5.5in (140mm) guns in single mountings; the six large destroyers of the 'Le Fantasque' class launched in 1933 and 1934 with a full-load displacement of 3,400 tons and a primary armament of five 5.5in guns in single mountings; the 12 small destroyers of the 'La Melpomène' class launched between 1935 and 1937 before completion with a full-load displacement of 900 tons and a primary armament of two 3.9in guns in single mountings; the two ships of the 'Mogador' class that were the epitome of large destroyer design and capability after launch in 1936 and 1937 before completion with a full-load displacement of 4,020 tons, a primary armament of eight 5.5in guns in four twin mountings, and a speed of 39 knots on the 92,000hp (75,265kW) delivered to two shafts by geared steam turbines; and the eight large destroyers of the 'Le Hardi' class launched between 1938 and 1939 before completion with a full-load displacement of 2,575 tons and a primary armament of six 5.1in guns in three twin mountings.

On the other side of the military divide were Germany, Italy and Japan. The first destroyers to be built in Germany were the 22 ships of the 'Type 34' or 'Maass' class, which were laid down from 1934 for launch in 1937 and 1938. Despite their attempts to keep abreast of current design trends during the time they had been denied the right to build such ships, the Germans found themselves with a number of problems, most notably in the

The *D'Estienne d'Orves*, lead ship of the French navy's large 'A69' class of frigates, fires one of its MM.38 Exocet anti-ship missiles. Completed between 1976 and 1984, these seventeen ships (with another three delivered to Argentina) have a full-load displacement of 1,250 tons, length of 262ft 6in (80.0m), armament of one 3.9in (100mm) dual-purpose gun in a single turret, two 20mm cannon in single mountings, two or four launchers for two or four MM.38 or MM.40 Exocet anti-ship missiles, one 14.75in (375mm) six-barrel anti-submarine rocket launcher and four 21.7in (550mm) tubes for anti-submarine and anti-ship torpedoes.

The *Glasgow* is the third unit of the 'Type 42 Batch 1' subclass of the 'Type 42' class of guided missile destroyers operated by the Royal Navy since the commissioning of all twelve of the ships between 1976 and 1985. The 'Type 42 Batch 1' subclass has less length and beam than the definitive 'Type 42 Batch 3' subclass and thus suffers in terms of seaworthiness and missile capacity, and the details of these four ships include a full-load displacement of 4,350 tons, length of 412ft 0in (125.6m), armament of one 4.5in (114mm) dual-purpose gun, two 20mm Vulcan six-barrel cannon in two Phalanx close-in weapon system mountings, four 20mm cannon in single mountings, one twin launcher for twenty-six Sea Dart surface-to-air missiles, six 12.75in (324mm) tubes in two triple mountings for lightweight anti-submarine torpedoes, and one helicopter.

The *Southampton* is one of the four ships of the 'Type 42 Batch 2' subclass within the 12-strong 'Type 42 class of guided missile destroyers operated by the Royal Navy.

Below: The *Erinomi* is a simple corvette of the 'Vosper Thornycroft Mk 9' class, of which the Nigerian navy operates two with a specification that includes a full-load displacement of 780 tons, length of 226ft 0in (69.0m), armament of one 3in (76mm) dual-purpose gun in a single turret, one 40mm anti-aircraft gun in a single mounting, two 20mm cannon in single mountings, one triple launcher for Seacat surface-to-air missiles and one 14.75in (375mm) three-barrel anti-submarine mortar.

propulsion arrangement, and the ships acquired an unfortunate but justified reputation for unreliability. Considerable size was chosen for advantages in weapon installation and seaworthiness, but the use of a short bow section with insufficient flare and freeboard meant that they were very wet ships in any sort of sea. In an attempt to match the projectile weight of the latest French destroyers, a new 5in (127mm) weapon was designed to supersede the well-proved 4.1in (105mm) gun, but although this was in itself a successful weapon it was installed in an obsolescent mounting that precluded its use as a dual-purpose weapon. The details of the ships included a full-load displacement of 3,160 tons, an armament of five 5in guns in single mountings, four 37mm anti-aircraft guns in two twin mountings, six 20mm cannon in single mountings and eight 21in torpedo tubes in two quadruple mountings, and a speed of 38 knots on the 70,000hp (52,200kW) provided to two shafts by geared steam turbines.

The survivors of these ships were complemented from the mid-war years by the 15 ships of the 'Type 36A' or 'Narvik' class, which was a development of the 'Type 34' design with greater weight of fire provided by a change to a main-armament calibre of 5.9in (150mm) in a gun that was difficult and slow to work. The details of this class included a full-load displacement of 3,600 tons, an armament of five 5.9in guns in one twin and three single turrets, four 37mm anti-aircraft guns in two twin mountings, five 20mm cannon in single mountings and eight 21in torpedo tubes in two quadruple mountings, and a speed of 36 knots on the 70,000hp (52,200kW) delivered to two shafts by geared steam turbines.

The problems with the main armament of the 'Type 36A' class persuaded the German naval high command that the switch to a 5.9in gun had been wrong, and the next type laid down was the 'Type 36B' class that reverted to the 5in gun. Only three of the ships were completed, with a full-load displacement of 3,505 tons, an armament of five 5in guns in single mountings, four 37mm anti-aircraft guns in twin mountings, fifteen 20mm cannon in three quadruple and three single mountings, eight 21in torpedo tubes in two quadruple mountings, and a speed of 36 knots on the 70,000hp (52,200kW) delivered to two shafts by geared steam turbines.

At the smaller end of the destroyer spectrum, Germany operated a number of ships including the twelve ships of the 'Albatros' and 'Iltis' classes laid down in the 1920s with an armament of three 4.1in guns in single mountings as well as a useful torpedo armament, 21 ships of the 'Type 35' and 'Type 37' classes that were too small for real utility, and then the 15 ships of the 'Type 39' or 'Elbing' class that were launched between 1942 and 1944. These were still comparatively small ships, but had an appearance sufficiently imposing that they were often mistaken for larger fleet destroyers. Their details included a full-load displacement of 1,755 tons, an armament of four 4.1in guns in single mountings, four 37mm anti-aircraft guns in two twin mountings, six 20mm cannon in single mountings and six 21in torpedo tubes in two triple mountings, and a speed of 33.5 knots on the 32,000hp (23,860kW) delivered to two shafts by geared steam turbines.

Italy also operated a mix of small and large (fleet) destroyers, some of them fairly old. The small type of destroyer was epitomised by a basic design originating in World War I with a 239ft 6in (73m) hull. The first of these were the eight 'Pilo' class ships of 1914-15 with an armament of five 4.1in guns in single mountings and four 17.3in (440mm) torpedo tubes in two twin mountings, and there followed the four 'Sirtori' class ships of 1916-17 with an extra gun, the eight 'La Masa' class ships of 1917-19 with the main armament restored to four guns, and the six 'Generale' class ships of 1921-22 with a full-load displacement of 890 tons, an armament of three 4in

(102mm) guns in single mountings, two 3in anti-aircraft guns in single mountings and four 17.3in torpedo tubes in two twin mountings, and a speed of 30 knots on the 15,000hp (11,185kW) delivered to two shafts by geared steam turbines.

A 269ft (82m) hull was used in the four 'Palestro' class ships of 1919-20 for almost a 50 per cent increase in power offering a higher speed with the same basic armament as the 'La Masa' class, and the same hull was retained for the improved 'Curtatone' class of 1922-23.

There followed a long gap in Italian small destroyer design and construction until the advent of the 32 'Spica' class ships from 1936. These had their boiler uptakes trunked into one funnel to maximise usable deck area, and their armament was based on a trio of 3.9in (100mm) guns in single mountings complemented by four 17.7in (450mm) torpedo tubes located initially as four single tubes but later as two twin mountings. Further development of the same concept resulted in the 'Ariete' class. Planned in 1941, the class was to have numbered more than 40 ships, but only 16 were laid down: only one of these was delivered to the Italian navy before Italy's September 1943 armistice with the Allies, but another 13 were later completed in northern Italy for German use. The type had a full-load displacement of 1,125 tons, an armament of two 3.9in guns in single mountings, two 37mm anti-aircraft guns in single mountings and six 17.7in torpedo tubes in two triple mountings, and a speed of 31 knots on the 22,000hp (16,405kW) delivered to two shafts by geared steam turbines.

Further development in Italian destroyer thinking resulted in the very similar 'Sauro' and 'Turbine' class destroyers of which four and eight respectively were built in the mid- and late 1920s with details that included, for the 'Turbine' class, a full-load displacement of 1,700 tons, an armament of four 4.7in (120mm) guns in two twin mountings, two 40mm anti-aircraft guns in single mountings and six 21in torpedo tubes in two triple mountings, and a speed of 36 knots on the 40,000hp (29,825kW) delivered to two shafts by geared steam turbines.

Between 1928 and 1930, and as successors to the four 'Sauro' class destroyers, the Italians produced, the 12 units of the 'Navigatore' class in which a heavy armament and considerable power were squeezed into a comparatively small hull for a full-load displacement of 2,580 tons, an armament of six 4.7in guns in three twin mountings, three 37mm anti-aircraft guns in single mountings and four or six 21in torpedo tubes in two twin or triple mountings, and a speed of 38 knots on the 50,000hp (37,280kW) delivered to two shafts by geared steam turbines.

During 1930-32, the Italian navy introduced the four ships of the 'Dardo' class in which maximum possible use of the deck area was facilitated by the trunking of the boiler uptakes into a single funnel. This permitted a main armament of four 4.7in guns in two twin mountings. Further development of the same concept led to the four destroyers of the improved 'Folgore' class with each gun mounting provided with its own director to make possible the simultaneous engagement of two targets. The main limitation of the 'Dardo' and 'Folgore' classes was their lack of seaworthiness, and in the following 1934 'Maestrale' class of four ships the hull was lengthened by some 32ft 9in (10m) and also increased in beam. Basically the same hull was used in the 1936 'Oriani' class of four ships. With the threat of war increasing at this time, the Italian navy in 1937 and 1938 placed orders for another twelve destroyers modelled on the 'Oriani' class design. These were the 'Soldato' class destroyers with a full-load displacement of 1,460 tons, and armament of four or five 4.7in guns in two twin and one single mounting, one 37mm anti-aircraft gun and six 21in torpedo tubes in two triple mountings, and a

The *Forbin* was one of the French navy's five 'Duperré' or 'T53' class destroyers completed in the mid-1950s as a development of the 'T47' class, with improved capability for the tracking and controlling of aircraft through the introduction of improved radar and specialised control equipment.

The *Athabaskan* is one of four 'Iroquois' or 'Tribal' class destroyers in service with the Canadian navy. The ships were commissioned in the first half of the 1970s as ocean escorts optimised for the anti-submarine role, but in the later 1980s were taken in hand for modernisation in the tribal update and modernization project (TRUMP) to re-emerge with a full-load displacement of 4,700 tons, length of 426ft 0in (129.8m), armament of one 3in (76mm) dual-purpose gun in a single turret and one 20mm Vulcan six-barrel cannon in a Phalanx close-in weapon system mounting, one vertical-launch system for 32 Standard Missile surface-to-air missiles, six 12.75in (324mm) tubes in two triple mountings for lightweight anti-submarine torpedoes and two large helicopters.

speed of 39 knots on the 48,000hp (35,790kW) delivered to two shafts by geared steam turbines.

Up to the end of World War I, the Japanese had adhered closely to British destroyer concepts, either buying directly from the UK or building ships based directly on British thinking, and worked within the overall scheme of large first- and smaller second-class destroyers. In the closing stages of World War I, however, the Japanese decided that there was something to be learned from German destroyer thinking especially in the matter of a well between the forecastle and the forward part of the superstructure to break the force of water streaming over the bows in any kind of weather. This resulted in the 13 'Minekaze' and 21 'Momi' class first- and second-class destroyers launched in the years immediately following World War I as what were basically large- and small-scale versions of the same basic design. The 'Minekaze' class ships had a full-load displacement of 1,650 tons, an armament of four 4.7in guns in single mountings and six 21in torpedo tubes in two triple mountings, and a speed of 39 knots on the 38,500hp (28,685kW) delivered to two shafts by geared steam turbines. The nine 'Kamikaze' class destroyers that followed were basically similar to the 'Minekaze' class ships, and further improvement of the same concept came with the twelve 'Mutsuki' class destroyers that introduced the 24in (610mm) torpedo as an exceptionally potent anti-ship weapon.

The Japanese launched the first of an eventual 20 'Fubuki' class first-class destroyers in 1927, and in the process created a type that was a trend-setter in destroyer design as it eschewed British and German design influences for a Japanese concept with a higher forecastle, no well between the forecastle and the forward part of the superstructure, and a strengthened superstructure

The *Scylla* is a 'Leander Batch 3A' frigate of the Royal Navy. One of the most successful warship types developed in the UK since World War II and built in large numbers for the export as well as domestic markets, the 'Leander' class was built in three basic forms in the 1960s, and the 'Leander Batch 3' or 'Broad-Beam Leander' class ships introduced greater beam for improved sea-keeping qualities. The specification for the 'Leander Batch 3' ships includes a full-load displacement of 2,960 tons, length of 372ft 0in (113.4m), armament of two 4.5in (114mm) dual-purpose guns in a twin turret, two or three 20mm cannon in single mountings, one quadruple launcher for Seacat surface-to-air missiles, one Limbo Mk 10 three-barrel anti-submarine mortar and one light helicopter. Some of the ships were later upgraded to 'Leander Batch 3A' standard, losing the 4.5in gun turret and Limbo mortar but gaining two twin launchers for four MM.38 Exocet anti-ship missiles, one sextuple launcher for 32 Sea Wolf surface-to-air missiles, and six 12.75in (324mm) tubes in two triple mountings for lightweight anti-submarine torpedoes.

The Royal Navy's eight 'County' class destroyers were commissioned between 1962 and 1980, and are here epitomised by the *Antrim*. The basic specification for these useful ships, which offered little short of cruiser capabilities, included a full-load displacement of 6,800 tons, length of 521ft 6in (158.9m), armament of four 4.5in (114mm) dual-purpose guns in two twin turrets, two 20mm cannon in single mountings, one twin launcher for Seaslug long-range surface-to-air missiles, two quadruple launchers for Seacat short-range surface-to-air missiles, and one helicopter; propulsion in the form of a combined steam and gas turbine (COSAG) arrangement with geared steam turbines delivering 30,000hp (22,370kW) and gas turbines delivering 30,000hp (22,370kW) to two shafts for a speed of 30 knots, and complement of 470. None of the ships remains in British service, four and one having been sold to Chile and Pakistan respectively in the 1980s.

The *Tromp* is the lead ship of the Dutch navy's two-ship class optimised for the air defence role and possessing the accommodation to support the commander of an anti-submarine escort squadron. The ships were commissioned in the mid-1970s and in their current form have a full-load displacement of 4,310 tons, length of 454ft 0in (138.4m), armament of two 4.7in (120mm) dual-purpose guns in a twin turret, one single launcher for 40 Standard Missile long-range surface-to-air missiles, one octuple launcher for 16 Sea Sparrow short-range surface-to-air missiles, two quadruple launchers for eight Harpoon anti-ship missiles, six 12.75in (324mm) tubes in two triple mountings for lightweight anti-submarine torpedoes, and one light helicopter.

that was thus considerably less prone to damage in heavy seas. These impressive ships had a standard displacement of 2,090 tons, an armament of six 5in (127mm) guns in three triple turrets and nine 24in torpedo tubes in three triple mountings with no fewer than 18 torpedoes, and a speed of 38 knots on the 50,000hp (37,280kW) delivered to two shafts by geared steam turbines.

In 1931 the Japanese introduced a small destroyer type as the 'Tomodzura' class, whose four units were planned to complete the destroyer tonnage allocated to the Japanese in the Washington Naval Treaty. These ships were designed for coastal operations off Japan and along the shore of eastern Asia, and were ambitious attempts to pack maximum capability into minimum hull, for with a standard displacement of only 650 tons, the ships carried an armament of three 5in guns in one twin and one single mounting as well as four 21in torpedo tubes in two twin mountings, and were capable of a speed of 30 knots on the 11,000hp (8,200kW) delivered to two shafts by geared steam turbines. That too much had been attempted on this hull was revealed by the top-heaviness of the class in general and the capsize of the lead ship in particular, and this problem was addressed in the following 'Ootori' class of eight ships launched between 1935 and 1937 with a longer but still very narrow hull and a reduced armament. The details of the 'Ootori' class included a full-load displacement of 1,050 tons, an armament of three 4.7in guns in single mountings, one 40mm anti-aircraft gun and three 21in torpedo tubes in a triple mounting, and a speed of 30 knots on the 19,000hp (14,165kW) delivered to two shafts by geared steam turbines.

Although the 'Fubuki' class destroyers had offered considerable capabilities at the time of their introduction – a

decade before the capable British 'J' class destroyers with a slightly inferior specification but a very high reputation – the trend-setting nature of the class had resulted in a number of operational problems that were addressed in succeeding classes. The first of these was the 'Akatsuki' class of four ships launched between 1931 and 1933 with a lightened topside structure on a shorter hull, and there followed the 'Hatsuhara' class of six destroyers with a hull that was shortened still further, resulting in the loss of one 5in gun mounting and one torpedo tube triple mounting, and a propulsion arrangement of reduced power as Japanese designers sought to comply with the limitations imposed by the first of the London Naval Agreements. Further development of the 'Hatsuhara' class design led to the 'Shiratsuyu' class of ten ships with a further shortening of the hull but an improvement in torpedo armament to eight 24in tubes in two quadruple mountings with reloads.

In 1937 there appeared the first of ten 'Asashio' class ships that ignored the London Naval Agreement limitations and were therefore very similar to

The *Boxer* is the lead ship of the six-strong 'Broadsword Batch 2' subclass of the Royal Navy's 'Broadsword' class of 10 guided missile frigates. The ships of the 'Broadsword Batch 1' subclass proved too short to carry the planned towed-array sonar and two medium helicopters, so the 'Broadsword Batch 2' subclass was lengthened by an appreciable degree and fitted with an uprated propulsion arrangement to create a highly effective type with excellent anti-ship, anti-aircraft and anti-submarine capabilities.

The *Duchess* was the last of the eight-strong 'Daring' class of standard gun-armed destroyers commissioned into the Royal Navy in the first half of the 1950s. The details of the class included a full-load displacement of 3,580 tons, length of 390ft 0in (118.8m), armament of six 4.5in (114mm) dual-purpose guns in three twin turrets, two 40mm anti-aircraft guns in single mountings and one 'Squid' anti-submarine projector, propulsion in the form of geared steam turbines delivering 54,000hp (40,260kW) to two shafts for a speed of 34.75 knots, and complement of 330.

The modular outfitting scheme devised in Germany by Blohm und Voss allows easy installation, repair, replacement and updating of equipment, weapons, sensors and other units installed in one of several types of standard module, and has resulted in the 'Meko' series of warships built in destroyer and frigate sizes. This is the *Aradu*, a 'Meko 360' class destroyer of the Nigerian navy.

the original 'Fubuki' class ships. The excellence of this basic design was further attested by the completion of 18 'Kagero' class destroyers that introduced a slightly beamier hull and were launched between 1938 and 1941 before completion to a standard that included a full-load displacement of 2,490 tons, an armament of six 5in guns in three twin mountings, four 25mm anti-aircraft guns in two twin mountings and eight 24in torpedo tubes in two quadruple mountings, and a speed of 35 knots on the 52,000hp (38,770kW) delivered to two shafts by geared steam turbines. So successful was the type considered, moreover, that the following 20 'Yugumo' class destroyers were basically similar.

The final type of large destroyer to be built by the Japanese in World War II was the 'Akitsuki' class, of which twelve units were launched between 1941 and 1944. These were planned as anti-aircraft escorts for major surface forces, and were designed to offer the same capabilities as the American 'Atlanta' and British 'Dido' class cruisers on a smaller hull that would therefore be cheaper and quicker to build. One of the keys to this capability was the adoption of a main gun of somewhat smaller calibre than those used in the Western ships, the loss of projectile weight in the Japanese gun being more than balanced by its considerably higher rate of fire. The details of the class included a full-load displacement of 3,700 tons, an armament of eight 3.9in (100mm) dual-purpose guns in two pairs of superfiring turrets, four 25mm anti-aircraft guns in two twin mountings and four 24in torpedo tubes in a quadruple mounting, and a speed of 33 knots on the 52,000hp (38,770kW) delivered to two shafts by geared steam turbines. During the course of the Pacific campaign, the Japanese came to appreciate that all their warships lacked adequate firepower to cope with saturation attacks by American warplanes, and in the surviving 'Akitsuki' class destroyers, the defensive anti-aircraft armament was steadily increased to fifty 25mm guns.

So far as convoy escorts were concerned, the Japanese were sadly let down by their high command, which had persistently based its plans on the winning of a quick victory and therefore had ignored the possibility of a protracted war and a long defensive effort in which Japan would be strangled by American submarine and air power unless vital convoys could be protected. The belated realisation that such ships were desperately needed resulted in the 'Matsu' class of escorts, of which only 17 of a planned 28 were completed in 1944 and 1945 with a full-load displacement of 1,530 tons, an armament of three 5in guns in one twin and one single mounting, twenty-four 25mm anti-aircraft guns in four triple and twelve single mountings, four 24in torpedo tubes in a quadruple mounting, and a speed of 27.5 knots on the 19,000hp (14,165kW) delivered to two shafts by geared steam turbines. Another and somewhat more austere escort was the 'Tachibana' class type of which more than 90 were planned, 27 laid down and only a few completed.

Since World War II, it has been the US Navy that has dominated the Western approach to destroyer design. Soon after the end of the war, relations between the USA and the USSR began to deteriorate rapidly, especially after the Soviet development of nuclear weapons, and as it became

The *Brave* is one of the six 'Broadsword Batch 2' class guided missile frigates currently operated by the Royal Navy.

clear that the Soviet navy was planning to develop a major submarine capability based on the design of the German 'Type XXI' class boat, the US Navy decided that a major upgrade of its escort forces was required to protect the carrier battle groups that were now the core of the service's operational thinking. Consequently, many of the surviving 'Fletcher', 'Gearing' and 'Allen M. Sumner' class fleet destroyers were revised to oceanic escort standard with a reduced gun armament but much improved anti-submarine capability. This made economic sense as the Americans had large numbers of these ships, which were still almost new, and the Soviet threat was slow to materialise in numbers and also in basic capability. Thus the conversions of World War II fleet destroyers into anti-submarine escorts provided the US Navy's main surface strength with a more than adequate defensive element, and the service could thus use its relatively limited funding to provide more modern escorts for the protection of convoys, which were seen to fall into two basic categories – as merchant ships providing fuel, food and raw materials for the USA's allies in Europe, and as amphibious warfare vessels transporting formations of the US Marine Corps and US Army for offensive operations in any part of the world.

These smaller ocean escorts, which were the equivalent of the destroyer escorts of World War II, were the 13 ships of the 'Dealey' class, four units of the 'Claud Jones' class, and two units of the 'Bronstein' class used as prototypes of more advanced types, the first two created in the 1950s and the last in the early 1960s with basically conventional weapons, although the 'Bronstein' class introduced the RUR-5 ASROC weapon which was a rocket used to deliver a homing torpedo or nuclear depth charge to the position of a target submarine detected and localised by sonar.

Further development of this ocean escort type, now generally reckoned to be a frigate rather than a destroyer, resulted in the ten ships of the 'Garcia' class, and the seven units of the 'Brooke' class that suffered in the replacement of one of the two 5in dual-purpose gun mountings by a launcher for sixteen RIM-24 Tartar surface-to-air missiles in recognition of the growing threat posed from the early 1960s by Soviet warplanes. This tendency was continued in the 46 ships of the 'Knox' class optimised for the anti-submarine role but offering a useful anti-aircraft capability with its octuple launcher for RIM-7 Sea Sparrow short-range SAMs.

The current mainstay of the US Navy's frigate force is the 'Oliver Hazard Perry' class of 51 ships commissioned from 1977. Although small, the type has a fair measure of electronic sophistication, and its primary details include a full-load displacement of 4,100 tons, an armament of one 3in dual-purpose gun, one 20mm Vulcan six-barrel cannon in a close-in weapon system mounting, one single-arm launcher for 40 missiles (generally four RGM-84 Harpoon anti-ship and 36 RIM-66 Standard Missile surface-to-air missiles), six 12.75in (324mm) torpedo tubes in two triple anti-submarine

Built for Iran but eventually taken into US Navy service, the *Chandler* is one of four 'Kidd' class guided missile destroyers developed from the 'Spruance' class and currently constituting one of the world's most potent destroyer classes with capabilities that verge on those of the cruiser. The details of the class include a full-load displacement of 9,750 tons, length of 563ft 4in (171.8m), armament of two 5in (127mm) dual-purpose guns in single mountings, two 20mm Vulcan six-barrel cannon in Phalanx close-in weapon system mountings, two twin launchers for 52 Standard Missile surface-to-air missiles and 16 ASROC anti-submarine rockets, two quadruple launchers for eight Harpoon anti-ship missiles, six 12.75in (324mm) tubes in two triple mountings for lightweight anti-submarine torpedoes, and two light helicopters, propulsion in the form of gas turbines delivering 80,000hp (59,655kW) to two shafts for a speed of 33 knots, and complement of 340.

mountings and, in some ships, provision for one anti-submarine helicopter, and a speed of 29 knots on the 41,000hp (30,570kW) delivered to one shaft by two General Electric LM2500 gas turbines.

In a slow process that started in the early 1950s, the mantle of fleet escort destroyer was gradually assumed from World War II conversions by new ships. The first of these were the four highly capable but also highly expensive destroyers of the 'Mitscher' class optimised for the anti-submarine role, then the ten destroyers of the 'Farragut' class optimised for the dual-role anti-submarine and anti-aircraft roles with ASROC missiles, homing torpedoes and one twin-arm launcher for 40 RIM-2 Terrier SAMs, and finally the 18 destroyers of the 'Forrest Sherman' class optimised for the general-purpose role with neither ASROC nor SAM weapons.

By the 1960s the Soviet threat was of a far higher order, and this led to the introduction of the 23 'Charles F. Adams' class destroyers with ASROC anti-submarine and RIM-24 anti-aircraft weapons, and then in the 1970s to the 31 'Spruance' and four 'Kidd' class destroyers with significant anti-submarine, anti-aircraft and anti-ship capabilities in the form of missiles, torpedoes and a multi-role helicopter. The final expression of this tendency,

This view of the stern section of the French destroyer *De Grasse* of the 'Tourville' or 'F67' class highlights the helicopter installation that lies at the heart of modern anti-submarine capability. Located just forward of the gear for the variable-depth sonar, that is one of the ship's key systems for the detection and localisation of submarines, is the helicopter platform and the fully enclosed hangar for two light anti-submarine helicopters that can also be outfitted for anti-ship operations. The hangar is topped by the Crotale Naval octuple launcher for short-range surface-to-air missiles.

which continued throughout the 1980s, is the 'Arleigh Burke' class, of which 26 are planned primarily for the anti-aircraft role with a slightly downgraded version of the AEGIS weapon system (SPY-1 radar and Standard Missile weapons) designed for the 'Ticonderoga' class cruisers.

These American leads have generally been followed in Western Europe, particularly in the UK, France, Italy, Germany and the Netherlands, and in the Far East, where Japan has built up an impressive destroyer and frigate force since the early 1960s.

The USSR also developed a major destroyer and frigate force from the late 1950s, and although the earlier of these classes were intended at the time of their introduction mainly for the destruction of American surface battle groups with large anti-ship missiles, later classes were completed to a more balanced standard with anti-submarine, anti-aircraft and anti-ship capabilities. The more modern of these classes, in order of introduction, were the 14 destroyers of the two 'Kashin' subclasses, the 22 destroyers of the 'Sovremenny' class and the twelve destroyers of the 'Udaloy' class; the 40 frigates of the three 'Krivak' subclasses and the three frigates of the 'Neustrashimy' class.

The most impressive of these are the 'Sovremenny' and 'Udaloy' class destroyers delivered from 1980. The 'Sovremenny' class design is optimised for the anti-ship and anti-aircraft roles with a full-load displacement of 7,300 tons, an armament of four 5.1in dual-purpose guns in two twin turrets, four 30mm six-barrel cannon in single mountings, two quadruple launchers for eight SS-N-22 'Sunburn' anti-ship missiles, two launchers for 44 SA-N-7 'Gadfly' SAMs, two 12-tube anti-submarine rocket launchers, four 21in torpedo tubes in two twin mountings, and one helicopter, and a speed of 32 knots on the 110,000hp (82,015kW) delivered to two shafts by geared steam turbines. The 'Udaloy' class design is optimised for the anti-submarine and anti-aircraft roles with a full-load displacement of 8,700 tons, an armament of two 5.1in dual-purpose guns in single turrets, four 30mm six-barrel cannon in single mountings, two quadruple launchers for eight SS-N-14 'Silex' anti-submarine missiles, eight octuple vertical launchers for 64 SA-N-9 SAMs, eight 21in torpedo tubes in two quadruple mountings, two 12-tube anti-submarine rocket launchers and two multi-role helicopters, and a speed of 30 knots on the 110,000hp (82,015kW) delivered to two shafts by a COGOG arrangement with four gas turbine engines.

This artist's impression conveys elements of the trends that may be incorporated in future frigates with a crew possibly as low as 50 through the incorporation of increased automation and highly sophisticated computer systems. Key features are the small size, with the helicopter located as near to the centre of movement as possible to minimise the ship's pitching on helicopter operations, the clean and uncluttered deck, and the inward slope of the small superstructure elements to minimise radar reflectivity.

Fast Attack Craft

Many of the world's navies, including a large number without any claim to a long-standing naval or even maritime tradition, now operate forces of small but comparatively heavily armed fast combat craft. These can be defined as vessels possessing a displacement of up to 600 tons and a top speed of 25 knots or more, and fall into two basic categories: the fast patrol boat (FPB) and fast attack craft (FAC). The FPB is generally fitted with only light armament (usually machine guns and cannon of up to 40mm calibre) together with minimal sensor and fire-control suites. The FAC is very formidable type usually capable of higher speeds and carrying a heavier, longer-ranged armament that can include anti-ship guided missiles, guns of up to 3in (76mm) calibre, heavyweight anti-ship torpedoes of up to 21in (533mm) calibre, and anti-submarine weapons such as lightweight homing torpedoes, rocket-propelled grenades and depth charges, all controlled with the aid of very sophisticated sensor and fire-control suites. The nature of the primary armament is generally indicated by a suffixed letter: thus the FAC(G) carries a medium-calibre gun, the FAC(M) carries anti-ship missiles, and the FAC(T) carries anti-ship torpedoes.

Recent developments have tended to obscure the fact that the FAC is a type with more than a century of pedigree behind it. The first small warship may be regarded as John I. Thornycroft's torpedo boat *Lightning* built for the Royal Navy in 1876-77. About ten years earlier Robert Whitehead had demonstrated the capabilities of his new invention, the locomotive torpedo, and since that time Thornycroft had urged the Admiralty for permission to develop a torpedo-armed launch based on his successful series of fast steam launches. Displacing 32.5 tons and possessing an overall length of 87ft (26.52m), the *Lightning* was powered by a compound steam engine delivering 460hp (343kW) to one shaft for a speed of 19 knots. By the beginning of the twentieth century, the Royal Navy alone had operated more than 100 such steam-powered boats. The later units displaced some 200 tons each and could reach 25 knots.

After the end of World War II, the Soviets undertook an intensive programme of missile development with the intention of creating a range of weapons across the tactical and strategic spectrum. In the late 1950s, this programme began to yield useful results in the field of surface-to-surface anti-ship missiles. The first Soviet experiments had been made in the immediate aftermath of the war with captured Fieseler Fi 103 (otherwise V-1) missiles, and led to spectacular success in the development of Soviet cruise missiles, which were placed in service some four years before the first Western equivalents. The first such type to reach operational status was the SS-N-1 'Scrubber', which entered service in 1958 as a large ship-launched weapon carrying a conventional or nuclear warhead to a maximum range of 115 miles (185km) with radar or infra-red homing. Although the 'Scrubber' was a considerable technical achievement and boded well for future Soviet developments, the missile was too large for truly practical use, and its deployment was limited to 'Kildin' and 'Krupny' class destroyers.

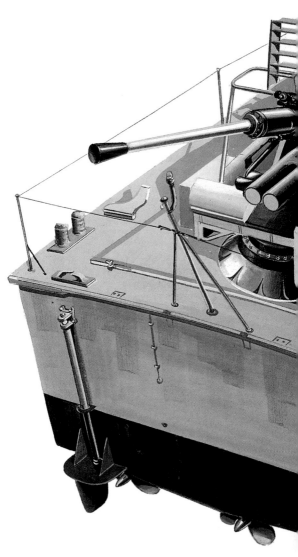

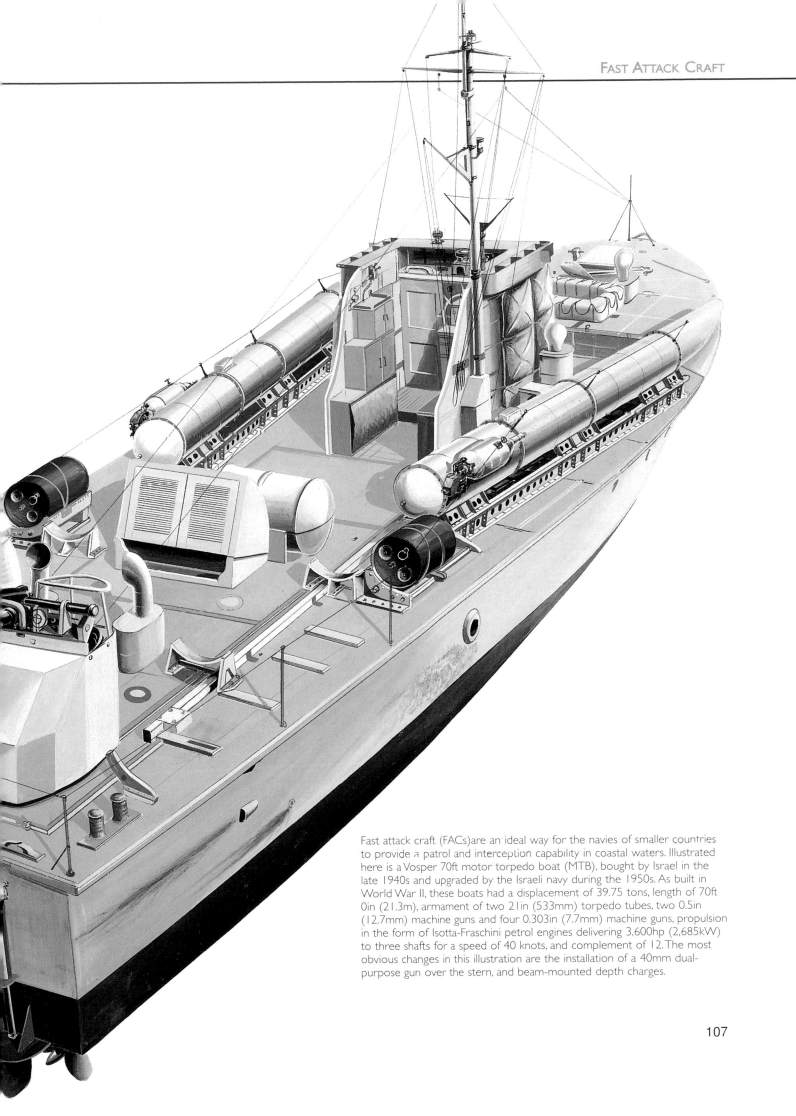

Fast attack craft (FACs) are an ideal way for the navies of smaller countries to provide a patrol and interception capability in coastal waters. Illustrated here is a Vosper 70ft motor torpedo boat (MTB), bought by Israel in the late 1940s and upgraded by the Israeli navy during the 1950s. As built in World War II, these boats had a displacement of 39.75 tons, length of 70ft 0in (21.3m), armament of two 21in (533mm) torpedo tubes, two 0.5in (12.7mm) machine guns and four 0.303in (7.7mm) machine guns, propulsion in the form of Isotta-Fraschini petrol engines delivering 3,600hp (2,685kW) to three shafts for a speed of 40 knots, and complement of 12. The most obvious changes in this illustration are the installation of a 40mm dual-purpose gun over the stern, and beam-mounted depth charges.

Yet the 'Scrubber' did pave the way for more practical weapons of the same aeroplane-type layout, and the first of these more effective weapons was the considerably smaller SS-N-2 'Styx', a missile that can truly be regarded as a weapon that revolutionised naval warfare. The 'Styx' weighed 6,614lb (3,000kg) with a 1,102lb (500kg) high explosive warhead, and its combination of a jettisonable solid-propellant rocket booster and a storable liquid-propellant sustainer rocket provided a theoretical maximum range of 53 miles (85km). The full range could only be usefully employed if mid-course updating of the guidance package was provided by a supporting helicopter (an extremely unlikely contingency in this period), so the effective range of the missile was 23 miles (37km) under the control of an autopilot with an active radar taking over for the terminal phase of the attack. The missile entered production in the late 1950s and reached initial operational capability in late 1958 or early 1959.

By this time the process of designing a specialist fast combat craft for the type was well advanced, but as an interim measure it was decided to convert a number of 'P 6' class torpedo craft into simple launch platforms. This resulted in a total of about 100 'Komar' class craft that entered service probably in late 1958, although the Western powers became aware of the type only in 1960. The Soviets classified this type of craft as the RK, standing for *Raketnyy Kater* (rocket cutter), and this designation has been retained for all later Soviet FAC(M)s. Of the 100 or so 'Komar' class craft completed in the USSR by 1961, some 78 were later transferred to the navies of satellite and client countries, and about 40 of the modified steel-hulled 'Hegu' class were built in China. The 'Komar' class was intended only as a stopgap, and the last craft had been retired from Soviet service by the early 1980s.

The naval operations of the Yom Kippur War saw the fast combat craft come of age in coastal warfare, but even before the war the manifest capabilities of the Israeli 'Saar' class craft had attracted an order for similar 'FPB/TNC-45' type craft from Argentina, which in 1970 ordered two West German-built craft, and these were

PT109 was an American pursuit torpedo (PT) boat of the Elco type built in World War II with a displacement of 38 tons, length of 80ft 0in (24.4m), armament of four 21in (533mm) torpedo tubes, two 20mm cannon in single mountings (or one 40mm gun and one 20mm cannon in single mountings) and four 0.5in (12.7mm) machine guns in two twin mountings, propulsion in the form of petrol engines delivering 4,050hp (3,020kW) to three shafts for a speed of 40 knots, and complement of 14.

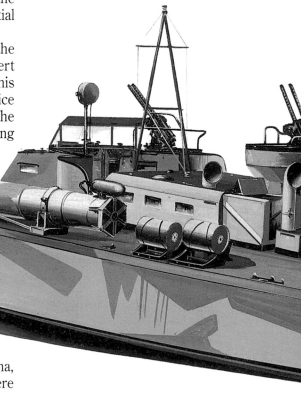

commissioned during 1974 in the FAC(G/T) role. Although there was no open warfare in the region, Argentina's possession of these two craft gave it a decided superiority that was only counterbalanced, and indeed reversed, in 1988 when Chile bought from Israel two of its 'Saar 3' class FAC(M)s. The next order came from South-East Asia, where the small nation of Singapore attests its strategic importance and wealth by maintaining moderately large and well-equipped armed forces for the preservation of peace in this potentially volatile region. Also in 1970, Singapore ordered six 'FPB/TNC-45' class FAC(M/G)s as two initial craft from West Germany to be followed by four indigenously built craft. The armament of these craft is a powerful and interesting combination of Swedish and Israeli weapons. The gun armament is Swedish, and comprises one 57mm Bofors SAK 57 weapon on the forecastle and one Bofors 40mm weapon aft. The missile armament initially comprised the first export installation of the Israeli Gabriel weapon, and consisted of five Gabriels in two fixed single container-launchers and one trainable triple container-launcher, though the latter can now be replaced by two twin container-launchers for an American weapon, the RGM-84 Harpoon. The Singapore order was followed by two other contracts from the same region. The first was placed by Malaysia for six licence-built craft completed to a less formidable FAC(G) standard with the same gun armament as the Singapore craft but less capable electronics and reduced performance based on a three- rather than four-shaft propulsion arrangement, and the second came from Thailand in the form of a contract for three licence-built units essentially similar to the Singapore craft. Other orders were received from Ecuador for three FAC(M/G)s with a notably useful armament that includes the 3in (76mm) OTO Melara Compact gun as well as the MM.38 early version of the French Exocet anti-ship missile, from three Persian Gulf states for a total of 17 FAC(M/G)s all carrying the OTO Melara Compact gun and the later MM.40 version of the Exocet missile, and from Ghana for two FAC(G)s with the OTO Melara Compact gun but only a modest two-shaft propulsion arrangement. The 'FPB/TNC-45' is still available, and further orders may yet be placed for this enduring design whose versatility means continued viability through the installation of modern weapons and sensors.

Despite the proved seaworthiness and endurance of the original 'Saar' class craft, Israel decided in the late 1960s that a new type of FAC(M) was required for longer-range operations in the Mediterranean and, to a lesser extent, the Red Sea. A major factor in this decision was the emergence as a major power in the Mediterranean theatre of Libya, a fervently Moslem state. A strong believer in pan-Arab power, Libya was using a very large percentage of its significant oil revenues for the creation of large and offensively oriented armed forces. These included a navy with a considerable missile capability in vessels ranging in size up to corvettes. The result of these Israeli concerns was the 'Saar 4' class of FAC(M)s derived by the Israelis from 1968 on the basis of their experience with the earlier 'Saars'. At a length of 190ft 3in (58.0m) and a full-load displacement of 450 tons, the type is somewhat larger than the 'Saar 2' and 'Saar 3' class units, but as range rather than speed was the prime performance requisite, the four-shaft propulsion arrangement remained essentially unaltered to yield a speed of 32 knots but a range of 4,600 miles (7,400km) instead of a speed of 40 knots or more and a range of 2,890 miles (4,650km). The 'Saar 4' proved its exceptional seaworthiness and range when four of the class made the passage from Israel's Mediterranean coast to the port of Eilat on the Red Sea coast, travelling around Africa via the Strait of Gibraltar and the Cape of Good Hope, and relying exclusively on refuelling at sea.

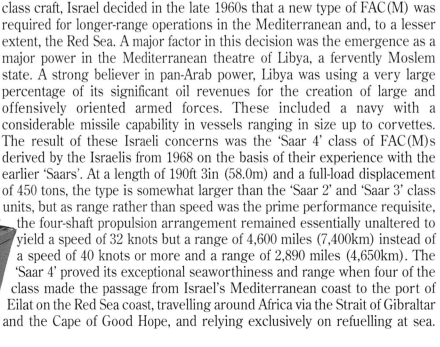

The American PT boats of World War II were operated with a number of armament fits, this boat having two 21in (533mm) torpedo tubes, eight depth charges, one 20mm cannon and four 0.5in (12.7mm) machine guns in two twin mountings.

Apart from additional fuel bunkerage, the greater volume and deck area of the 'Saar 4' class units are used for greater habitability, improved electronics, a superior weapons layout, and significantly upgraded sensor and countermeasures capabilities. In their original form, the 'Saar 4' class craft each carried two 3in OTO Melara Compact guns, two 20mm Oerlikon cannon in single mountings and/or a maximum of six 0.5in machine guns in twin mountings, and six container-launchers for Gabriel missiles. The after gun mounting was later replaced by a 20mm six-barrel cannon in an American-supplied Phalanx close-in weapon system mounting for improved last-ditch defence against sea-skimming anti-ship missiles, and from 1978 the missile armament was revised after Israel began to receive the RGM-84 Harpoon anti-ship missile, which can be installed in one or two twin or quadruple container-launchers replacing a similar number of Gabriel container-launchers for further enhancement of the 'cocktail' attack concept.

Israel built 10 'Saar 4' class craft for its own use, but subsequently sold two of them to Chile. Another three units of the original configuration were built in the same Israeli yard for South Africa, where another nine were built under licence.

The commissioning of 'Saar 4' class units gave the Israeli navy an impressive force of modern and sophisticated fast combat craft. Early experience in the 1967 war, confirmed by operations in the 1973 war, indicated that these forces could be deployed more effectively in flotillas led by a more sophisticated flotilla leader with specialised equipment and accommodation for the flotilla commander and his staff. This resulted in the 'Saar 4.5' class which was based on the hull, propulsion arrangement, armament (in upgraded form) and electronics of the 'Saar 4' class. The hull was lengthened to allow the incorporation in two units, at the expense of part of the missile armament, of a hangar and deck pad for a single light helicopter used in the surveillance and missile targeting update roles. The Israelis later decided that despite its longer hull, the 'Saar 4.5' class design was not ideally suited to helicopter operations, and this was one of the primary reasons for the design of the 'Saar 5' class of guided-missile corvettes.

The proven success of the 'Saar 2' and 'Saar 3' classes in Israeli service was a very useful advertisement for the quality of Lürssen fast combat craft designs, and resulted in a steady stream of orders for craft based on the 'FPB/TNC-45' design. Lürssen also took a further step up the size ladder, for the company recognised that the type of weapon and electronic fit demanded by its customers was on the verge of swamping the capabilities of the 'FPB/TNC-45' design. Lürssen thus appreciated that greater size would not only facilitate the installation of current weapons and sensors as

In the period before and during World War II, the Italians were some of the most skilled exponents of light craft, which in their MTB forms were designated as MAS craft.

well as a new generation of these items, but would also fit in with the procurement plans of many of the world's smaller navies. Many of these navies belonged to Third-World countries only recently emerged from colonial rule into independence, and for financial and technical reasons thought that their expansion should not encompass major warships optimised for a single role. Instead, they favoured a type one step up from the medium-sized FAC, namely a large fast combat craft type offering multi-role capability through the adoption of a combination of hull and propulsion arrangement that would support later upgrading with more and/or better weapons and sensors.

The two main British designers of fast combat craft are Brooke Marine and Vosper Thornycroft. In general terms, Brooke Marine specialises in robust craft well suited to the demands of Third-World navies with difficulties in finding adequate numbers of trained personnel, while Vosper Thornycroft specialises in the more sophisticated end of the market where an advanced hull and propulsion arrangement are combined with an integrated suite of modern weapons and capable electronics.

Within the spectrum of fast craft, the smallest of Brooke Marine's standard hull types are the 80 and 95ft (24.5 and 29m) designs, and these have proved successful in securing considerable export orders. These are mostly patrol craft of limited performance and light armament, however, and thus fall outside the fast combat craft category. Next up in size, however, is the 107ft (32.6m) design that has formed the basis for two types of fast combat craft, both delivered to African nations and featuring a two-shaft propulsion arrangement for low purchase cost but also low performance. For example, the three units for Kenya were delivered as patrol craft, but as the Kenyan navy became better trained and more experienced it recognised the latent capabilities of the design, and contracted for the craft to be upgraded to limited FAC(M) standard. The original gun armament of two 40mm Bofors guns in single mountings was replaced by the more modern fit of two 30mm Oerlikon cannon in a twin mounting under control of an optronic director, and this core armament was supplemented by four container-launchers for Gabriel II anti-ship missiles.

Amongst Brooke Marine's core designs is the larger 123ft (37.5m) type. This retains a low-powered two-shaft propulsion arrangement similar in concept to that of the 'Brooke Marine 32.6m' design, although with more highly powered engines for better performance. The greater size of the hull provides better seakeeping qualities, and also offers the right combination of larger area and greater volume for a more effective armament layout. Placed by Oman, the first order covered three examples of the 'Al Bushra'

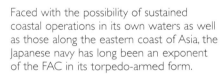

Faced with the possibility of sustained coastal operations in its own waters as well as those along the eastern coast of Asia, the Japanese navy has long been an exponent of the FAC in its torpedo-armed form.

class of FAC(G)s, armed with two 40mm Bofors guns in single mountings forward and aft. These were commissioned in 1973, and were revised between 1977 and 1978 as FAC(M/Gs) with two container-launchers for MM.38 Exocet missiles. Another four units were delivered in 1977 as FAC(G)s with a 3in OTO Melara Compact gun on the forecastle under control of an optical director, this useful main gun being supplemented by one 20mm cannon and two medium machine guns. The other main operator of the 'Brooke Marine 37.5m' design is Algeria, which has two British- and seven Algerian-built craft of the 'Kebir' class. This is an FAC(G) type of modest performance, and the armament comprises one 3in OTO Melara Compact gun on the forecastle as well as two 23mm Soviet cannon in a twin mounting aft, where they replace a single 20mm Oerlikon cannon.

The largest of Brooke Marine's designs currently in service is the 137ft (41.8m) type, which is used by Australia in the form of the 'Fremantle' class. This comprises 15 simple FAC(G)s with limited armament, and the craft are used mainly for patrol duties.

The UK had done little with the concept of fast combat craft since the end of World War II. In the second half of the 1960s, however, the Royal Navy became sufficiently concerned with the threat posed by fast combat craft to order a class of three FACs to train the crews of its major warships in the tactics to counter their attacks. The 'Scimitar' class was designed and built by Vosper Thornycroft, and the three craft were delivered in 1969 and 1970. With a full-load displacement of 102 tons on a laminated wooden hull measuring 100ft 0in (30.5m), the craft were each fitted with a CODOG propulsion arrangement whose two shafts were powered by two 90hp (67kW) Foden diesels for cruising or two 4,500hp (3,355kW) Rolls-Royce Proteus gas turbines for a maximum speed of 40 knots. At much the same time, Vosper Thornycroft evolved its 'Tenacity' class design and built a single craft as a private venture. This had a full-load displacement of 220 tons on a hull that measured 144ft 8in (44.1m) in length. The propulsion arrangement was of the CODOG type with the three shafts powered by two 600hp (445kW) Paxman diesels for cruising or three 4,250hp (3,170kW) Rolls-Royce Proteus gas turbines for a maximum speed of 39 knots. This design experience is reflected in a number of types which Vosper Thornycroft evolved for the export market during the 1960s and early 1970s. Typical of these are the 'Vosper Thornycroft 103ft', 'Vosper Thornycroft

Typical features of the British MTBt in World War II were the primary armament of two 21in (533mm) torpedo tubes and a secondary armament of two 0.5in (12.7mm) machine guns in a 'pulpit' twin mounting abaft the bridge and complemented by two or four 0.303in (7.7mm) machine guns in single or twin mountings.

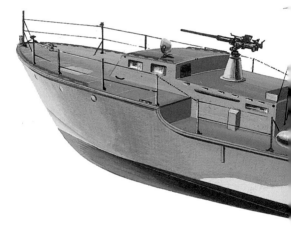

With its Schnellboote developed in the period after 1920, Germany opted for a larger type of attack craft that offered greater weapon capability and better sea-keeping qualities at the expense of outright speed. The S10, for example, had a displacement of 78 tons, length of 106ft 4in (32.4m), armament of two 21in (533mm) torpedo tubes and one 20mm cannon, propulsion in the form of three Daimler-Benz MB 502 diesel engines delivering 3,960hp (2,955kW) to three shafts for a speed of 35 knots, and complement of 20.

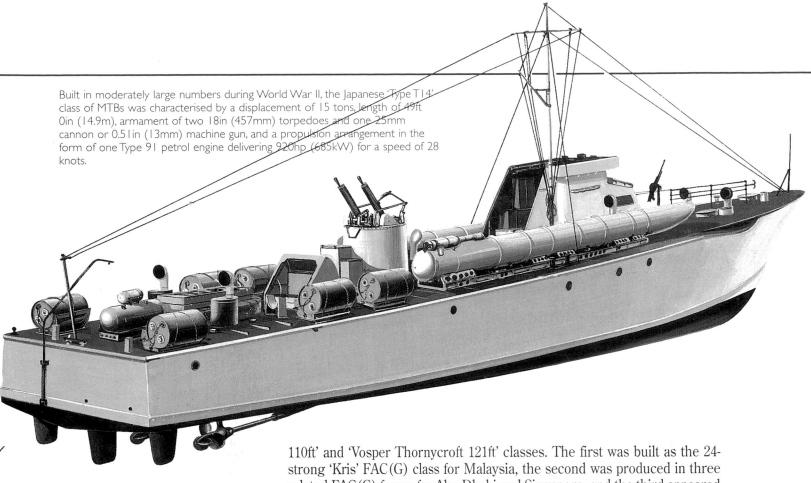

Built in moderately large numbers during World War II, the Japanese 'Type T14' class of MTBs was characterised by a displacement of 15 tons, length of 49ft 0in (14.9m), armament of two 18in (457mm) torpedoes and one 25mm cannon or 0.51in (13mm) machine gun, and a propulsion arrangement in the form of one Type 91 petrol engine delivering 920hp (685kW) for a speed of 28 knots.

110ft' and 'Vosper Thornycroft 121ft' classes. The first was built as the 24-strong 'Kris' FAC(G) class for Malaysia, the second was produced in three related FAC(G) forms for Abu Dhabi and Singapore, and the third appeared in three forms including a dedicated FAC(M) type for Brunei and related FAC(G) and FAC(M) variants for Venezuela.

The different conceptual approaches of Vosper Thornycroft and Brooke Marine to the design of fast combat craft is highlighted by the superior combat potential of the 'Tenacity' design to Brooke Marine's less powerful types. This superiority received concrete expression in 1977, when Egypt ordered six FAC(M)s to a design which Vosper Thornycroft extrapolated from that of the 'Tenacity' type. The design of the 'Ramadan' class is a good example of the way in which careful design thinking can pack maximum offensive capability into a comparatively small hull, in this instance possessing a full-load displacement of 310 tons on a length of 170ft 7in (52.0m). The armament is impressive and of Italian origins, and comprises two twin container-launchers for Otomat Mk 1 missiles between the superstructure and the deck house, one 3in OTO Melara Compact gun on the forecastle, and two 40mm Bofors guns in a Breda Compact twin mounting over the stern. The propulsion arrangement is based on West German diesels powering four shafts for a maximum speed of 40 knots.

From the design of the 'Ramadan' class, Vosper Thornycroft developed the 'Province' FAC(M/G) design for Oman, which ordered three craft in the early 1980s and followed with a contract for the fourth in 1986. The design of the 'Province' class provides slightly greater dimensions for a hull of proportionately finer line and, despite the greater displacement, this ensures high performance with a four-shaft propulsion arrangement with basically the same power as that in the 'Ramadan' class. The craft were delivered in two differing standards, for while all have the same barrelled armament of one 3in OTO Melara Compact gun and two 40mm Bofors guns in a Breda Compact twin mounting, the first and last three units have respectively two triple and quadruple container-launchers for the MM.40 variant of the Exocet. The same basic type was ordered by Kenya, which thus received two craft with a well-balanced weapon fit with lighter missile armament than the Omani units.

In the 15 years after World War II, the USA had produced or funded for overseas construction a considerable number of motor gun boats (MGBs) (PGM 33-83, PGM 91 and PGM 102-124), but these were for allied rather than American use. In the early 1960s, however, the Cuban missile crisis highlighted the US Navy's lack of fast combat craft for use in confined waters such as the Gulf of Mexico. It was therefore decided to built a 22-strong class of MGBs, though the classification was altered to 'patrol combatant' during 1967. The resulting 'Asheville' class was developed for coastal patrol and blockade, but in the event only 17 of the class were completed between 1966 and 1971 by Tacoma Boatbuilding and Peterson Builders. The type has a CODOG propulsion arrangement for long range at a modest cruising speed and high speed for combat, and the armament is based on a 3in gun in an enclosed mounting forward of the bridge and a 40mm Bofors gun in an open mounting over the stern. Most of these craft saw extensive patrol service in the Vietnam War, and in the mid-1970s four of them were adapted as FAC(M)s with an armament of four Standard Missiles (in its anti-radar form) for service in the Mediterranean as counters to Soviet 'tattletale' vessels. The craft had a very good reputation for seaworthiness, but were decidedly uncomfortable in any sort of sea and suffered propeller cavitation problems that prevented them from attaining their theoretical maximum speed of 40 knots or more.

Below: As well as being heavier, larger and better armed than their earlier brethren, the German *Schnellboote* built in the later part of World War II were fitted with an armoured bridge. This was originally a cast unit of curved shape, but production difficulties meant that most of these bridge units were of the polygonal type illustrated here. The boats had a normal displacement in the order of 105 tons, length of 114ft 6in (34.9m), armament of two 21in (533mm) torpedo tubes and varying numbers of 37mm and 20mm cannon, propulsion in the form of Daimler-Benz diesel engines delivering 7,500hp (5,590kW) to three shafts for a speed of 39 knots, and complement of 15-20.

In the late 1950s, the US Navy also began to acquire an interest in hydrofoil craft for very high speeds, but the sole class to emerge has been the 'Pegasus' class of six high-speed hydrofoils each armed with a single 3in Mk 75 gun forward of the bridge structure and two quadruple container-launchers for eight RGM-84 Harpoon missiles above the stern. As such, the craft are the US Navy's most potent combatants on the basis of firepower per displacement ton. The craft can be highly effective in the right conditions, but they lack the range, endurance and versatility of larger warships. The 'Pegasus' class FAH(M/G)s thus fall outside the main tactical organisation of their operating service, which is concerned primarily with deep-water operations.

Even though the 'Asheville' class failed to find any real favour with the US Navy, Tacoma Boatbuilding was confident that the basic type had an export potential, especially amongst East and South-East Asian nations. The company therefore used the 'Asheville' design as the basis of its Patrol Ship Multi-Mission Mk 5 (PSMM Mk 5) type with a two-shaft COGOG propulsion arrangement using no fewer than six gas turbines. The first customer for the type was South Korea, which operates a large force of fast combat craft against the constant threat of North Korean aggression. The parent company built the first four of the eight craft, the initial three of them reflecting the type's ancestry in a missile armament of four Standard Missiles (each carrying a seeker designed to home on the target vessel's radar emissions) and an American 3in gun. The last American-built unit switched to the definitive armament of two twin container-launchers for the RGM-84 Harpoon missile and the 3in OTO Melara Compact gun. Construction of the last four units was undertaken by a South Korean subsidiary, and this has also built four somewhat different 'Dagger' class FAC(M)s for Indonesia, with a CODOG propulsion arrangement and the revised armament of two twin container-launchers for four MM.38 Exocet missiles, one 57mm Bofors SAK 57 Mk 1 gun, one 40mm Bofors gun and two 20mm cannon. Another customer for the 'PSMM Mk 5' class was Taiwan, the island nation that until very recently regarded itself as being at war with the communist regime on the Chinese mainland. Clearly, the main Chinese threat to Taiwan's continued independence was a seaborne invasion, and against this threat Taiwan maintains powerful naval defences including a force of FACs for the destruction of any elements of the invading force that break through the main offshore defences. Tacoma Boatbuilding thus produced the first unit of the Taiwanese 'Lung Chiang' class, a type similar to the South Korean class with a two-shaft CODOG propulsion arrangement and a barrelled armament of one 3in OTO Melara Compact gun backed by two 30mm Oerlikon cannon in an Emerson Electric twin mounting. The missile armament comprises four container-launchers for the Hsiung Feng I (licence-built version of the Israeli Gabriel) missile. The second unit was licence-built in Taiwan, which planned a large class with the RGM-84 Harpoon missile and an American fire-control system. Under Chinese pressure, the Americans refused to export the Harpoon to Taiwan, which then dropped its plan for a major 'Lung Chiang' class. The only other operator of the 'PSMM Mk 5' type is Thailand, which has six 'Sattahip' class craft that are FAC(G)s, useful mainly for patrol and training with their low-powered propulsion arrangement and comparatively light gun armament.

Peterson Builders also have construction capability for a range of ship types and sizes, and this is reflected in the company's main export success in the field of fast combat craft, the nine units of the 'Al Siddiq' class of FAC(M/G)s for Saudi Arabia. These feature toward the upper end of the fast combat craft size scale, but have a two-shaft CODOG propulsion

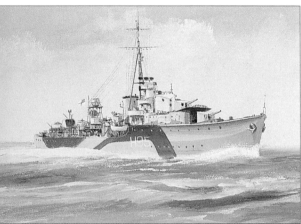

Above: Bahrain is one of 11 countries that operates the 'Lürssen FPB/TNC-45' type of FAC. These four FAC(M)s have a full-load displacement of 259 tons, length of 147ft 4in (44.9m), armament of two twin launchers for four MM.40 Exocet anti-ship missiles, one 3in (76mm) dual-purpose gun in a single turret and two 40mm dual-purpose guns in a twin mounting, propulsion in the form of four MTU diesel engines delivering 15,395hp (11,480kW) to four shafts for a speed of 41.5 knots, and complement of 36.

arrangement for high gas turbine-engined speed and good diesel-engined range. The craft were designed specifically for the anti-ship role, and the armament of each unit is centred on one 3in OTO Melara Compact gun, located on the forecastle forward of the superstructure, and the modest anti-ship missile fit of two twin container-launchers for the RGM-84 Harpoon weapon, located near the stern. Aft of the missile installation is the Phalanx close-in weapon system mounting, whose 20mm six-barrel rotary cannon has excellent fields of fire for its primary task of destroying incoming anti-ship missiles.

By far the world's largest operator of fast combat craft is China, whose navy has been confined almost exclusively to the coast defence role until very recent times, when deeper strategic thinking combined with the possibility of natural resources in the South China Sea to persuade the Chinese to begin development of a technologically more advanced navy possessing offshore capability. China has a long coastline whose many good harbours are supplemented by even larger numbers of well-positioned smaller harbours. With no real naval threat but the posturing and nuisance raids of Taiwan to fear, China rightly decided that the best way to ensure coastal security, and at the same time build the nucleus of a strong navy, lay with the creation of a large force of fast combat craft that could become technologically more sophisticated as Chinese industry and service personnel evolved the necessary skills. The core of this operational philosophy began in the early 1950s, when the Chinese navy used armed examples of local craft. On this basis, and with considerable technical and material assistance from the Soviets, the Chinese began to develop a more advanced fast combat craft capability toward the middle of the decade. Precise details are lacking, but it seems that from 1952, more than 70 'P 4' class motor torpedo boats (MTBs) were transferred from the USSR to China. It is probable that a comparatively small number of improved 'P 6' class MTBs were transferred at a slightly later date, and that these were used as pattern craft for Chinese construction of about 80 boats. This experience allowed the Chinese to begin development of their own types, starting with the 'Huchuan' FAH(T) that entered production in 1966 as the world's first foil-equipped naval vessel. Despite the fact that the type was only of the semi-foil variety, with the forward part of the hull lifted by the foil and the rear part planing, the design was clearly successful in meeting Chinese expectations, and production totalled just under 200 units.

Like the Soviets, however, the Chinese had seen the virtue of combining torpedo- and missile-armed FACs for the type of two-handed punch that could take an enemy force off balance and inflict severe losses. In the early 1960s, the Chinese navy had received from the USSR some seven or eight 'Komar' class FAC(M)s, and from this simple type the Chinese evolved the 'Hegu' design with a steel rather than wooden hull of slightly modified form and the position of the missile container-launchers moved slightly inboard by comparison with the Soviet original. These were limited but effective FAC(M)s, but the Chinese have maintained the type in service long past the time when simple electronic countermeasures have made it easy for any modestly sophisticated navy to defeat the missile carried by the 'Hegu' class craft.

As in the pattern established earlier with the MTBs, the Soviets followed deliveries of the 'Komar' class craft with some four examples of the two improved 'Osa I' class (in this instance with four 30mm rather than 25mm cannon in two twin mountings) as well as the technical information that allowed the Chinese to build this type as the 'Huangfen' class. The Chinese-built craft differ in detail from the Soviet original, and for an unexplained reason the class is credited with a maximum speed of 41 knots to the Soviet type's 35 knots. The 'Huangfen' class is still the backbone of the Chinese fast combat craft force but, as with the 'Hegu' class operating the same missile, its combat capability has been virtually removed in recent years by the widespread adoption of electronic countermeasures by potentially hostile navies. This fact has been recognised by China, which is now retrofitting a more modern type of anti-ship missile, which has the additional advantages of smaller size and reduced weight so that a greater number of missiles can be installed. In recent years, the Chinese have made considerable but mostly unsuccessful attempts to upgrade their fast combat craft capability, often with the aid of Western companies. Older missiles have been supplemented and largely replaced by more modern weapons, but the Chinese government's suppression of the emergent democracy movement has led to the effective halt on all programmes of Western technical support for types such as the 'H3' class.

Thus in many parts of the world the concept of fast combat craft is alive and flourishing. Many emerging countries find such craft an ideal way to begin development of their navies, with larger and more sophisticated craft bought to match their developing skills and increased operational ambitions. Many less affluent countries have discovered that such craft are a cost effective method of maintaining a national presence in territorial waters and offshore zones of possible commercial importance. But in general the countries that make the greatest and potentially most effective use of fast combat craft are those with confined coastal waters or chokepoints where major maritime routes are constricted by geographical factors. It is therefore no coincidence that areas where concentrations of fast combat craft are to be found include the Baltic Sea and its exit into the North Sea; the Mediterranean (especially at its western end near the Strait of Gibraltar, its centre near the Sicilian Narrows, its north offshoot in the Adriatic Sea, its north-eastern corner into the Aegean Sea, and its eastern end where Israel and several Arab nations vie with each other); the Persian Gulf; South-East Asia where there are several chokepoints such as the Malacca Strait; the eastern coast of Asia; and various parts of South America where limited finance and confined waters combine with nationalistic and economic rivalries.

The Aircraft Carrier

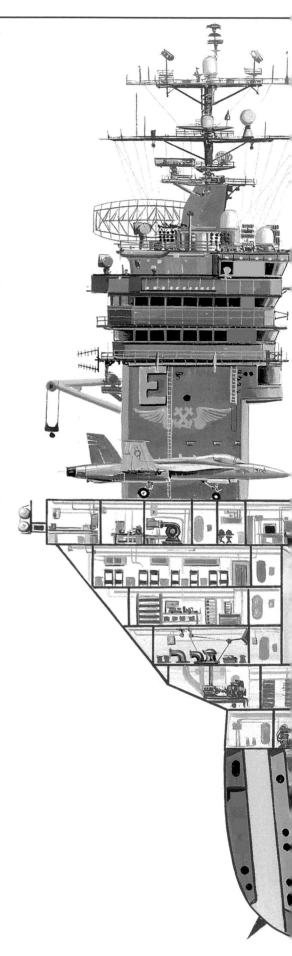

I T was an American who made the first take-off from and first landing on a ship. In November 1909 Eugene Ely flew off the cruiser *Birmingham* and in January 1911 he landed on the cruiser *Pennsylvania*, in both instances using a Curtiss biplane. The mantle then passed to the British, and in 1912 the first British aircraft operations began with a take-off from the moored battleship *Hibernia* during January and continued with a take-off from the moving battleship *Africa* in May. This capability was seen at the time as experimental, and more serious consideration was given to the use of aircraft in their flying boat and floatplane forms as adjuncts of naval operations. The first ship completed for this task was the *Ark Royal*, which was converted during construction from a collier into a seaplane carrier with internal accommodation for seaplanes that were lifted into and out of the water by a crane. Although successful in basic terms, the *Ark Royal* lacked the speed and range to support fleet operations, and the faster English Channel ferries *Empress*, *Engadine*, *Riviera*, *Ben-my-Chree*, *Manxman*, *Vindex*, *Pegasus* and *Nairana* were converted into seaplane carriers and saw valuable service, and these were supplemented by the converted liner *Campania*. Seaplane operations were cumbersome, however, and several of the ships were later fitted with a flying-off platform allowing the operation of wheeled aircraft, which were initially converted floatplanes but later standard 'landplane' types.

As World War I continued, the importance of aircraft for all surface operations, sea as well as land, increased dramatically and thought was given to the creation of larger ships to carry a greater number of aircraft that could be operated from longer platforms at higher weights. The light battle-cruiser *Furious* was converted into an aircraft carrier for service from March 1918, and was supplemented from October 1918 by the *Vindictive* and *Argus*, which had been laid down as a cruiser and a liner respectively. As the war ended in November 1918, the UK was building two more aircraft carriers as the *Eagle*, whose hull had been laid down as that of a sister ship to the battleship *Canada*, and the *Hermes* that was the first ship to be designed as an aircraft carrier.

During the 1920s, *Furious* was rebuilt to full aircraft carrier standard with a flush flightdeck, and her two light battle-cruiser half-sisters *Courageous* and *Glorious* were also converted to this standard, with a starboard-side 'island', in the period between 1924 and 1930. This gave the British a force of four large battleships by the mid-1930s. The two 'Courageous' class ships each had a displacement of 22,500 tons, an armament by the beginning of World War II of sixteen 4.7in (120mm) anti-aircraft guns in single mountings as well as provision for 48 aircraft, protection in the form of a 3in (76mm) belt and deck, and a speed of 30.5 knots on the 90,000hp (67,105kW) delivered to four shafts by geared steam turbines. The *Furious* had a displacement of 22,450 tons, an armament by the beginning of World War II of twelve 4in (102mm) anti-aircraft guns in six twin mountings and twenty-four 2pdr anti-aircraft guns in three octuple mountings as well as provision for 33 aircraft, protection in the form of a 3in (76mm) belt and deck, and a speed of 30.5 knots on the 90,000hp (67,105kW) delivered to four shafts by geared steam turbines. The *Eagle* had a displacement of 22,600 tons, an armament by the beginning of World War II of nine 6in (152mm) guns in single mountings, four 4in anti-aircraft guns in single mountings and eight 2pdr anti-aircraft guns in an octuple mounting as well as provision for 21 aircraft, protection in the form of a 7in (178mm) belt and 4in (102mm) deck, and a speed of 24 knots on the 50,000hp (37,280kW) delivered to four shafts by geared steam turbines.

Experience with these large carriers as well as a few small carriers benefited the British between the world wars, and in the later part of the 1930s they produced a new *Ark Royal* to embody the lessons of this experience in an altogether larger ship with better protection (passive armour as well as active guns) and a large aircraft complement of which most could be accommodated in a large two-storied hangar under the full-length flightdeck. The ship had a displacement of 22,000 tons, an armament of sixteen 4.5in (114mm) anti-aircraft guns in eight twin mountings, forty-eight 2pdr anti-aircraft guns in six octuple mountings and thirty-two 0.5in (12.7mm) machine guns in eight quadruple mountings, as well as 72 aircraft, protection in the form of a 4.5in (114mm) belt and 3in (76mm) deck, and a speed of 30.75 knots on the 102,000hp.

By the period immediately preceding World War II, the British had decided that the threat posed by aircraft to the aircraft carrier had reached such a level that the demands of survivability could only be met by the adoption of an armoured hangar below an armoured flightdeck, and the greater topweight generated by this change dictated that a single-level

This cross-section reveals the great size and complexity of the modern aircraft carrier, in this instance the *Abraham Lincoln* of the US Navy's superb 'Nimitz' class of nuclear-powered ships.

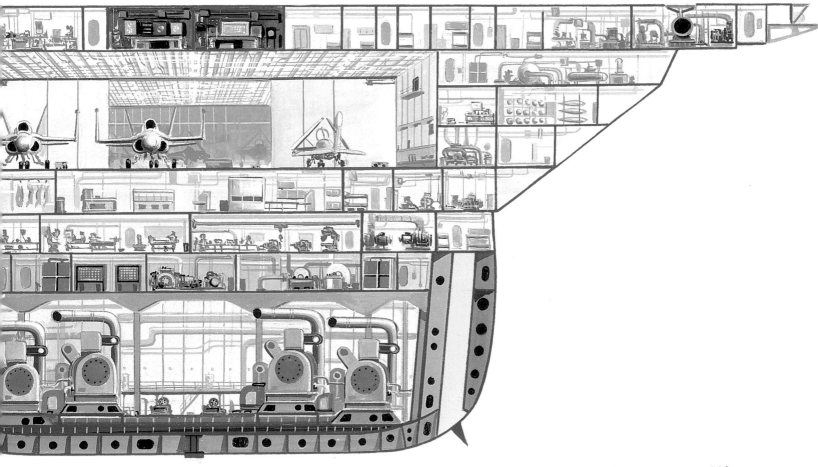

hangar had to be used with a consequent reduction in aircraft capacity to 36 in the 'Illustrious' class carriers, which were the first full series-built carriers to reach British service. The class was planned as six ships, but while the first three were completed to the originally planned standard, the last three were delivered to a modified standard with an additional half-hangar aft even though this meant a reduction in the armouring of the ships' upper sections. The original four 'Illustrious' class carriers were delivered in the first half of World War II and each had a displacement of 23,000 tons, an armament of sixteen 4.5in anti-aircraft guns in eight twin mountings, forty-eight 2pdr anti-aircraft guns in six octuple mountings and eight 20mm cannon in single mountings, as well as 36 aircraft, protection in the form of a 4.5in (114mm) belt and hangar side and 3in (76mm) deck, and a speed of 31 knots on the 110,000hp (82,015kW) delivered to four shafts by geared steam turbines. The last two carriers of the class were delivered later in World War II and each had a displacement of 26,000 tons, an armament of sixteen 4.5in anti-aircraft guns in eight twin mountings, forty-eight 2pdr anti-aircraft guns in six octuple mountings and thirty-eight 20mm cannon in 17 twin and four single mountings, as well as 72 aircraft, protection in the form of a 4.5in (114mm) belt, 1.5in (38mm) hangar side and 3in (76mm) deck, and a speed of 32 knots on the 148,000hp (110,350kW) delivered to four shafts by geared steam turbines.

These were the last fleet carriers to be completed in the UK during World War II, although two of four 'Audacious' class fleet carriers were completed after the end of the war, and further aircraft deliveries were therefore for the light and escort carriers. The light carriers were essentially scaled-down fleet carriers, and the first of them in British service were the 10 units of the 'Colossus' class, of which only six were operational by the end of World War II in the form of four light carriers and two maintenance carriers. The light carriers were completed to a standard that included a displacement of 13,190 tons, an armament of twenty-four 2pdr anti-aircraft guns in six quadruple mountings and nineteen 40mm anti-aircraft guns in single mountings, as well as 48 aircraft, only light protection, and a speed of 25 knots on the 42,000hp (31,315kW) delivered to two shafts by geared steam turbines. The two maintenance carriers had lighter gun armament and no

Seen here in the late 1930s, the *Enterprise* was one of the three aircraft carriers of the US Navy's 'Yorktown' class, and the ship's details included a full-load displacement of 22,900 tons, length of 827ft 4in (252.2m), armament of eight 5in (127mm) guns in single mountings and 81 aircraft launched with the aid of three catapults, propulsion in the form of geared steam turbines delivering 120,000hp (89,470kW) to four shafts for a speed of 33 knots, and complement of 2,920 in war.

aircraft, and were designed for support of the British naval force operating with the US Pacific Fleet. The other four ships were completed after the war, and four of the class were later transferred to friendly nations (Australia, Brazil, Canada, Argentina, France, and the Netherlands).

There followed five of six light carriers of the 'Majestic' class that were launched during the war but completed after it, with a displacement of 14,000 tons, an armament of thirty 40mm anti-aircraft guns in six twin and 18 single mountings, as well as 34 aircraft, only light protection, and a speed of 24.5 knots on the 42,000hp (31,315kW) delivered to two shafts by geared steam turbines. All of these ships were later transferred or sold to friendly nations (two to Australia, two to Canada and one to India)

There should have followed eight units of the larger and more capable 'Hermes' class 'intermediate fleet carrier' type with somewhat higher performance as a result of their considerably more powerful propulsion arrangement, but only four of these were laid down for launch and completion after the end of the war, with a displacement of 18,300 tons, an armament of thirty-two 40mm anti-aircraft guns in two sextuple, eight twin and four single mountings, as well as 50 aircraft, protection in the form of a 1in (25mm) deck, and a speed of 29.5 knots on the 83,000hp (61,885kW) delivered to four shafts by geared steam turbines.

The escort carrier was built to a small and less capable standard as it was designed originally for the convoy escort role and later used additionally for the support of amphibious operations. The ships were initially converted from large merchant ships but later were built specifically for the task although generally to mercantile standards. Most of the ships were of American origin, and the vessels used by the Royal Navy included the five units of the 'Archer' class, 26 units of the 'Ruler' class, and four miscellaneous ships. The 'Ruler' class may be taken as typical of the breed, and its details included a full-length hangar under the flightdeck, a displacement of 11,420 tons, an armament of two 4in anti-aircraft guns in single mountings, sixteen 40mm anti-aircraft guns in eight twin mountings and twenty 20mm cannon in single mountings, as well as 24 aircraft, no protection, and a speed of 17 knots on the 9,350hp (6,970kW) delivered to one shaft by a geared steam turbine.

In the period after World War II, the UK was financially straitened and was already beginning its retreat from empire, so no new aircraft carriers were laid down for some time and the Royal Navy relied on its existing units, albeit in forms that were often upgraded to a

Seen in the background is the British aircraft carrier *Argus*, which was the first ship of its type with a full-length flightdeck. Completed in the last stages of World War I, the ship was used mainly as an aircraft ferry and training carrier in World War II before succumbing to the attentions of the breakers immediately after the end of that war.

The *Amagi* and *Akagi* were Japanese battle-cruisers taken in hand during construction for conversion into aircraft carriers, but the *Amagi* became a constructive total loss while still incomplete during the course of a 1923 earthquake, and was scrapped.

significant degree with features such as the angled flightdeck and the mirror landing system, which were both British inventions. The force available by the middle of the 1950s included the three units of the 'Hermes' class revised as the 'Centaur' class, the lead ship of the 'Audacious' class completed as the sole 'Eagle' class ship with a full-load displacement of 53,390 tons and provision for up to 60 aircraft, the other unit of the 'Audacious' class completed as the sole unit of the 'Ark Royal' class with a full-load displacement of 53,060 tons and provision for up to 36 aircraft, and the *Victorious* of the 'Illustrious' class revised to a more modern standard with a full-load displacement of 35,500 tons and provision for up to 36 aircraft.

The sole later addition in the 1950s was the 'Hermes' class carrier with a full-load displacement of 28,700 tons and provision for up to 28 aircraft. In the late 1960s, the UK decided that large aircraft carriers were no longer appropriate to the country's reduced world status and were also too expensive in maintenance and construction, and they were gradually phased out of service in the 1970s, although two units enjoyed a further lease of life into the early 1980s as commando carriers.

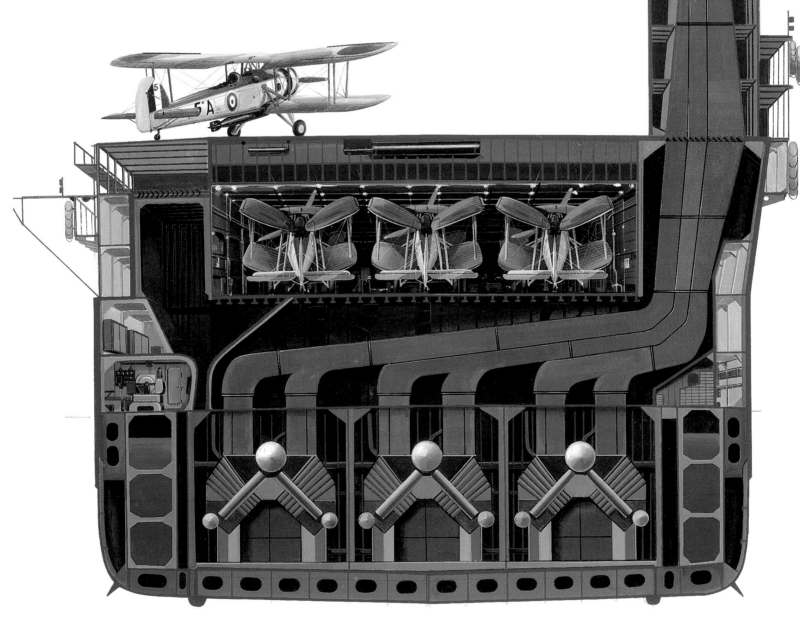

Right: This cross-section of an American aircraft carrier of the World War II period reveals the extensive compartmentalisation and double skinning which, in concert with comparatively lavish and well-disposed armour, made such ships difficult targets for torpedoes and gunfire. The 'aircraft' part of the ship was built as an added superstructure, however, and being considerably less well protected was distinctly vulnerable to bombing attack.

Opposite: This cross-section of the *Illustrious*, a British aircraft carrier of the World War II period, reveals the British system of incorporating the 'aircraft' part of the ship into the main hull, thereby affording it considerably better protection than the comparable section of American aircraft carriers.

The last British aircraft carriers, which are still in useful service after launch between 1977 and 1981, are the three light carriers of the 'Invincible' class, which were designed to carry helicopters and fixed-wing aircraft of the short take-off, vertical landing STOVL type, the latter in the form of the British Aerospace Sea Harrier. These carriers each have a full-load displacement of some 23,000 tons, an armament of one twin-arm launcher for Sea Dart surface-to-air missiles and two 20mm Vulcan six-barrel cannon in Phalanx close-in weapon system mountings, as well as 14 aircraft, and a speed of 28 knots on the 112,000shp (83,505kW) delivered to two shafts by a COGOG propulsion arrangement with four Rolls-Royce Olympus gas turbines.

The American involvement with carrierborne aviation began in 1922 with the conversion of the collier *Jupiter* into the aircraft carrier *Langley*. This ship provided the fledgling naval air arm with initial experience, and this facilitated the entry into service late in the same decade of the two fleet carriers of the 'Saratoga' class which, as a result of the Washington Naval Treaty limitation on capital ship construction, were converted during construction from battle-cruisers into aircraft carriers. When completed, the ships were the largest and probably the most advanced aircraft carriers in the world with a full-load displacement of 39,000 tons, an armament of eight 8in (203mm) guns in four twin turrets and twelve 5in (127mm) anti-aircraft guns in single mountings, as well as 90 aircraft, protection in the form of a 6in (152mm) belt and 3in (76mm) deck, and a speed of 34 knots on the 180,000hp (134,210kW) delivered to four shafts by a turbo-electric propulsion arrangement.

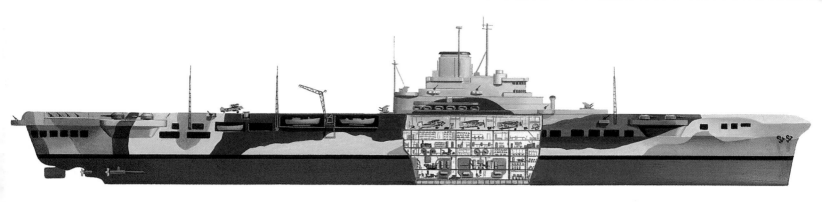

The first American aircraft carrier designed as such was the following *Ranger*, which was launched in 1933 and completed to a standard that included a displacement of 14,500 tons, an armament of eight 5in (127mm) anti-aircraft guns in single mountings, as well as 86 aircraft, protection in the form of a 2in (51mm) belt and 1in (25mm) deck, and a speed of 29.5 knots on the 53,500hp (39,890kW) delivered to two shafts by geared steam turbines.

Experience indicated that the *Ranger*, built to Treaty limitations and therefore lacking in protection and performance to ensure that a large number of aircraft could be embarked, was inadequate as a first-line aircraft carrier. The two following units of the 'Yorktown' class, both launched in 1936, were therefore completed to a larger and more capable standard with a full-load displacement of 25,500 tons, an armament of eight 5in anti-aircraft guns in single mountings, as well as 100 aircraft, protection in the form of a 4in (102mm) belt and 3in (76mm) deck, and a speed of 34 knots on the 120,000hp (82.015kW) delivered to four shafts by geared steam turbines. These two ships were the *Yorktown* and the *Enterprise*, and in 1940 a half-sister was launched as the *Hornet* with a slightly larger flightdeck and a number of other improved features.

The last American aircraft carrier completed before the entry of the USA into World War II was the *Wasp*, which was a small carrier along the lines of the *Ranger* and designed to fill the American quota for aircraft carrier tonnage under the terms of the Washington Naval Treaty. The American philosophy at this time was that all must be subordinated to aircraft-carrying capability, and as the *Wasp* carried very nearly as many aircraft as the ships of the 'Yorktown' class, major sacrifices had to be made in protection and speed. As completed, the ship had details including a full-load displacement

The *Formidable* was a unit of the first subclass of the 'Illustrious' class of British fleet aircraft carriers, and was launched in 1939 for service through World War II before being scrapped in 1953. The details of the ship included a displacement of 23,000 tons, length of 753ft 6in (229.7m), armament of sixteen 4.5in (114mm) dual-purpose guns in eight twin turrets, forty-eight 2pdr anti-aircraft guns in six quadruple mountings, eight 20mm cannon in single mountings, and 36 aircraft, protection in the form of a 4.5in (114mm) belt and hangar sides and 3in (76mm) deck, propulsion in the form of geared steam turbines delivering 110,000hp (82,015kW) to three shafts for a speed of 31 knots, and complement of 1,390.

Seen here in 1950, the *Oriskany* was one of the 15 units of the 'Modified Essex' class of fleet aircraft carriers delivered in the later stages of World War II. The details of the ship included a full-load displacement of 38,000 tons, length of 888ft 0in (270.7m), armament of twelve 5in (127mm) anti-aircraft guns in four twin and four single turrets, seventy-two 40mm anti-aircraft guns in 18 quadruple mountings, 52 20mm cannon in single mountings, and 80 aircraft launched with the aid of two catapults, propulsion in the form of steam turbines delivering 150,000hp (111,840kW) to four shafts for a speed of 33 knots, and complement of 3,450.

of 21,000 tons, an armament of eight 5in (127mm) anti-aircraft guns in single mountings, as well as 84 aircraft, protection in the form of a 4in (102mm) belt and 1.5in (38mm) deck, and a speed of 29.5 knots on the 75,000hp (55,920kW) delivered to two shafts by geared steam turbines.

By the late 1930s, the radical worsening of international relations combined with the US Navy's considerable experience in carrier operations to make feasible the design of a completely new type of aircraft carrier. This was the 'Essex' class, which became the mainstay of the US Navy's carrier force in World War II and was built to the final extent of 26 ships. The design included a size comparable with that of the 'Saratoga' class battle-cruiser conversions with the pure aircraft carrier design features of the 'Ranger', 'Yorktown' and 'Wasp' classes, in a type that was optimised for far-ranging operations through the incorporation of more 'ship' qualities, much improved protection based not so much on thicker armour as on increased compartmentalisation and, for maximum aircraft operating capability (including the possibility of upgrade to larger and heavier warplane types), a large flightdeck with an overhanging port side, two catapults and three large elevators (including one deck-edge rather than inset unit) connecting the hangar and flightdeck. The one weak point of the design, certainly relative to British practice at this time, was the installation of the flightdeck as an essentially unarmoured superstructure element rather than as an intrinsic and armoured part of the hull. Even so, the 'Essex' class carriers were superb warships that possessed the ability to survive considerable combat damage.

The details of the 'Essex' class aircraft carrier included a full-load displacement of 33,000 tons, an armament of twelve 5in anti-aircraft guns in four twin and four single mountings, between forty-four and seventy-two 40mm anti-aircraft guns in 11 to 18 quadruple mountings and fifty-two 20mm cannon in single mountings, as well as 100 aircraft, protection in the form of a 4in (102mm) belt and 3in (76mm) deck, and a speed of 33 knots on the 150,000hp (111,840kW) delivered to four shafts by geared steam turbines.

Experience with the 'Essex' class aircraft carriers showed that while these were excellent ships with considerable offensive and

The Brazilian navy's aircraft carrier *Minas Gerais* was originally constructed as the *Vengeance* of the British 'Colossus' class in World War II, but after purchase by Brazil in the mid-1950s was rebuilt in the Netherlands to a more advanced standard with an angled flightdeck, mirror landing system and a single steam catapult.

Seen in 1972, the year in which it was deleted, the *Albion* was laid down in World War II as a 'Hermes' class light carrier but completed after the war as one of three 'Centaur' class carriers with a full-load displacement of 27,000 tons, length of 737ft 9in (224.8m), armament of thirty-two 40mm anti-aircraft guns in two sextuple, eight twin and four single mountings, as well as 26 aircraft, propulsion in the form of geared steam turbines delivering 78,000hp (58,155kW) to two shafts for a speed of 28 knots, and complement of 1,100 excluding an air group of 300.

The *Clemenceau*, lead ship of a two-strong class of French aircraft carriers, was completed in 1961 with a full-load displacement of 32,780 tons, length of 869ft 5in (265.0m), provision for 38 aircraft, speed of 32 knots, and complement of 1,340.

Lead ship of a four-strong class that was the first type of aircraft carrier designed after World War II, the US Navy's *Forrestal* was completed in 1955 with details that include a full-load displacement of 80,385 tons, length of 1,086ft 0in (331.0m).

defensive capability, they were hampered by their lack of protection on and below the flightdeck. In the 'Midway' class, of which six were ordered but only three completed in the period after World War II, the opportunity was taken to increase size and displacement by an appreciable degree. This allowed improved horizontal and vertical armour to be worked into the design, and also provided for the carriage of a larger complement of current aircraft or a smaller number of newer and larger types as these entered service. Other features were the two aircraft-launching catapults, three elevators including one deck-edge unit, and the location of virtually all of the defensive armament in long sponsons along the sides of the hull. The details of this class included a full-load displacement of 60,000 tons, an armament of eighteen 5in dual-purpose guns in single turrets, eighty-four 40mm anti-

aircraft guns in 21 quadruple mountings and eighty-two 20mm cannon, as well as 137 aircraft, protection in the form of an 8in (203mm) belt and armoured decks, and a speed of 33 knots on the 212,000hp (158,065kW) delivered to four shafts by geared steam turbines.

Although the US Navy was a firm believer in the overall superiority of the large fleet carrier, the crisis in which it found itself in the days after the Japanese attack on Pearl Harbor persuaded the service to plan for the rapid introduction of a light carrier element based on the hulls of nine incomplete 'Cleveland' class cruisers. Such was the urgency of the programme that all of these very successful ships entered service in 1943, providing the US Navy with an excellent interim carrier capability until the larger 'Essex' class carriers could enter service. The details of this class included a full-load displacement of 15,100 tons, an armament of four 5in dual-purpose guns in single turrets, twenty-six 40mm anti-aircraft guns in two quadruple and nine twin mountings and forty 20mm cannon in single mountings, as well as 45 aircraft launched with the aid of two catapults, protection in the form of a 5in (127mm) belt and 3in (76mm) deck, and a speed of 32 knots on the 100,000hp (74,560kW) delivered to four shafts by geared steam turbines.

The same reasoning that led the British to the concept of the escort carrier was also relevant to the Americans, who saw in this type the possibility of large numbers built in a short time for tasks ranging from

Built basically to mercantile standards and equipped more austerely than fleet carriers, the small escort carriers produced in the USA during World War II were nonetheless vital ships that played a major strategic role in tasks such as convoy escort and the provision of air support for amphibious operations.

The *Ark Royal*, seen here in 1977, was the UK's last large fleet carrier. The ship was completed in 1955 and broken up in 1980, and its details included a full-load displacement of 53,060 tons, length of 811ft 9in (247.4m), provision for 36 aircraft, protection in the form of a 4.5in (114mm) belt, 1.5in (38mm) hangar side and 4in (102mm) deck, propulsion in the form of geared steam turbines delivering 152,000hp (113,330kW) to four shafts for a speed of 31.5 knots, and complement of 2,640 including the air group.

'The Great Marianas Turkey Shoot'

AFTER the US capture of the Gilbert and Marshall Islands between November 1943 and February 1944, the Imperial Japanese navy planned the long-sought 'decisive battle' of the naval war in the Pacific. Admiral Mineichi Koga, commander of the Combined Fleet, and Admiral Soemu Toyoda, succeeding Koga after the latter's death in an air accident on 1 April 1944, appreciated that the next forward move would take the Americans to the Mariana Islands on the Japanese home islands' strategic doorstep. This would enable them to strike at Japan, Iwo Jima in the Volcano Islands, Okinawa in the Ryukyu Islands, and Formosa with the intention of severing Japan's maritime links with the Philippines, South-East Asia and all their raw materials. The resulting Operation 'A' called for the American invasion force off the Marianas (in the event, Vice Admiral Raymond A. Spruance's 5th Fleet with the 5th Amphibious Force and Vice Admiral Marc Mitscher's Task Force 58) to be attacked by powerful surface forces moving in from the south-west, where they were based close to vital oil supplies. The operation was launched on 15 June 1944 under the command of Vice Admiral Jisaburo Ozawa, whose 1st Mobile Fleet from Tawitawi was supported by Vice Admiral Matome Ugaki's Southern Force from Batjan, the two forces rendezvousing east of the Philippines on 16 June, one day after the US forces landed on Saipan in the Marianas. The rendezvous gave Ozawa a fleet of three fleet and six light aircraft carriers (carrying 473 obsolescent warplanes including 222 fighters and about 200 attack aircraft, all manned by indifferent aircrew with a maximum of a mere six months' training), five battleships, 10 heavy and two light cruisers, and 22 destroyers. Task Force 58 comprised seven fleet and eight light aircraft carriers (with 956 modern warplanes manned by skilled aircrew, of whom even the least experienced had two years' training and 300 hours in the air), seven battleships, eight heavy and 13 light cruisers, and 69 destroyers.

The Japanese plan became apparent to Mitscher after the Japanese rendezvous was spotted by US patrol submarines, and the scene was thus set for the climactic Battle of the Philippine Sea (soon to become known as 'The Great Marianas Turkey Shoot') on 19/20 June 1944. Ozawa thought that the land-based warplanes commanded by Vice Admiral Kakuji Kakuta on Guam, Rota and Yap Islands had already struck hard blows at the US ships, and planned that his attack aircraft would rearm and refuel on these island bases. In reality the Japanese land-based aircraft had been virtually wiped out by American carrierborne aircraft, and the island airfields were being kept under constant attack: neither of these facts was reported by Kakuta to Ozawa. The Japanese carriers launched a first air strike early on 19 June, but the radar-warned Americans intercepted this initial wave 50 miles (80km) short of the US force, shooting down more than 200 Japanese aircraft. US submarines had meanwhile attacked Ozawa's force, torpedoeing the carriers *Taiho* and *Shokaku*, both of which sank. The Japanese second strike of 125 aircraft was intercepted on its way to Guam: once more, the Japanese aircraft were decimated, some 100 being lost. Two more Japanese attacks were handled in the same way; thus by the end of the first day, Ozawa had lost two carriers and 346 aircraft, whereas Mitscher had lost some 35 aircraft (29 of them in combat) and suffered damage to one battleship.

It was now the turn of the Americans to go over to the offensive, and Mitscher launched his aircraft from 16.24 on 20 June as TF58 pursued the Japanese fleet that was withdrawing to the north-west to refuel. The American strike sank two tankers and the carrier *Hiyo*, damaged the carriers *Zuikaku*, *Junyo* and *Chiyoda* plus the heavy cruiser *Maya*, and destroyed another 65 Japanese aircraft, for the loss of 20 of their own aircraft. It was night by the time the American aircraft headed for their parent carriers, which Mitscher ordered to turn on their lights as an aid to the pilots. Nevertheless some 80 US aircraft ran out of fuel and ditched, most of their crews being saved. Operation 'A' and the resultant Battle of the Philippine Sea may thus be seen as marking the end of the Imperial Japanese Navy's air arm as an effective weapon.

convoy escort and anti-submarine warfare to support of amphibious operations via the resupply of larger carriers (both fleet and light) and the reinforcement of island bases in the Pacific. The first of these classes was the 'Long Island' type, of which two were retained by the US Navy and the other four passed to the Royal Navy, and further construction yielded the 'Bogue' class of 11 ships excluding 26 transferred to the Royal Navy, the 'Sangamon' class of four ships, the 'Casablanca' class of 50 ships that were the first of the type built from the keel up as escort or 'jeep' carriers, and the 'Commencement Bay' class of 19 ships. The details of the 'Casablanca' class included a full-load displacement of 10,400 tons, an armament of one 5in dual-purpose gun, sixteen 40mm anti-aircraft guns in eight twin mountings and twenty-four 20mm cannon in single mountings, as well as 28 aircraft launched with the aid of one catapult, no protection, and a speed of 19 knots on the 9,000hp (6,710kW) delivered to two shafts by triple-expansion steam engines.

In the aftermath of World War II, the US Navy concentrated on the restoration of its war-weary carrier force to full capability and on the completion of those ships in the final stages of construction. The 1947 fleet strength therefore included 22 'Essex', three 'Midway', three 'Independence', two 'Saipan', four 'Bogue', six 'Casablanca' and 12 'Commencement Bay' class carriers. These ships remained in service or were taken in hand for conversion, either to an improved standard or for other roles, as the US Navy analysed the lessons of World War II. These included the inescapable conclusion that the aircraft carrier had replaced the battleship as the real capital ship, and the development of the US Navy's surface capability was now concentrated even more strongly on the operation of carrier battle groups as the core of American naval strength.

Shipbuilding resumed during the Korean War (1950-53), and included in this first generation of new ships were the four aircraft carriers of the

The *Independence* was the last of the four 'Forrestal' class conventionally powered aircraft carriers to be completed for the US Navy, which commissioned the ship in January 1959. The flightdeck arrangement of this ship includes a fore-and-aft bow section with two steam catapults, an angled section with two steam catapults and four sets of arrester wires, and four large deck-edge elevators located at three on the starboard side (one forward of the island and two abaft it) and one on the port side (near the forward edge of the angled flightdeck section).

Commissioned in the first half of the 1980s, the Royal Navy's three small carriers of the 'Invincible' class, here epitomised by the *Illustrious* photographed in 1983, were designed for the operation only of VTOL and STOVL aircraft, the former represented by helicopters and the latter by BAe Sea Harrier multi-role warplanes that are able to lift off at a moderately high weight as a result of their thrust-vectoring engine configuration and the 'ski jump' forward edge of the flightdeck. The details of the 'Invincible' class include a full-load displacement of 19,500 tons, length of 677ft 0in (206.6m), armament of two 20mm Vulcan six-barrel cannon in two Phalanx close-in weapon system mountings, two 20mm cannon in single mountings, one twin launcher for Sea Wolf surface-to-air missiles, and 21 aircraft (12 rotary-wing and nine fixed-wing machines), propulsion in the form of a COGAG arrangement with gas turbines delivering 94,000hp (70,085kW) to two shafts for a speed of 28 knots, and complement of 785 excluding an air group of 400.

Although larger than the 'Invincible' class ships, the three units of the USSR's 'Kiev' class bear a similarity to the British ships in being designed for the operation only of VTOL and STOVL aircraft. The ships are in effect hybrid missile cruisers and V/STOL aircraft carriers.

'Forrestal' class to a design scaled down from that of the *United States*, a large ship laid down (but then cancelled) as the carrier of the US Navy's new generation of strategic attack warplanes armed with free-fall nuclear weapons. The 'Forrestal' class ships were completed between 1955 and 1959 with all the latest aircraft developments including the angled flightdeck and mirror landing system, and its flightdeck carried four deck-edge elevators as well as four catapults. The details of this epoch-making class included a full-load displacement of 78,510 tons, an armament of eight 5in dual-purpose guns in single turrets, as well as 90 aircraft, unspecified protection, and a speed of 33 knots on the 280,000hp (208,770kW) delivered to four shafts by geared steam turbines.

The next four ships were completed between 1961 and 1968 as the 'Kitty Hawk' class to an improved 'Forrestal' class design, with a full-load displacement of 80,945 tons, an armament of two twin-arm launchers for 80 RIM-2 Terrier surface-to-air missiles, as well as 90 aircraft, unspecified protection, and a speed of 33.6 knots on the 280,000hp (208,770kW) delivered to four shafts by geared steam turbines. The last of the ships to be completed was the *John F. Kennedy*, which differs from the other ships in its improved underwater protection of the type developed for the first American nuclear-powered carrier.

This was the *Enterprise*, which was completed in 1961 with a full-load displacement of 89,085 tons, an armament of 90 aircraft supplemented by three octuple launchers for RIM-7 Sea Sparrow surface-to-air missiles, unspecified protection, and a speed of 32 knots on the 280,000hp (208,770kW) delivered to four shafts by the geared steam turbines supplied from eight Westinghouse A2W pressurised water-cooled reactors. The importance of this ship was enormous, for it opened the possibility of operational cruises of extreme range and endurance. The ship has virtually unlimited range without any need for oil fuel, and this leaves all the bunkerage for aviation fuel with consequent advantages in the amount of flying that can be undertaken before the bunkers need replenishment from supply ships: the real limitations to the length of an operational cruise are crew efficiency and the rate at which consumables (food and other manpower requirements, warplane spares, ammunition and bombs, and warplane fuel) can be replenished.

Opposite below: Although larger than the 'Invincible' class ships, the three units of the USSR's 'Kiev' class bear a similarity to the British ships in being designed for the operation only of VTOL and STOVL aircraft. The ships are in effect hybrid missile cruisers and V/STOL aircraft carriers, and their details include a full-load displacement of 37,100 tons, length of 895ft 9in (273.0m), armament of four 3in (76mm) dual-purpose guns in two twin turrets, eight 30mm six-barrel cannon in eight close-in weapon system mountings, four twin launchers for eight SS-N-12 'Sandbox' anti-ship missiles, two twin launchers for 72 SA-N-3 'Goblet' surface-to-air missiles, two twin launchers for 40 SA-N-4 'Gecko' surface-to-air missiles or, in one ship only, six octuple vertical launchers for 96 SA-N-9 surface-to-air missiles, one twin launcher for 20 FRAS anti-submarine rockets, two 12-tube anti-submarine rocket launchers, 10 21in (533mm) torpedo tubes in two quintuple mountings and 32 aircraft in the form of 19 rotary-wing and 13 fixed-wing machines, propulsion in the form of geared steam turbines delivering 201,180hp (150,000kW) to four shafts for a speed of 32 knots, and complement of 1,200 excluding an air group of unrevealed size.

Aircraft Carrier Attack on Pearl Harbor

OPERATION 'Z' was the Japanese attack on the US Pacific Fleet in Pearl Harbor on 7 December 1941, and this attack marked the entry of Japan into World War II. The operation was designed by Admiral Isoroku Yamamoto, Commander-in-Chief of the Combined Fleet, as a decisive stroke to eliminate Admiral Husband E. Kimmel's US Pacific Fleet at its base on Oahu Island in the Hawaiian group.

The force selected for the attack was Vice Admiral Chuichi Nagumo's 1st Air Fleet, comprising the fleet carriers Akagi, Kaga, Hiryu, Soryu, Shokaku and Zuikaku, the light cruiser Abukuma and nine destroyers, supported by the battleships Hiei and Kirishima, and by the heavy cruisers Tone and Chikuma; there were also three submarines for reconnaissance of the approach route for the 1st Air Fleet, two destroyers for the operation against Midway Island planned on the return journey, and a fleet train of eight tankers and supply ships. The 1st Air Fleet assembled in Tankan Bay in the Kurile Islands from 22 November 1941, and began to sail on 26 November, a circuitous northern route being selected to reduce the chances of detection. At 06.00 Nagumo began to launch his first strike force, consisting of 43 Mitsubishi A6M fighters, 51 Aichi D3A dive-bombers and 89 Nakajima B5N bombers (49 carrying 1,600lb/726kg armour-piercing shells modified as bombs and the other 40 carrying torpedoes specially modified for shallow running).

Shortly before 08.00 the attack began, the fighters peeling off to strafe airfields and the bombers beginning a decisive blow against Pearl Harbor. Only three of the battleships were not hit, and as the Japanese pulled out at 08.35 the West Virginia was sinking, the Arizona had settled on the bottom, the Oklahoma had capsized, the Tennessee was on fire, and the damaged Nevada was making for the harbour mouth. But already a second strike force was approaching the harbour, the pattern was similar to that of the first wave when the attack started at 09.15, and the Nevada was forced to beach herself while the Pennsylvania was severely damaged. The Japanese pulled out at 09.45. American losses were three battleships sunk, one battleship capsized, four battleships severely damaged, three light cruisers and three destroyers damaged, 65 out of 231 US Army aircraft destroyed, 200 out of 250 US Navy and Marine Corps aircraft destroyed, and some 3,225 Americans killed plus another 1,272 wounded.

The Japanese had scored a decisive victory, but this was only of a tactical or perhaps operational nature, the great strategic prizes being missed as the Pacific Fleet's three carriers (Enterprise, Lexington and Saratoga) were absent, and as Nagumo refused his air commanders' pleas for a third strike to eliminate the Pacific Fleet's unprotected oil tank farms and maintenance facilities.

The success of the *Enterprise* paved the way for the US Navy's current generation of carriers, which comprise the eight ships of the 'Nimitz' class delivered from 1975 to an improved 'Forrestal' class design with a smaller nuclear propulsion arrangement. These huge and extremely capable ships each have a full-load displacement of 102,000 tons, an armament of three octuple launchers for RIM-7 Sea Sparrow surface-to-air missiles and four 20mm Vulcan six-barrel cannon in Phalanx close-in weapon system mountings, as well as 90 aircraft, unspecified protection, and a speed of 30 knots or more on the 260,000hp (193,855kW) delivered to four shafts by the geared steam turbines supplied from two Westinghouse A4W or General Electric A1G pressurised water-cooled reactors.

The only other country to have built aircraft carriers in significant numbers is Japan, which completed its first carrier in 1922 as the *Hosho*. This was a small ship of limited operational capability, but provided the Japanese navy with the right type of experience to progress to the design and operation of larger and more capable fleet aircraft carriers. The first of these were two conversions from capital ships whose completion was prevented by the Washington Naval Treaty: the *Kaga* and *Akagi* were conversions from related battleship and battle-cruiser designs respectively. The details of the *Kaga* included a displacement of 26,900 tons, an armament of ten 7.9in (200mm) guns in two twin and six single turrets and twelve 4.7in

guns in six twin mountings, as well as 60 aircraft, protection in the form of an 11in (280mm) belt, and a speed of 27 knots on the 91,000hp (67,850kW) delivered to four shafts by geared steam turbines, while the details of the *Akagi* included a displacement of 26,900 tons, an armament of ten 7.9in guns in two twin and six single turrets and twelve 4.7in guns in six twin mountings, as well as 60 aircraft, protection in the form of a 10in (255mm) belt, and a speed of 31 knots on the 131,200hp (97,825kW) delivered to four shafts by geared steam turbines.

In 1929, Japan laid down its second purpose-designed carrier as the *Ryujo*, which as a result of Washington Naval Treaty limitations had a displacement of less than 10,000 tons as such carriers were not included in Japan's limit of 80,000 tons of carriers. The ship was found to be limited in many operational respects, and after its 1936 refit had details that included a displacement of 10,600 tons, an armament of eight 5in anti-aircraft guns in four twin mountings and twenty-four 25mm anti-aircraft guns in 12 twin mountings, as well as 48 aircraft (36 operational and 12 spare), unspecified but limited protection, and a speed of 29 knots on the 65,000hp (48,465kW) delivered to two shafts by geared steam turbines.

Japan used its experience with these early carriers to plan its first large fleet carriers designed as such from the keel up. These were the two ships of the 'Soryu' class that were completed in 1937 and 1939 with a

Laid down in June 1944 as the Elephant, fifth light carrier of the 'Hermes' class, this ship was completed in November 1959 as the *Hermes* of the 'Centaur' class. This long building period allowed a thorough revision of the ship, which thus emerged with an angled flightdeck and a deck-edge elevator, the latter complementing an inset elevator in the after part of the flightdeck. The deck-edge elevator was adopted as the forward inset elevator originally planned had to be eliminated to allow the incorporation of two steam catapults in the forward end of the fore-and-aft section of the flightdeck. The ship was completed with a full-load displacement of 28,700 tons, length of 744ft 4in (226.9m), armament of ten 40mm anti-aircraft guns in five twin mountings, and 28 aircraft, propulsion in the form of geared steam turbines delivering 76,000hp (56,665kW) to two shafts for a speed of 28 knots, and complement of 1,830 excluding an air group of 270. The ship was later revised with two triple launchers for Seacat surface-to-air missiles in place of the 40mm guns, and in its final form became a carrier of VTOL and STOVL warplanes in the form of up to 10 Westland Sea King anti-submarine helicopters and 20 BAe Sea Harrier multi-role warplanes, the latter launched at high weights with the aid of the 'ski jump' raised section installed at the forward end of the flightdeck. The Hermes was the flagship of the British forces despatched to free the Falkland Islands from Argentine occupation in 1982, and was deleted shortly after this.

Opposite top: The *Coral Sea* was an American fleet carrier of the 'Midway' class built in World War II, but was modernised and survived into the later 1980s, finally as a training carrier based on the American west coast.

Opposite below: Represented here by the lead ship, photographed in 1988, the four fleet aircraft carriers of the 'Kitty Hawk' class were completed in the 1960s to an improved 'Forrestal' class design with a full-load displacement of 80,945 tons, length of 1,947ft 6in (319.4m), armament of two twin launchers for 40 RIM-2 Terrier surface-to-air missiles, and 90 aircraft launched with the aid of four steam catapults, propulsion in the form of geared steam turbines delivering 280,000hp (208,770kW) to four shafts for a speed of 33.6 knots, and complement of 3,305 excluding an air group of 1,380.

Right: The *Ark Royal* was completed in 1978 as the third unit of the Royal Navy's three-strong 'Invincible' class of light aircraft carriers, and differs from the other two ships in details such as its higher-angled 'ski jump', full-load displacement of 20,000 tons, greater length of 685ft 10in (209.1m) and improved defensive armament.

displacement of 15,900 and 17,300 tons respectively, an armament of twelve 5in anti-aircraft guns in six twin mountings and between twenty-eight and thirty-one 25mm anti-aircraft guns in 14 twin mountings or in seven triple and five twin mountings, as well as 69 aircraft (53 operational and 16 spare), moderate but unspecified protection, and a speed of 34.5 knots on the 152,000hp (113,330kW) delivered to four shafts by geared steam turbines.

Further improvement of the concept embodied in the 'Soryu' class and the expiry of Treaty limitations allowed Japan's next pair of carriers to be the somewhat larger ships of the 'Shokaku' class completed in 1941 with a displacement of 25,675 tons, an armament of sixteen 5in anti-aircraft guns in eight twin mountings and thirty-six 25mm anti-aircraft guns in 12 triple mountings, as well as 84 aircraft (72 operational and 12 spare), protection in the form of an 8.5in (215mm) belt and 6.75in (170mm) deck, and a speed of 34.25 knots on the 160,000hp (119,135kW) delivered to four shafts by geared steam turbines.

These were the most important aircraft carriers operated by the Japanese navy up to the time of the Battle of Midway (June 1942), when the service lost no fewer than four of the ships together with most of its experienced naval aviators. The Japanese carrierborne arm then went into a decline from

which it never recovered despite the delivery of new and improved aircraft, fresh aircrews who lacked the experience and the skills of their predecessors, as well as a number of new aircraft carriers to supplement the ships surviving from the early operations of World War II. The other ships included the two 'Soho' class light carriers completed in 1939 and 1940 with a displacement of 11,260 tons and 30 aircraft; the three 'Taiyo' class escort carriers completed in 1940 and 1941 with a displacement of 17,830 tons and between 27 and 30 aircraft; the two 'Hiyo' class fleet carriers completed in 1942 with a displacement of 24,140 tons and an armament of 53 aircraft; the single 'Taiho' class fleet carrier completed in 1944 with a displacement of 29,300 tons and an armament of 74 aircraft; the single 'Ryuho' class light carrier completed in 1942 with a displacement of 13,360 tons and an armament of 31 aircraft; the single 'Shinano' class fleet carrier converted from a 'Yamato' class battleship and completed in 1944 with a displacement of 62,000 tons and an armament of 47 aircraft; the single 'Shinyo' class light

These two views highlight the huge size of the flightdeck of the US Navy's 'Nimitz' class of nuclear-powered aircraft carriers, planned as a total of nine ships. The ship shown is the *Abraham Lincoln*, which was commissioned in November 1989 with a full-load displacement of 102,000 tons, length of 1,092ft 0in (332.9m), armament of four 20mm Vulcan six-barrel cannon in four Phalanx close-in weapon system mountings, three octuple launchers for Sea Sparrow surface-to-air missiles, and 81 fixed-wing and six rotary-wing aircraft, propulsion in the form of nuclear-powered geared steam turbines delivering 260,000hp (193,855kW) to four shafts for a speed of 30 or more knots, and complement of 3,185 excluding an air group of 2,800. The flightdeck, which extends over the full length of the ship, is 252ft 0in (76.8m) wide, served by one starboard- and three port-side deck-edge elevators, carries two steam catapults on the fore-and-aft section of the flightdeck and on the angled section two steam catapults and five sets of arrester wires.

carrier completed in 1943 as a conversion of a German liner with a displacement of 17,500 tons and an armament of 33 aircraft; the single 'Kaiyo' class escort carrier completed in 1943 with a displacement of 13,600 tons and an armament of 24 aircraft; the two 'Chiyoda' class light carriers completed in 1943 and 1944 with a displacement of 11,190 tons and an armament of 30 aircraft; and the three 'Unryu' class light fleet carriers completed in 1944 with a displacement of 17,150 tons and 64 aircraft.

Germany and Italy designed and started work on aircraft carriers for service in World War II, but none of these was completed. The only other countries that have completed true aircraft carriers are France (one before and two after World War II with two others currently building or planned) and the USSR (four 'Kiev' and two 'Kuznetsov' class ships), although Italy and Spain have in recent years each completed one light aircraft carrier suitable for the operation of helicopters and STOVL warplanes.

The *Nimitz* was completed in May 1975 as the lead ship of this important aircraft carrier class, and is seen here with examples of the wide assortment of aircraft that can be carried on these huge machines. The current air group includes 20 Northrop Grumman F-14 Tomcat fleet defence fighters, 20 McDonnell Douglas F/A-18 Hornet dual-role fighter and attack aircraft, 20 Northrop Grumman A-6 Intruder attack aircraft, 10 Lockheed Martin S-3 Viking anti-submarine aircraft, six Northrop Grumman EA-6 Prowler electronic warfare aircraft and five Northrop Grumman E-2 Hawkeye airborne early warning aircraft as well as six Sikorsky SH-3 Sea King or Sikorsky SH-60 Seahawk helicopters.

Although somewhat smaller than the latest 'Nimitz' class nuclear-powered aircraft carriers, the *Forrestal* and its conventionally powered three sister ships are still very substantial warships.

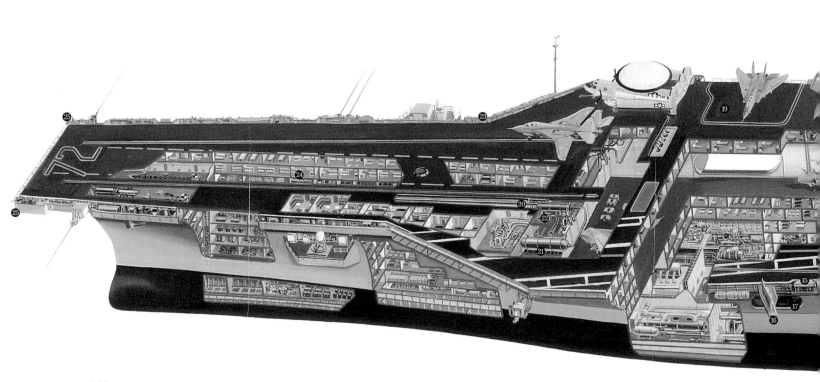

Annotation key

1. Aviation jet engine shop
2. Phalanx 20mm close-in weapons system
3. NATO Sea Sparrow Mk 29 launcher
4. Ship's boats
5. Squadron ready rooms
6. Landing signal officer platform
7. Mk 7 Mod 3 arrester gear engine
8. Aircraft elevator
9. Air search radar
10. Mobile crane
11. Jet blast deflector
12. Missile arming/de-arming platform
13. Island: Primary flight control/air boss, navigation bridge, radar and electronics, chart room, flight deck control, flight deck TV camera
14. Main engine room (arrangemernt notional)
15. Catapult officer launch control station
16. Optical landing system
17. Ship's whaler
18. Main deck (hanger bay)
19. Aircraft elevator
20. Type C-13-2 catapult
21. Catapult steam vessel
22. Catapult piping room
23. Saluting gun
24. Crew living spaces
25. .50-caliber machine gun

One of the two defensive weapons now carried by American aircraft carriers, the RIM-7 Sea Sparrow (seen here being fired from the *John F. Kennedy*) is a development of the AIM-7 Sparrow air-to-air missile intended for the short-range protection of major warships.

This cutaway illustration of the *Abraham Lincoln* reveals the extraordinary complexity of the huge 'Nimitz' class aircraft carriers.

Submarines

Introduction

THE submarine is a vessel designed and built to operate under the surface of the sea so that it can avoid the comparatively easy detection that is the fate of vessels operating on the surface of the sea: this 'cloak of invisibility' has the twin advantages of allowing the undetected submarine to avoid the easy interception that can swiftly lead to destruction, and to 'sneak up' on the enemy and inflict a telling blow before this enemy has been able to undertake anything in the way of evasive manoeuvres and/or defensive measures. This cloak of invisibility has long been a desire of armed forces, and the notion of a submarine vessel therefore had great attraction from early times. There were almost certainly designs (if not prototypes) in the period up to the end of the sixteenth century, but no known records of these efforts survive.

In the years between 1575 and 1765 many submarines were designed, and the designs of at least 17 survive today. The four men who made the greatest strides in this difficult field were the Englishman William Bourne, the Dutchman Cornelius van Drebbel, and the Americans David Bushnell and Robert Fulton. It was the two Americans who made the most notable contributions.

Bushnell was born in 1742 and graduated from Yale in 1775, just before the beginning of the War of Independence (1776-83). Bushnell was bitter in his opposition to the British, and designed a small 'submarine' as the means whereby the Americans, who lacked any form of effective navy, might be able to attack the fleet on which the British relied for the shipment of men, matériel and supplies from England, and also for transport and tactical mobility along the eastern litoral of the North American continent. Bushnell's *Turtle* was shaped like an egg, and by the flooding of two small internal tanks it could be trimmed right down in the water so that its conning tower was awash. Propulsion was provided by a hand-cranked propeller, and offensive capability rested with a 150lb charge of gunpowder that was designed to be attached to the

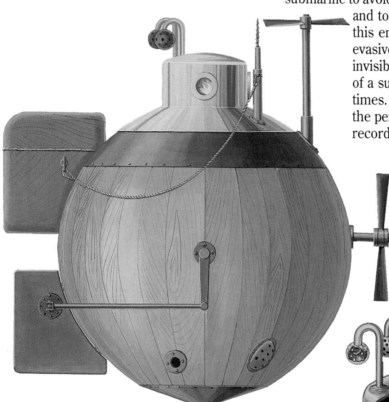

With hand-powered propellers for horizontal and vertical propulsion and snorkel-type tubes for the admission of breathing air, the *Turtle* designed by David Bushnell was the first 'practical' submarine in history, and was in fact a semi-submersible that could be trimmed right down into the water for concealed attacks with the 150lb (58kg) black powder charge contained in the hollowed-out oak container carried on the back of the vehicle and designed to be attached to the target by a screw. The boat was used operationally on at least one occasion in September 1776, but was defeated on its attack on a British battleship by the thick copper plating used to prevent infestation of the lower hull by shipworm.

underside of the target ship by a screw. In 1776, the Bushnell 'submarine' was launched against the British fleet lying off New York: manned by Sergeant Ezra Lee, the 'submarine' reached the *Eagle*, flagship of Admiral Lord Howe, but could not deposit its charge as Bushnell had forgotten that British warships were plated with copper that resisted the penetration of the screw. Two other unsuccessful efforts were made later in the war, but in 1782 Bushnell gave up his efforts and became a doctor.

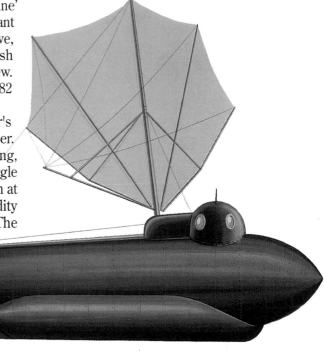

Fulton was born in 1765 and, after an early working life as a jeweller's apprentice and portrait painter, decided that engineering should be his career. In 1794, he travelled to England and became involved in canal engineering, but, in 1797, he moved to France and turned his attention to an uphill struggle to persuade the French that they needed submarines to defeat the British at sea. In 1801, Fulton managed to persuade Napoleon of his concept's validity and received 10,000 francs to design and build a prototype, the *Nautilus*. The submarine was ellipsoid in shape, 21ft (6.40m) long and 7ft (2.13m) in maximum diameter, and could be submerged by opening cocks to flood internal tanks. Surface propulsion was provided by a collapsible mast and sail, and underwater propulsion by hand-cranked propeller. A first test in Brest was successful when the *Nautilus* placed an external charge under a schooner anchored in the harbour, but the French marine ministry remained sceptical. Fulton then tried his luck in Britain with equal lack of success, and then returned to the USA, where his concept was also turned down. In 1812, Fulton devised his 'turtle-boat', a semi-submersible for operations against the British in the War of 1812: this boat was propelled by a hand-cranked propeller and designed to flood down to a freeboard of only 6in (0.15m) so that the craft could, at night, be mistaken for a floating log. The 'weapon' carried by the turtle-boat was a series of towed floating charges which could be swung against the target vessel and detonated from a safe distance with a lanyard. The first trial was not successful, and the turtle-boat was then destroyed by a British raiding party before further trials could be undertaken. Fulton went on to make his name as a pioneer of steam power for ships.

The semi-submersible was also used in the American Civil War (1861-65). The type used by the Confederate navy carried the name 'David'. The 'Davids', of which some 20 were built, were intended to redress the considerable numerical superiority of the Union navy and came in two basic forms, using steam or hand power. The best known exploit of a steam-powered 'David' was the attack on the Federal ship *New Ironsides* in Charleston harbour in October 1863: under the command of Lieutenant Glassel, the 'David' did not get its spar torpedo (a 132lb/60kg explosive charge at the end of a long pole) deep enough under the water before the charge was exploded by its impact fuses, and the resulting waves swamped and sank the 'David' without causing more than limited damage to its target. More success attended a hand-propelled 'David', the *H.L. Hunley*, committed against the Federal ship *Housatonic* just as she was about to set sail in February 1864: the *Housatonic* was holed and opened to the sea. She sank, taking down with her the successful 'David', whose crew of nine was found inside the sunken vessel when divers went down to the wrecks some years later.

A successful submarine clearly depended on a number of primary requirements: a hull of circular section to withstand water pressure when

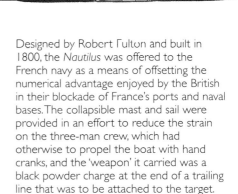

Designed by Robert Fulton and built in 1800, the *Nautilus* was offered to the French navy as a means of offsetting the numerical advantage enjoyed by the British in their blockade of France's ports and naval bases. The collapsible mast and sail were provided in an effort to reduce the strain on the three-man crew, which had otherwise to propel the boat with hand cranks, and the 'weapon' it carried was a black powder charge at the end of a trailing line that was to be attached to the target.

143

submerged, ballast tanks that could be filled with water to make the submarine sink and then refilled with air to restore the buoyancy to bring the boat back to the surface once more, a powerplant able to function without a constantly replenished supply of air when the submarine was submerged, a rudder to provide directional control, and horizontal rudders (hydroplanes) to provide longitudinal control. The hydroplanes also needed to be controllable either collectively so that, for example, a positive angle on both planes would bring the submarine upwards without changing its longitudinal angle, or differentially for a bow-up or bow-down angle to speed surfacing or submerging respectively.

The development of metal construction (initially iron and later steel) opened the possibility of ships and also of submarines with a watertight hull of considerable strength without excessive thickness and, during the second half of the nineteenth century, American and French inventors developed a number of designs up to model form. None of them secured the official backing that could have turned them into full-size hardware. This was perhaps just as well, for the major problems yet to be overcome were underwater propulsion and an effective underwater weapon. Steam power could be used for surface propulsion, of course, but was impractical because of the time needed to damp down the boilers before submerging and to get up a head of steam after surfacing. The practical solution appeared in 1885 with the invention of the internal-combustion engine by Gottlieb Daimler: some years had to elapse before it had been made powerful and reliable enough to use on board ships, but it offered the possibility of instant shut-down and start-up. However, such an engine cannot be used under water, since it needs a

The *Plongeur Marin was* designed during 1850 by the Bavarian Wilhelm Bauer, and its propulsive momentum was provided by the iron weight that could be moved fore and aft to plane forward in a series of undulating dives and climbs. The threat of the boat, built at Kiel, was sufficient to keep the Danish navy at a respectful distance from Kiel in the Prusso-Danish dispute over Schleswig-Holstein until the boat sank in February 1851 after a structural failure. Bauer and his two crew members became the first to survive a submarine accident.

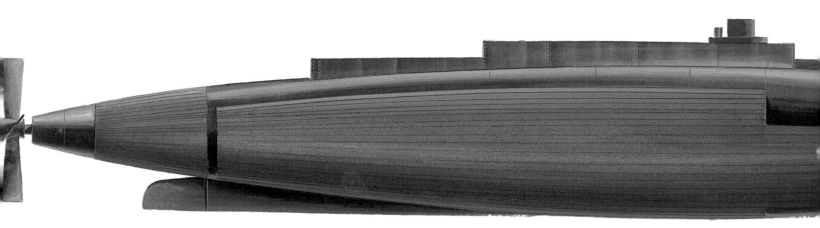

supply of air so large that the engine would exhaust the submarine's supply of compressed breathing and ballast-blowing air in a very short time.

For underwater running, a combination of electric engines and a massive array of batteries provided one solution. This combination had its limitations, however. Surface running could be entrusted to the internal-combustion engine, which could also be used to charge the batteries of the underwater system. The main drawback to the idea was the need for the submarine to surface periodically to recharge the batteries, but this problem could be reduced by surfacing at night or in safe conditions. This means, though, that the submarine with combined internal-combustion and electrical propulsion should perhaps be thought of as a submersible rather than as a true submarine as the type cannot be genuinely independent of the surface.

The right weapon was found in the locomotive torpedo, a free-running weapon developed into an effective type by Robert Whitehead, a British engineer working at Fiume in Austria-Hungary. The torpedo used compressed air for motive power and had a hydrostatic valve (later a pendulum system) for stability of depth. The first trials were undertaken in 1867, and by 1869 the locomotive torpedo was a practical weapon that was rapidly adopted by most of the world's more advanced navies. The type was still limited, but progress was made steadily in improving the torpedo's range, speed and course-keeping, the last with the aid of a gyroscopic system invented in Trieste by L. Obry in 1881. The first production torpedo emerged for the Royal Laboratory at Woolwich, England, in the early 1870s: it was a 16in (406mm) weapon with contra-rotating propellers (in which the torque reaction of each unit cancelled that of the other and therefore removed the tendency of single-propeller torpedoes to roll and thus change course in the direction of the roll), for a range of 1,000 yards (915m) at 7 knots or 300 yards (275m) at 12.5 knots. The pace of development is indicated by the fact that in 1909 the standard Whitehead torpedo was an 18in (457mm) weapon with a range of 2,000 yards (1830m) at 35 knots or 4,000 yards (3660m) at 29 knots. Further development was in the pipeline through the enrichment of the torpedo's air oxidant: the British developed a steam/gas engine in which water was evaporated and superheated by a shale-oil jet, while the Americans produced the Bliss-Leavitt type with a turbine driven by steam heated by an alcohol torch.

Lacking the resources to match the large fleets that the Union was able to create in the American Civil War (1861-65), the Confederacy opted for a 'high-technology' response to its opponent's surface warships. This was the combination of the spar torpedo (a large explosive charge at the end of a wooden spar extended over the bow) and the submarine, and given their planned task of killing the Union 'giants', these boats received the generic name 'Davids'. The first such boat was the *David*, funded by Theodore Stoney and built at Charleston, South Carolina, before being presented to the Confederate navy. The boat was constructed largely of boiler plate, and was based on a cylindrical central section with conical fore and after ends. A small boiler in the forward part of the boat generated the steam that powered the single engine powering the four-blade propeller at the extreme stern. Being unable to submerge completely, the *David* was not a true submarine but rather a semi-submersible: water was allowed to flood ballast tanks that trimmed the boat down into the water so that only some 10ft (3.05m) of the superstructure, including the hatch and the cylindrical funnel, were awash and could, it was hoped, be mistaken for a floating log or other such natural phenomenon. The *David* was 54ft (16.45m) long and was armed with a spar torpedo extending from the bow: this was designed to be lowered below the surface so that the detonation of its 134lb (60.8kg) of gunpowder, under the influence of seven chemical impact fuses, would blow a large hole in the side of the target below the waterline. The dangers of such a boat even under non-operational conditions were revealed when it was swamped and sunk by the wash of a ship during its trials, but the boat was raised and readied for action. In October 1863 the *David*, with a volunteer crew under the command of Lieutenant Glassell, attacked the broadside ironclad New Ironsides. The *David* was seen and challenged by the watch of the Union warship, but the Union sailors were disconcerted by a volley of rifle fire from the *David*'s hatch, which killed one Union officer and provided enough time for the spar torpedo to hit the ship abreast the engine room. The resulting explosion was too near the waterline to cause fatal damage, but sprang the wooden side of the ship for some 4 to 5in (0.10 to 0.127m) over a length of 50ft (15.25m). The explosion also swamped the *David*, putting out the boiler fire and washing Glassell overboard. Glassell and two other members of the crew swam to safety.

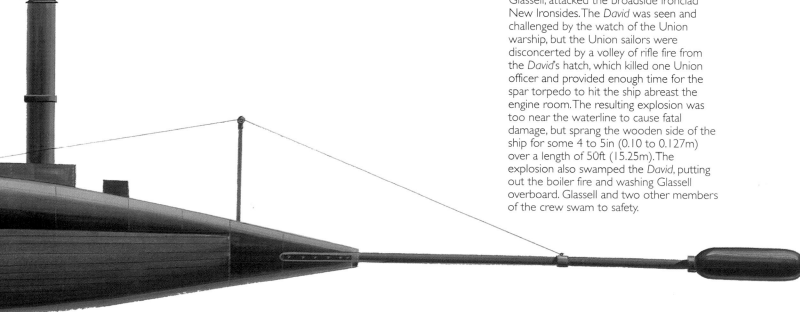

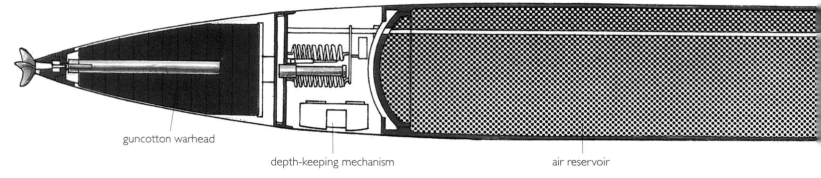

guncotton warhead

depth-keeping mechanism

air reservoir

By 1914, torpedoes were generally of 18 or 21in (457 or 533mm) diameter, with lengths of 17.5 and 22ft (5.33 and 6.71m) respectively and ranges of 3,750 yards (3,430m) at 44 knots or 10,000 yards (9,145m) at 28 knots.

The torpedo was thus the ideal weapon for the submarine: it was designed to run underwater in any case, and in submarines it could be launched by either of two methods: in the drop-collar method the torpedoes were carried externally and merely released from their mountings, and in the tube-launched method the torpedoes were fired by compressed air out of flooded tubes that could then be purged of water by the closing of the bow doors and reloaded from inside the submarine if the vessel was large enough to carry a reserve supply. The latter method fairly rapidly became the norm as it offered lower drag and therefore higher underwater speed, and allowed the withdrawal of the torpedo from its tube for limited maintenance if required.

These features all combined in the fertile mind of an Irish-born American, John P. Holland, who may be regarded as the father of the true submarine. The first Holland submarine was the *Plunger*, a design commissioned by the US Navy and built by the Columbian Iron Works in 1896. Because of the naval requirements the design was too complex for its small size, and the *Plunger* was not successful. The contract was cancelled in 1900, the year in which the US Navy bought the sole example of Holland's next design, which had been designed as a private venture and built by Crescent. This seven-man vessel had surfaced and submerged displacements of 64 and 74 tons on a length of 53.75ft (16.38m), and with 50hp (37.3kW) available from its gasoline or electric

The device that was eventually to make the submarine a viable weapon of war was the Whitehead locomotive torpedo, seen here in its first effective form of 1868. From nose to tail, the primary features are the guncotton warhead with impact fuse, the depth-keeping mechanism, the compressed air reservoir, the compressed air motor, and the tail section with its rudders and contra-rotating propeller unit.

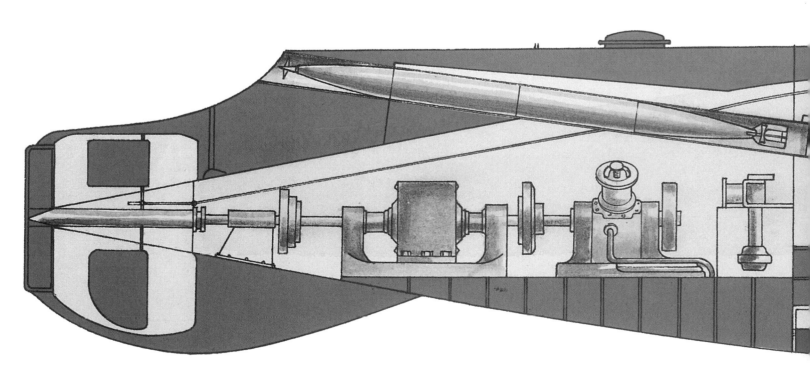

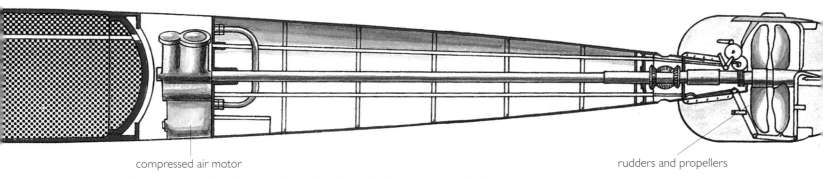

compressed air motor   rudders and propellers

engines had surfaced and submerged speeds of 8 and 5 knots respectively. The armament included one 18 in (457mm) torpedo tube and one 8in (203mm) dynamite gun. The concept clearly held promise, and there followed a group of seven 'A' class submarines which were slightly larger and provided improved underwater performance.

Several other countries began to develop submarines around the turn of the century. Germany was an exception, as its navy preferred to wait for the perfection of the considerably safer and more economical compression (rather than spark) ignition engine invented by Diesel and which ran on comparatively heavy oil instead of volatile gasoline, which made for considerably greater safety in the confined spaces inside a submarine and which, incidentally, offered much superior fuel economy. This last factor gradually came to assume a significant importance as the greater range possible, on a given volume of fuel, allowed the development of the diesel-engined boat as an independent long-range weapon for commerce raiding rather than a subordinate medium-range weapon associated with battle fleet evolutions on the surface.

The first diesel-engined submarine was the French *Aigrette*, which was launched in January 1904, and this was followed in 1906, 1910 and 1911 by the Russian *Minoga*, British D2 and American *Skipjack*.

The first submarine design by John Holland, arguably the true 'father' of the submarine, was the *Plunger* ordered by the US Navy in 1895 but never accepted by the US Navy as the type was an unsuccessful effort to fit too much capability into a design limited in size by the navy's lack of resources and then constantly altered during the course of construction in the light of changing naval opinions.

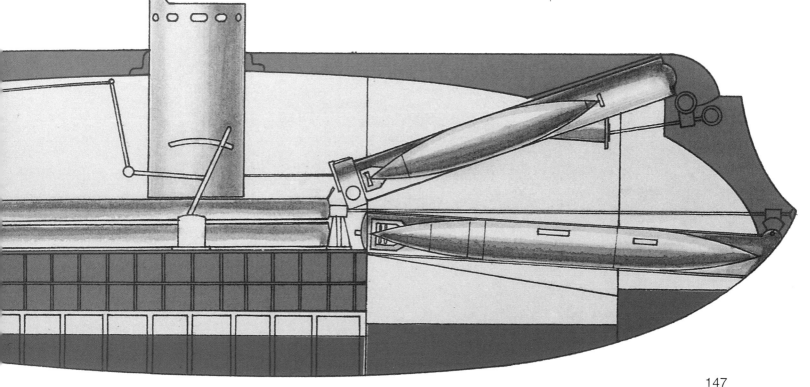

The Submarine in World War I

THE first German *Unterseeboot* (underwater boat, otherwise submarine) was the U1 that appeared in 1906 as a 19-man vessel that was 139ft (42.37m) long. At surfaced and underwater displacements of 238 and 283 tons, it was capable of 10.7 and 7 knots respectively on its gasoline or electric motors, each developing 400hp. The armament was still limited, made up of just one 17.7in (450mm) torpedo tube. This was a 'traditional' boat with the generally unsuccessful combination of a gasoline engine for surfaced running and battery charging, and an electric motor for submerged running. The progress made in the next few years is indicated by the size and capabilities of the four boats of the 'U19' class that were all delivered in 1913 from Danzig Dockyard as the Imperial German navy's first four diesel-engined submarines. These boats were each manned by 39 men, were 210.5ft (64.15m) long, possessed a surfaced and submerged displacement of 650 and 837 tons respectively, were capable of surfaced and submerged speeds of 15.5 and 9.5 knots respectively on their powerplant of 1,700hp (1,267.5kW) diesel engines or 1,200hp (895kW) electric motors, and carried an armament of one 86 or 105mm (3.4 or 4.1in) deck gun and four 17.7in (450mm) torpedo tubes.

The installation of the deck gun is signal evidence of a gradual shift in emphasis for the submarine's role. The torpedo was still seen as the primary weapon for the destruction of larger warships and merchant vessels at medium range, but was an expensive and bulky weapon of which only a relatively few could be carried. The deck gun, on the other hand, could be added without too much sacrifice of internal volume except for an ammunition magazine, and offered the possibility of comparatively cheap shell fire for the destruction of smaller naval vessels and larger merchant vessels. The rules of war dictated that the latter had to be stopped, searched and permitted to evacuate their crews and passengers before being sunk, and this was effectively impossible without the submarine surfacing, when the deck gun became a more cost-effective weapon than the torpedo.

Technical progress in the years before World War I (1914-18) was rapid, and by the beginning of the war there were about 400 submarines in service with 16 navies. The British and French mustered about half of this total, but whereas these vessels were generally of the small coastal type with

Below: The French *Gymnote* was the first successful modern submarine when it first appeared in 1888. In its original form the boat had virtually no superstructure and very poor depth-keeping capability, and was twice rebuilt to appear in 1898 to the form illustrated with a raised conning tower, an extended deck casing, and external drop collars for two torpedoes. In reality, however, the *Gymnote* was too small and rudimentary to be anything more than an experimental type.

Below left: These are the outline plans for the Holland-designed 'A' class submarine *Plunger*, later renamed as the A-1 and the lead boat of a seven-strong group that was the US Navy's first operational submarine class. The boats were completed between 1901 and 1903. All except the A-1 were transferred to the Philippines in 1909 and expended as targets in 1922, the year in which the A-1 was sold for scrap.

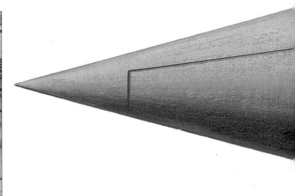

displacements of about 300 tons, the Germans used the larger type suitable for open-sea operations on a displacement between 550 and 850 tons. The Royal Navy had 71 operational submarines with another 31 being built, and the Germans had 33 with another 28 in production. The British and most other navies saw their submarines as companions to their large surface fleets used to scout and ambush the enemy's warships, but the Germans rapidly came to the conclusion that the submarine could and should be used as a deep-sea raider independent of the surface forces.

The first submarine operations of World War I were extremely limited, for none of the combatants had any experience in the use of such vessels under wartime conditions. The majority of navies and their senior officers viewed the submarine as an adjunct to their surface forces, which they deemed to be the real arbiters of any naval battle. Thus the submarine was seen primarily as a covert reconnaissance machine, and in the first days of the war the Germans sent some of their boats north through the North Sea to watch for the activities of the Grand Fleet, which was based on Rosyth and Scapa Flow in Scotland, while the British despatched some of their submarines into the south-east quadrant of the North Sea in the Heligoland Bight to watch for any sortie of the High Seas Fleet from its base at Wilhelmshaven. In the course of these initial operations the Germans lost two of the 10 boats they sent out: *U13* failed to return, probably as a result of hitting a mine, while *U15* was sighted, rammed and cut in two by a British cruiser.

Striking evidence of what might be achieved was soon provided by *U9*, which on one day sank the British armoured cruisers *Hogue*, *Aboukir* and *Cressy*, and then only three weeks later sank the cruiser *Hawke*: the British death toll was more than 1,600 men as well as four cruisers, albeit of types that were thoroughly obsolete and provided with indifferent protection against torpedo attack. Such was the fear of the submarine now instilled in the British that henceforward the major units of the Royal Navy ventured from port only when escorted by an outer screen of destroyers.

The British, and indeed all who sought to counter the threat of the submarine, were severely hampered by the lack of any means to detect a

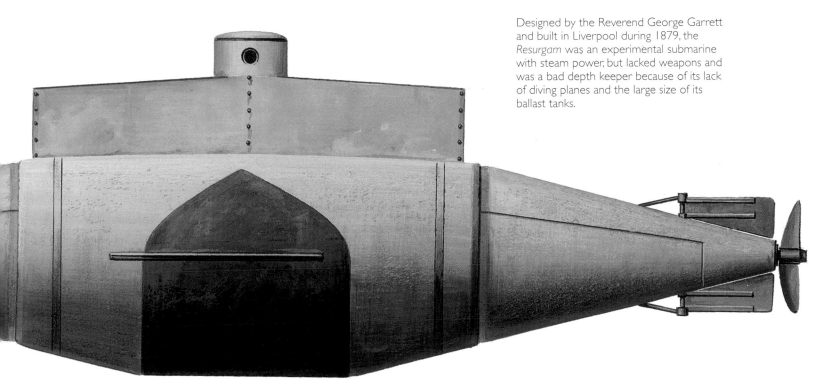

Designed by the Reverend George Garrett and built in Liverpool during 1879, the *Resurgam* was an experimental submarine with steam power, but lacked weapons and was a bad depth keeper because of its lack of diving planes and the large size of its ballast tanks.

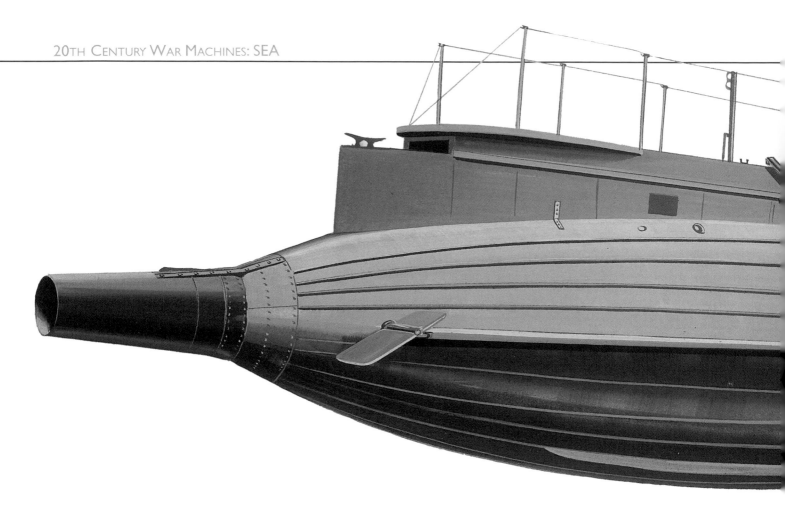

submerged submarine: only the sighting of a raised periscope, or the conning tower of a poorly trimmed boat breaking through the surface of the water, could provide advance warning of an event otherwise signalled by the thunderous explosion of a torpedo against the side of a hapless warship. Moreover, even when they sighted a submarine, the crew of a surface warship could achieve little in the way of securing the boat's destruction: new-construction destroyers and light cruisers were fitted with a reinforced foot on the stem for a ramming attack, and all vessels could respond with gunfire in the hope of holing the conning tower or carrying away a periscope.

The submarines of the period were just about fast enough on the surface to provide a scouting capability for forces of cruising warships but lacked the pace to keep up with them after these moved off at maximum speed, and they also lacked the underwater endurance and speed to serve as adjuncts to major surface forces except by lurking off the enemy's ports to report the sortie of such forces and perhaps torpedo one warship if the opportunity offered. Moreover, after a few brief flurries in 1914 and the first part of 1915, the British and German major fleets seemed content to remain in harbour and await the opportunity for a single climactic battle that would decide the outcome of World War I.

Thus there seemed little part for the submarine to play in the course of conventional naval warfare, so other methods were sought in which the new weapon could profitably be employed. Small numbers of submarines were detached to the confined waters such as the south-western corner of the North Sea, the Strait of Otranto and the Dardanelles,

Resulting from the development work carried out by the Norwegian armaments manufacturer Nordenfelt, this was one of two submarines built in Germany in 1890. The type was not successful, and little is known of its details, although it is thought that the bow-mounted 'snout' was probably a torpedo tube.

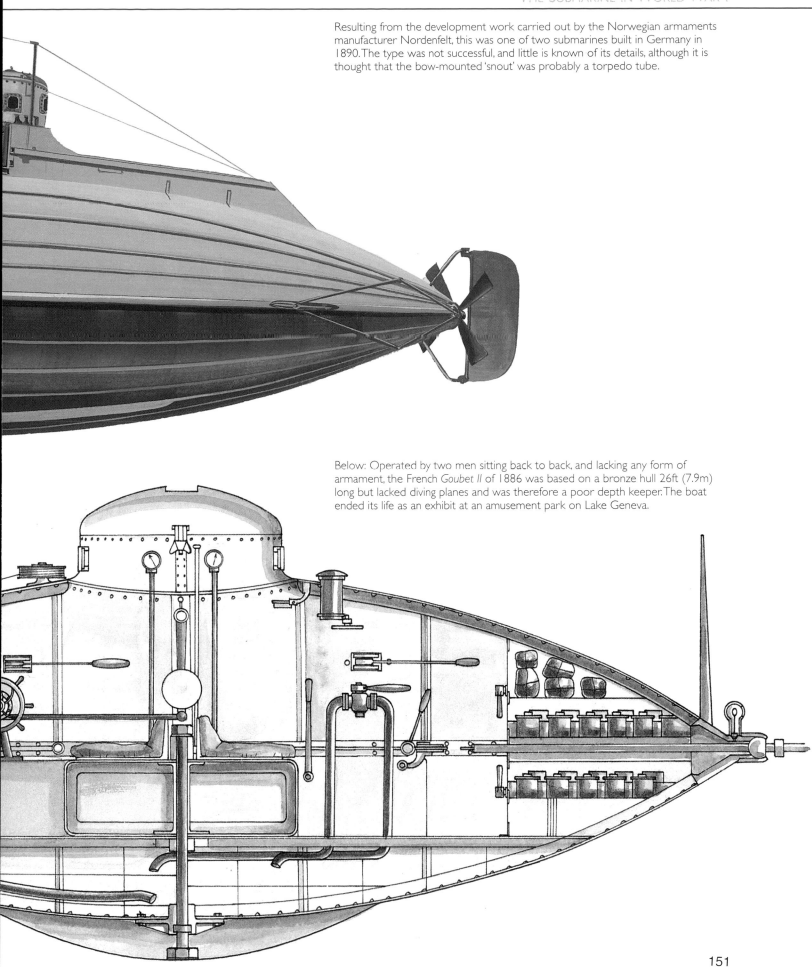

Below: Operated by two men sitting back to back, and lacking any form of armament, the French *Goubet II* of 1886 was based on a bronze hull 26ft (7.9m) long but lacked diving planes and was therefore a poor depth keeper. The boat ended its life as an exhibit at an amusement park on Lake Geneva.

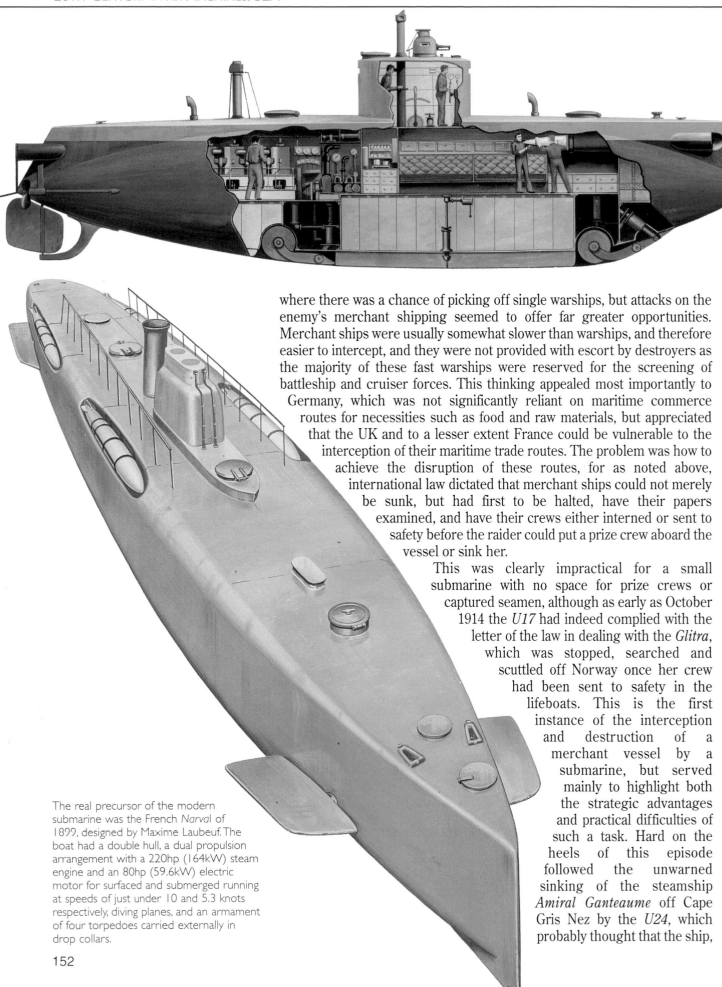

The real precursor of the modern submarine was the French *Narval* of 1899, designed by Maxime Laubeuf. The boat had a double hull, a dual propulsion arrangement with a 220hp (164kW) steam engine and an 80hp (59.6kW) electric motor for surfaced and submerged running at speeds of just under 10 and 5.3 knots respectively, diving planes, and an armament of four torpedoes carried externally in drop collars.

where there was a chance of picking off single warships, but attacks on the enemy's merchant shipping seemed to offer far greater opportunities. Merchant ships were usually somewhat slower than warships, and therefore easier to intercept, and they were not provided with escort by destroyers as the majority of these fast warships were reserved for the screening of battleship and cruiser forces. This thinking appealed most importantly to Germany, which was not significantly reliant on maritime commerce routes for necessities such as food and raw materials, but appreciated that the UK and to a lesser extent France could be vulnerable to the interception of their maritime trade routes. The problem was how to achieve the disruption of these routes, for as noted above, international law dictated that merchant ships could not merely be sunk, but had first to be halted, have their papers examined, and have their crews either interned or sent to safety before the raider could put a prize crew aboard the vessel or sink her.

This was clearly impractical for a small submarine with no space for prize crews or captured seamen, although as early as October 1914 the *U17* had indeed complied with the letter of the law in dealing with the *Glitra*, which was stopped, searched and scuttled off Norway once her crew had been sent to safety in the lifeboats. This is the first instance of the interception and destruction of a merchant vessel by a submarine, but served mainly to highlight both the strategic advantages and practical difficulties of such a task. Hard on the heels of this episode followed the unwarned sinking of the steamship *Amiral Ganteaume* off Cape Gris Nez by the *U24*, which probably thought that the ship,

Opposite: Rivalling John Holland as the father of the American submarine, Simon Lake produced the *Protector* in 1901 with extending wheels in the bottom of the hull so that the boat could travel along the sea bed. The boat was armed with three torpedo tubes (two in the bows and one in the stern), and was in most respects superior to the rival Holland No.8. It is possible that the US Navy ignored the *Protector*'s capabilities and greater 'developability' because of the oddity represented by the wheels, so Lake sold the boat to Russia, which then ordered another four. All five boats were shipped in sections to Vladivostok in eastern Siberia, and there assembled in time for service during the Russo-Japanese War (1904-05), in which they achieved nothing of note other than the deterrence of any Japanese naval attack on Vladivostok.

Right: The first submarine to be completed for the US Navy was the Holland-designed *Holland*, which was commissioned in 1900 with surfaced and submerged displacements of 64 and 74 tons respectively, a length of 53ft 9in (16.38m), a propulsion arrangement of one 45hp (33.5kW) petrol engine and one 50hp (37.3kW) electric motor for surfaced and submerged speeds of 8 and 5 knots respectively, a crew of 7, and an armament of one 18in (457mm) torpedo tube and one 8in (203mm) dynamite gun, although the original design had included two of each type. The boat was discarded in 1910.

Below: One of the Union's answers to the Confederacy's 'Davids' in the American Civil War (1861-65) was the Intelligent Whale, which was a carefully considered design that relied on manual propulsion, lacked a suitable weapon, was difficult to manoeuvre and, because of the war's end, was never used operationally.

in fact loaded with Belgian refugees, was a troopship and therefore a legitimate target.

The sinking of the *Amiral Ganteaume* was regarded by the Allies as a German atrocity, but was in fact a portent of the future for the submarine as World War I descended to the level of total war, in which the whole of the nation rather than just its armed strength was regarded as 'fair game'. In February 1915 Germany announced that the waters round the UK were now a war zone and that any British or French ship in it was liable to summary destruction without warning, and that as a result of the submarines' limitations (such as indifferent periscope quality) it was also impossible to guarantee the safety of neutral ships in the zone. The effect of this change soon made itself apparent: in January 1915 the British and French had lost 47,900 tons of merchant shipping, but after the declaration of the German war zone this total rose to 185,400 tons, 148,000 tons of it represented by British hulls.

Above left: Seen in the early 1900s, this is the view looking forward in a Holland-designed 'B' class submarine, which was the second type of boat adopted by the US Navy as a development of the ideas embodied in the 'A' class. Visible are the side-by-side pair of 18in (457mm) torpedo tubes and, because the deck plates have been lifted, the batteries. The data for the three 'B' class submarines included surfaced and submerged displacements of 145 and 173 tons respectively, a length of 82ft 6in (25.15m), a propulsion arrangement of 250hp (186kW) petrol engines and a 150hp (112kW) electric motor for surfaced and submerged speeds of 9 and 8 knots respectively, and a crew of 10.

Left: The view aft from the control space in the 'B' class submarine is dominated by the engines for the single-propeller propulsion arrangement. The three boats were completed in 1906 and 1907, transported to the Philippines in 1912, and expended as targets in 1922.

Opposite: Completed in 1902, this is the Royal Navy's 'Holland' class submarine *Holland No.4* photographed in 1904. Of the five boats, *Holland No.1* and *Holland No.2* were sold in 1913, *Holland No.3* was sunk in experiments during 1911, *Holland No.4* was dismantled in 1912, and *Holland No.5* sank while on tow to the breaker's yard in 1912.

At this time the sole threat to Germany and its submarines was not British and French countermeasures, which were wholly ineffective, but the total opposition of world opinion, with that of America to the fore as its commercial interests were severely threatened. This hard-headed financial response to the threat of the German submarine offensive was strengthened by the weight of public opinion in May 1915, when the *U20* torpedoed the large liner *Lusitania*, which sank with the loss of many civilian lives including a number of Americans. This was not the first time in which civilians, particularly American civilians, had died as a result of submarine attack, but the scale of the losses combined with an astute British propaganda effort to swing American public opinion firmly behind the Allies paved the way for the USA's eventual entry into World War I in April 1917.

As the pace of the submarine war around the British and French coasts was increasing in the last months of 1914 and the first months of 1915, and as the Germans were preparing to shift toward a type of unrestricted submarine warfare not only in these areas but in the deeper waters of the North Atlantic Ocean, a relatively intense period of submarine warfare was becoming apparent in the Mediterranean. Most of France's submarines were located in this theatre, whose main base was Toulon in the south of France, but in the first months of the war there was little submarine activity as the British and French surface forces were sufficient to contain the considerably smaller and generally less effective navies of the Austro-Hungarian and Turkish empires. It was therefore left to the Austro-Hungarians, who initially possessed only seven submarines, to take the offensive in a bold attempt to redress the Mediterranean balance of naval power: in January 1915 the *XII* torpedoed and severely damaged the battleship Jean Bart, and four months later the *V* torpedoed and sank the armoured cruiser *Léon Gambetta*. By this time Turkey had entered the war, and after reinforcing her navally inept new partner with the *U21* sent into the Mediterranean via the Strait of Gibraltar, Germany decided that it would be more cost-effective to move six dismantled UB-type coastal submarines by rail to the Austro-Hungarian port of Cattaro (now Kotor), where they would be reassembled for operations under the German flag.

Three of the boats were then sent to Turkey, one disappearing *en route* and the other two reaching Constantinople (now Istanbul), where they joined forces with the *U21*, which in May 1915 torpedoed and sank the British battleships *Triumph* and *Majestic* off the Dardanelles. These elderly battleships had virtually no anti-submarine protection, but such was the fear

Above: Seen here as its crew wash it down while lying alongside *Holland No.4*, one of the four-strong second group of the 'Holland' class, the *Holland No.1* was the first submarine accepted by the Royal Navy after design by John Holland and construction by Vickers. The *Holland No.1* had surfaced and submerged displacements of 104 and 122 tons respectively, a length of 63ft 4in (19.3m), a propulsion arrangement of one 160hp (119kW) petrol engine and one 74hp (55.2kW) electric motor for surfaced and submerged speeds of 8 and 5 knots respectively, a crew of seven and an armament of one 14in (356mm) torpedo tube. The last four boats differed only in their submerged displacement of 150 tons and 250hp (186kW) petrol engine.

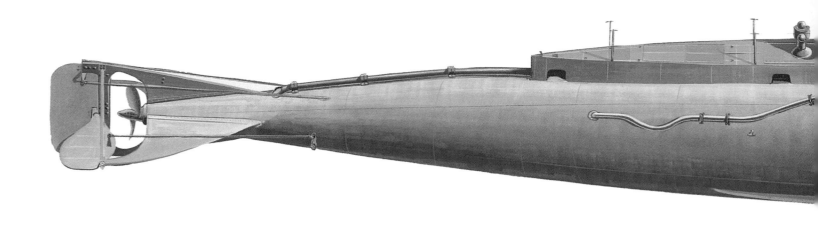

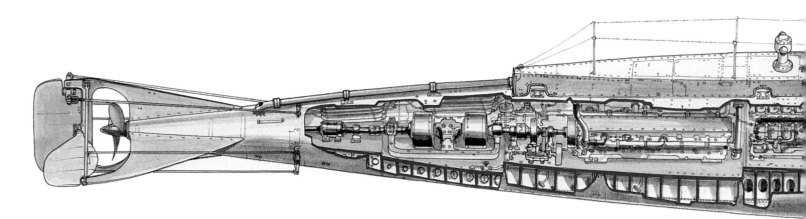

of submarine attack by the British naval forces off the Dardanelles that the local commander ordered all his larger warships back to anchor in the harbour of the Greek island of Mudros, thereby leaving the Allied infantry on Gallipoli with virtually no naval gunfire support.

By this time Italy had entered the war on the Allied side, and soon came to feel the effect of the new type of warfare as the submarines *Medusa* and *Nereide* and the cruisers *Amalfi* and *Giuseppe Garibaldi* were lost to submarine attack. Meanwhile, the squadron of six German boats in Turkey was continuing its run of success in the Black Sea and the Sea of Marmara. It was not all one-sided traffic, however, for the British and French respectively sent three and two obsolescent boats to blockade the mouth of the Dardanelles in case the Germans attempted to unleash their two most powerful ships in the area, the battle-cruiser Goeben and the light cruiser Breslau, which had reached Constantinople just before Turkey's entry into the war on the side of the Central Powers. The British then felt that it would be worth the effort to force their way past the Turkish anti-submarine defences in an effort to reach the Sea of Marmara, where they might find unwary Turkish targets.

This proved to be the case, and the *B11* there sank the old Turkish warship *Messudieh*. The Turkish ship was of no real operational value, but the fact that it had been reached and sunk encouraged the British to send no fewer than seven of the newer 'E' class boats to reinforce their submarine

Seen above in exterior and cutaway views, the Royal Navy's 'B' class of submarines totalled 11 boats all built by Vickers and completed in 1905 and 1906. The design represented what was basically the second stage of development from the original 'Holland' class of five boats via the 13 boats of the 'A' class also built by Vickers and completed between 1903 and 1905, but was limited by two factors. These were its small size, which made the boats capable of little more than harbour defence, and its use of petrol engines for surfaced running. The data for the class included surfaced and submerged displacements of 280 and 313 tons respectively, a length of 135ft 0in (41.15m), a propulsion arrangement of 600hp (447kW) petrol engines and a 190hp (142kW) electric motor for surfaced and submerged speeds of 12-13 and 7-9 knots respectively, a crew of 16, and an armament of two 18in (457mm) torpedo tubes in the bows. The B2 was lost during 1912 in a collision off Dover and the *B10* was bombed and sunk in 1916 in Venice harbour, but the other nine boats survived World War I (1914-18) to be sold and scrapped in the period after its conclusion.

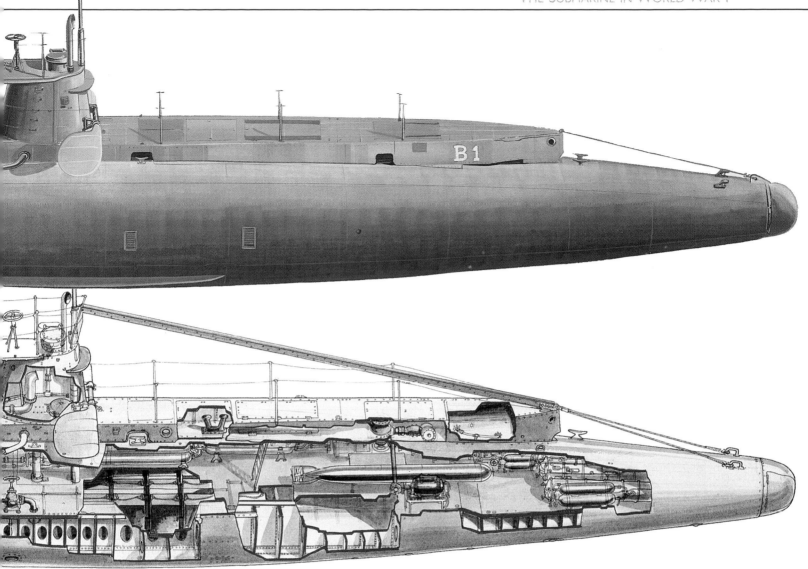

strength off Turkey. There followed a small but extremely brave and classic submarine campaign as these limited boats, complemented by a small number of French submarines, got through to the Sea of Marmara on several occasions and wrought considerable havoc in this Turkish 'pond'. Some of this havoc was wrought with torpedoes against larger ships, but much useful work was achieved with the submarines' newly provided deck guns against smaller ships and also upon Turkish trains plying the rail route along the coast. The Allied submarines continued to operate into the Sea of Marmara up to January 1916, when the Allies finally conceded the failure of their land campaign on each side of the Dardanelles and completed a superb amphibious evacuation.

The captains who had developed such skills were returned to the UK to continue their efforts in the North Sea, but the surviving submarines were used to strengthen the Allied force watching the mine barrage across the Strait of Otranto, which the Austro-Hungarian navy would have to penetrate in the course of any effort to break out into the Mediterranean.

The submarine campaign in the confined waters of the Strait of Otranto and around the Dardanelles was mirrored by a somewhat different campaign in the close, shallow and very heavily mined waters of the Baltic Sea, where the Germans faced the Russians, who were supported by a small number of British submarines. The first two out of three British boats despatched from a Scottish base arrived at the Russian base of Lapvik in the

Gulf of Finland during October 1914. Here the task of the British, and to a lesser extent the Russians (who were generally short of new submarines as the engines for their latest craft had been ordered from Germany), was not only to sink German ships but also to upset German fleet dispositions and training, of which the latter was habitually carried out in the 'safe' waters off the eastern end of the Kiel Canal and along the German Baltic coast. Even though the British boats at first enjoyed only limited success, this was sufficient to persuade the German naval commander-in-chief that the British had deployed at least a flotilla of submarines to the Baltic and that his two squadrons of large warships had to be retired to harbour until the flotilla's imagined depot ship had been located and destroyed.

Below: The US Navy's first submarine class, the seven boats of the 'A' class, slightly preceded the British 'Holland' class, which differed from the American original only in insignificant details. The 'A' class was notable for its fat cigar-shaped hull, very small deck casing, and vestigial conning tower.

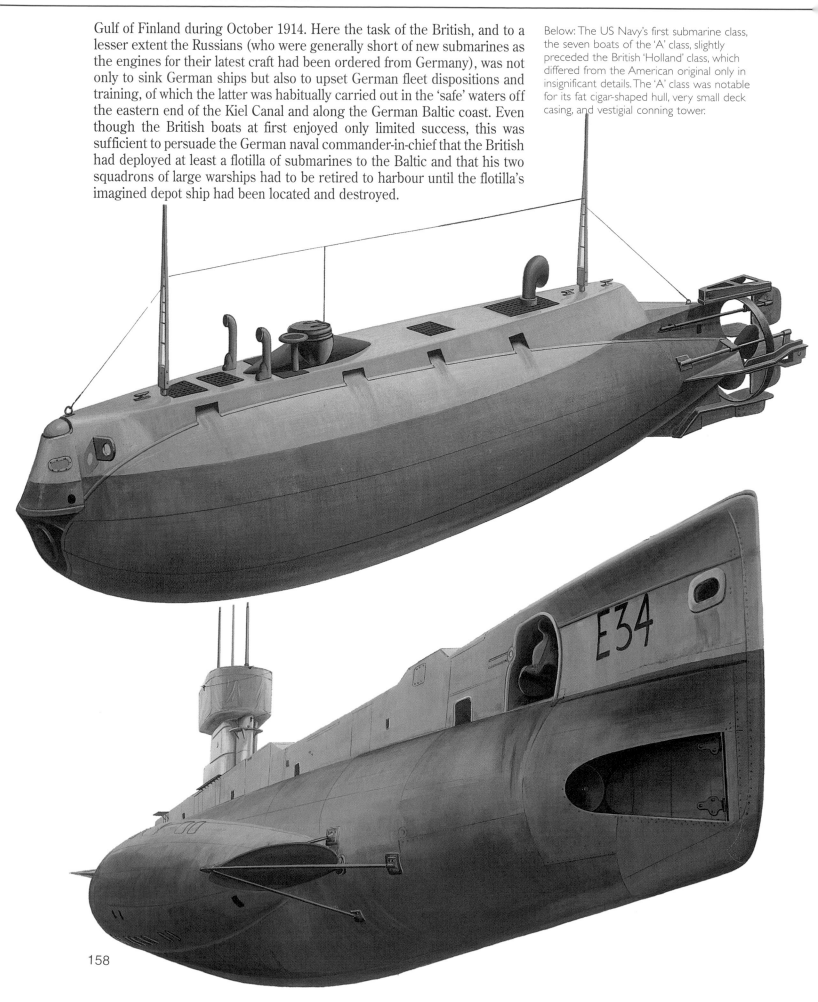

158

Opposite bottom: The 'E' class was the most successful British submarine type of World War I (1914-18), and was built to the extent of 55 boats including the *AE1* and *AE2* for the Royal Australian Navy. The class was built in three major subvariants (the 'E1', 'E7' and 'E21' types). Illustrated here is the *E34* completed in 1917 by Thornycroft as one of the six minelayers with the otherwise standard pair of 18in (457mm) beam torpedo tubes omitted to allow the incorporation of tubes for 20 mines. The submarine was lost in 1918 when it was itself mined in the Heligoland Bight.

This had an adverse effect on German naval planning, but more important was the success from the spring of 1915, when the Baltic unfroze, of the British boats on the merchant shipping used to transport high-grade iron ore from Sweden to Germany. A number of German warships were also attacked by Russian and British boats, and the success of the campaign in the Baltic soon persuaded the Admiralty to send additional boats to the Baltic. Four more 'E' class boats made the dangerous run through the Kattegat between Denmark and Norway/Sweden, one being lost in transit after running aground, while four older 'C' class boats sailed to the Arctic port of Arhangelsk, from which they were moved to Lapvik by rail and barge. By the late summer of 1915 the British and Russian submarine force

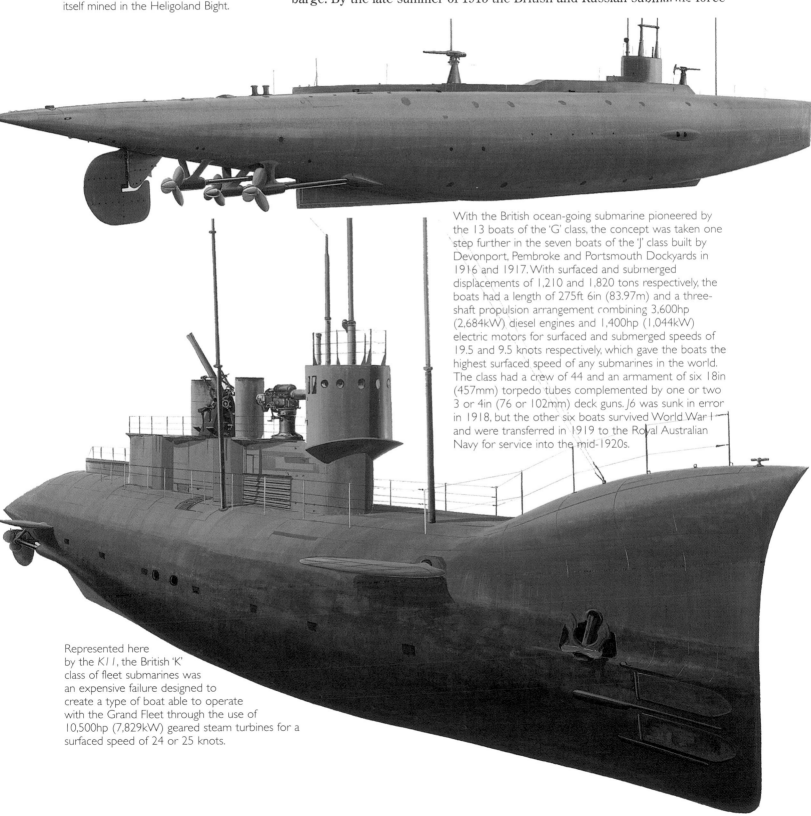

With the British ocean-going submarine pioneered by the 13 boats of the 'G' class, the concept was taken one step further in the seven boats of the 'J' class built by Devonport, Pembroke and Portsmouth Dockyards in 1916 and 1917. With surfaced and submerged displacements of 1,210 and 1,820 tons respectively, the boats had a length of 275ft 6in (83.97m) and a three-shaft propulsion arrangement combining 3,600hp (2,684kW) diesel engines and 1,400hp (1,044kW) electric motors for surfaced and submerged speeds of 19.5 and 9.5 knots respectively, which gave the boats the highest surfaced speed of any submarines in the world. The class had a crew of 44 and an armament of six 18in (457mm) torpedo tubes complemented by one or two 3 or 4in (76 or 102mm) deck guns. *J6* was sunk in error in 1918, but the other six boats survived World War I and were transferred in 1919 to the Royal Australian Navy for service into the mid-1920s.

Represented here by the *K11*, the British 'K' class of fleet submarines was an expensive failure designed to create a type of boat able to operate with the Grand Fleet through the use of 10,500hp (7,829kW) geared steam turbines for a surfaced speed of 24 or 25 knots.

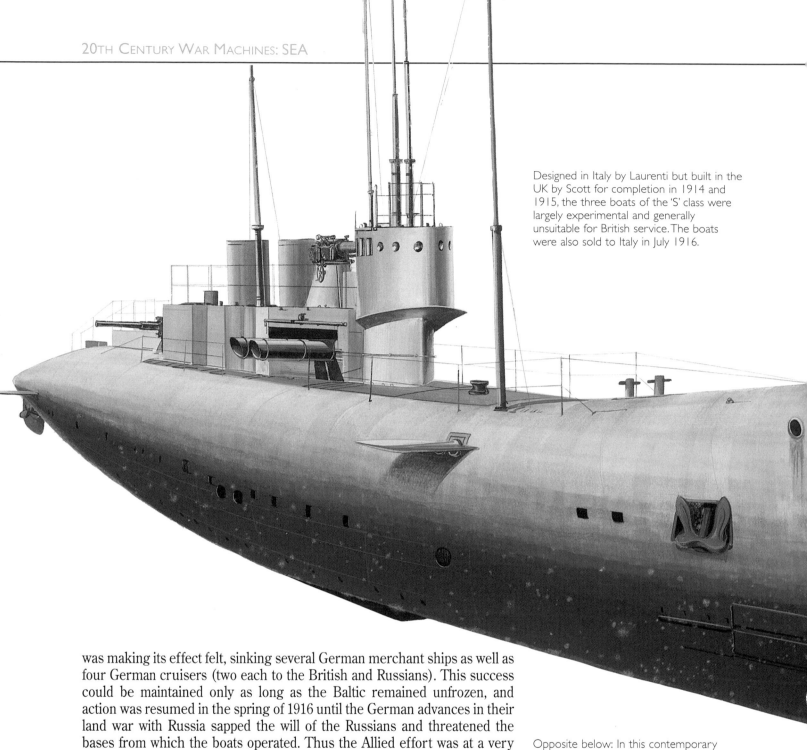

Designed in Italy by Laurenti but built in the UK by Scott for completion in 1914 and 1915, the three boats of the 'S' class were largely experimental and generally unsuitable for British service. The boats were also sold to Italy in July 1916.

was making its effect felt, sinking several German merchant ships as well as four German cruisers (two each to the British and Russians). This success could be maintained only as long as the Baltic remained unfrozen, and action was resumed in the spring of 1916 until the German advances in their land war with Russia sapped the will of the Russians and threatened the bases from which the boats operated. Thus the Allied effort was at a very low ebb when the advent of winter in 1916 ended operations for the year, and the full resumption of submarine activities in the spring of 1917 was made all but impossible by the effect of the first Russian revolution in March of that year. More concerned with internal matters and the continued land pressure exerted by the Germans, the Russians were unable to provide the technical support required by the British boats. There followed the second Russian revolution in November 1917 and the establishment of the communist regime, which reached a settlement with the Germans at Brest-Litovsk in the early part of the following year. As part of this settlement, the Soviets agreed to surrender the British submarines to the Germans, but before this condition could be exercised, an ice-breaker manned by anti-communist Russians opened a path into the Baltic from the base at Helsingfors (now Helsinki) so that the surviving submarines could be taken to deeper water and scuttled.

So far as the British and German naval commanders were concerned,

Opposite below: In this contemporary illustration, the British submarine *B11* is seen running on the surface after torpedoing the elderly Turkish warship *Messudieh* in December 1914. Despite the age and general inefficiency of the target, this was a remarkable feat for which the submarine had first to dive under five rows of mines and then escape in the face of gunfire and torpedo boat attack. The *B11*'s commander was awarded the Victoria Cross.

however, the Mediterranean and Baltic were side-show theatres compared with the North Sea, in which the two main protagonists, the British Grand Fleet and the German High Seas Fleet, confronted each other directly in a region that was generally accepted as being that in which the decisive naval engagement would be fought. In was for this theatre, therefore, that each side reserved its best boats and successively introduced its latest classes.

At the beginning of the war, the Germans had a modest number of boats in service in this theatre, and were building another 19 (*U31* to *U41* and *U43* to *U50*), with another six (*U51* to *U56*) soon ordered. All these boats were generally similar, with a displacement in the order of 720 tons, armament of four 19.7in (500mm) torpedo tubes located equally in the bow and stern, and a propulsion arrangement that combined two 1,100hp (820kW) diesel engines for surfaced running and two 550hp (410kW) electric motors for submerged running. It soon became clear that the torpedo was hardly a cost-effective weapon against the small coastal shipping that became the German submarines' main target, and the original 37mm gun, located on a retractable mounting, was rapidly replaced by a 3.465 or 4.13in (88 or 105mm) deck gun.

There followed the six, three and five boats of the '*U57*', '*U63*' and '*U66*' classes with a submerged displacement in the order of 830 tons, an armament of two or four bow and one or two stern tubes, all firing the 19.7in (500mm) torpedo, as well as a deck gun, and paired diesels and electric motors for surfaced and submerged speeds in the order of 15.5-17.5 knots and 8-9 knots respectively. These boats were known as the 'Mittel-U' types, and were the workhorses of the German submarine effort during 1915 and 1916.

This was not the limit of the German submarine-building effort, however, for in November 1914 it became clear that there would be no immediate victory on land and, faced with the prospect of a long war, the German naval high command decided to increase its submarine capabilities with two new types of boat, namely the 'UB' and 'UC' types optimised respectively for the coastal and minelaying roles. Both types were originally small, but they proved highly successful and were developed in later classes to considerably greater size and in these improved forms were generally superior in all operational respects to the 'Mittel-U' boats: the 'UB I' class, for example had a submerged displacement of only 142 tons and carried an armament of two 17.7in (450mm) torpedo tubes, while the final 'UB 133' class had a submerged displacement of 656 tons and carried an armament of five 19.7in (500mm) torpedo tubes and one 4.13in (105mm) gun; the 'UC I' class had a submerged displacement of only 183 tons and carried an armament of only 12 mines without any torpedo tubes, while the final 'UC III' class had a submerged displacement of 571 tons and carried an armament of three 19.7in (500mm) torpedo tubes, one 4.13in (105mm) gun and 14 mines.

The 'UB' boats proved very successful against coastal shipping and light warships in the waters around the coasts of the UK and northern France as well as in the central Mediterranean, while the 'UC' boats had an inauspicious start but then developed into highly successful types whose ability to lay new minefields quickly and accurately resulted in several spates of Allied losses.

The British followed a similar course to the Germans, but their construction programmes were generally a response to German leads

The *AE2* was one of two Royal Australian Navy 'E' class submarines built by Vickers and commissioned in 1914. The first boat was lost during 1914 in the Pacific, possibly after striking an uncharted reef, and this second boat was involved in the Dardanelles campaign, and was lost in 1915 after attacks by Turkish warships in the Sea of Marmara.

Opposite: *O-1*, seen here in a New York dry dock during 1918, was the lead boat of the 16-strong 'O' class of American coastal submarines completed in 1917 and 1918. The first two boats were built by Portsmouth and Puget Sound Navy Yards to provide the US Navy with experience in submarine construction, and the other 14 boats were built by commercial yards. The first 10 and last six boats formed two distinct subclasses, of which the lattes had a slightly longer but thinner hull, modestly reduced displacements, and an uprated propulsion arrangement. The basic data for the earlier subclass included surfaced and submerged displacements of 521 and 629 tons, a length of 172ft 3in (52.50m), a two-shaft propulsion arrangement combining 880hp (656kW) diesel engines and 740hp (552kW) electric motors for surfaced and submerged speeds of 14 and 10.5 knots, a crew of 29, and an armament of four 18in (457mm) torpedo tubes and one 3in (76mm) deck gun.

rather than the results of original thinking. Unlike the Germans, however, the British had started the war with a number of experimental types for the evaluation of new ideas: the three 'S' class boats were to an Italian design by Laurenti with diesel engines by Fiat, the four 'W' class boats were to a French design by Schneider-Lauboeuf, and the four 'V' class boats were to a Vickers design, while there were also the *Nautilus* and *Swordfish*, the former a large ocean-going boat and the latter a steam-powered boat designed to achieve greater surface speeds than was possible with current diesel-powered boats. After the outbreak of war, the Admiralty decided that the time for leisurely experimentation was past, and between October 1915 and August 1916 all seven units of the 'S' and 'W' classes were transferred to Italy.

The first response of the Admiralty to the outbreak of war and to the revelation that there would be no rapid outcome, was an order for an additional 38 boats of the successful 'E' class, supplemented by contracts to Canadian Vickers and the American yard at Fore River for a total of 20 'H' class boats using steel bought from the Bethlehem Steel Company. The boats were basically similar to the America's 'H' and Russian navy's 'AG' class boats, and a further eight boats were ordered from Canadian Vickers by Italy. The group of 10 American-built boats was finally released to the UK only after the USA's entry into the war in April 1917, and even then six of them were transferred to Chile in recompense for Chilean warships impressed by the British earlier in the war.

A member of the prolific 'E' class of British submarines, the E20 was the fourteenth and last of the 'E7' subclass, and was completed in 1915 after construction by Vickers. The boat was lost in the same year that it was commissioned, being torpedoed and sunk by the German coastal submarine *UB-14* in the Sea of Marmara.

As work on the 'H' class boats was starting, the Admiralty received reports (subsequently found to be erroneous) that the Germans were building a class of high-speed submarines, and decided to respond with its own class, which was to be capable of a surfaced speed of 20 knots and possess long-range radio, so that the boats could be used to create a reconnaissance line deep in the Heligoland Bight to watch for the emergence of the High Seas Fleet and instantly radio this information to the UK. The result was the seven-strong 'J' class, whose design included a length of more than 100ft (30.5m) – greater than that of the 'D' and 'E' classes – and a surfaced powerplant of three 1,200hp (895kW) Vickers diesel engines for a speed of 19.5 knots, which made them the fastest boats in the world.

The most unfortunate effect of the success of the 'J' class was the fact that it persuaded the Admiralty of the feasibility of using high-speed submarines as part of the main surface force. This led to the design and construction of the 17-strong 'K' class. This extraordinary type of 'fleet submarine', intended to scout for the Grand Fleet, was designed to exceed the maximum 21-knot speed of current battleships. Such a speed was clearly impossible with the current or even foreseeable generation of diesel engines, so Vickers designed the boat with a 10,000hp (7,456kW) geared turbine steam powerplant for surfaced propulsion at 24 knots. Moreover, the fleet task planned for these boats was further reflected in the armament, which included four fixed 18in (457mm) torpedo tubes in the bows, two trainable 18in (457mm) torpedo tubes on each beam to allow the engagement of targets off the submarine's high-speed surface course, and up to three guns including one anti-aircraft weapon.

The 'K' class boats were designed for entirely the wrong role, for the submarine had no place in close proximity to surface warships as it lacked the manoeuvrability and strength of its surface brethren, and naval personnel had so high a dread of submarine attack that they were likely to

Being small, technically complex and subjected to intense operational strains, submarines have always required considerable maintenance. There is little internal volume for the carriage of a large volume of spares, so the tendency has been for submarines to be supported by a depot ship providing specialist maintenance crews with well-equipped workshops and a large quantity of spares. The depot ships, such as that seen here with the British submarines R2, R3 and H3 alongside in World War I, also carried fuel and torpedoes to replenish her boats' bunkers and tubes, as well as comparatively spacious accommodation and recreation spaces for the crews of the boats alongside.

open fire as soon as they saw a submarine. This faulty tactical origin was matched by the complexity of the 'K' class design's propulsion arrangement, which was based on two steam boiler units each with its own funnel and air inlet. Before the boat could dive, therefore, the boiler had to be damped down, the funnels retracted, and all openings sealed against water ingress. It was, as one observer of the time said, a question of 'too many damned holes'. The 2,650-ton 'K' class boats were thus unsuccessful, as confirmed most unfortunately by the 'Battle of May Island' in January 1918 when K22 (the renamed K13 after the boat had foundered on its maiden voyage and had been raised) suffered a jammed helm while two flotillas of 'K' boats were exercising the battle-cruiser force: the K4 rammed and sank the K6, and the K17 was sunk by a cruiser.

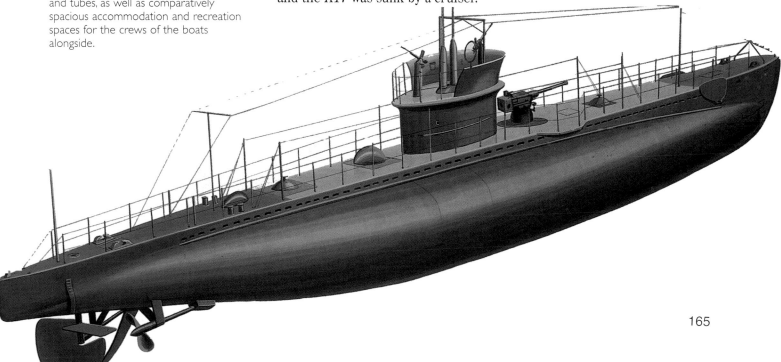

After the completion of the *D1* as a semi-prototype with surfaced propulsion by diesel engines for the first time in a British submarine, the 'D' class was completed to a total of eight boats by another seven submarines to a slightly revised design with greater displacement, greater power for higher submerged speed, a larger conning tower, a revised deck profile and, for the first time in a British submarine class, a deck gun that was first installed on the *D4* (illustrated). The basic details for the 'D' class included surfaced and submerged displacements of 550 and 620 tons respectively, a length of 162ft 0in (49.38m), a two-shaft propulsion arrangement with 1,750hp (1,305kW) diesel engines and 550hp (410kW) electric motors for surfaced and submerged speeds of 16 and 10 knots respectively, a crew of 25, and an armament of three 18in (457mm) torpedo tubes and one (later two) 12pdr deck guns. The *D4* was notable for torpedoeing and sinking the German coastal submarine *UB-72* in the English Channel during May 1918.

German influence was also discernible in two other types of British submarine. After they had captured and examined a 'UC' type minelayer, the British modified six 'E' class boats to a similar capability with five mine chutes, each containing two mines, externally in each of the two ballast tanks rather than internally, the additional weight of the mining installation resulting in the omission of the two beam torpedo tubes that were otherwise standard in the 'E' class boats. Another British development was a response to the Germans' submarine cruisers, which were armed with 5.91in (150mm) guns for the destruction of small warships and merchant ships in the deep ocean areas. The Admiralty responded with an order for four 'M' class submarines each armed with a single turreted 12in (305mm) gun in addition to four 18in (457mm) torpedo tubes in the bows. In the event only three of these extraordinary boats were completed, only one of them in World War I, and two of these were lost in peacetime accidents.

During this period the large 'E' class (55 boats in three subvariants) had been proving its continued worth, and was followed by 36 units of the 'L' class, which was also produced in three subvariants as an enlargement of the 'E' class design and with a number of detail improvements.

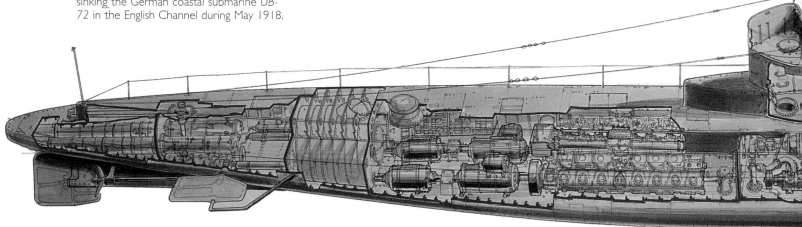

The British and, to a more limited extent, the Germans placed emphasis on the use of submarines with their surface fleets during World War I. Although it had not been established by May 1916, the month in which the climactic Battle of Jutland was fought, there should have been a flotilla of 12 submarines, based at Blyth in Northumberland and complemented by four destroyers for communications relay duties. This flotilla was to join the fleet 'in time to take part in a fleet action in the middle or southern part of the North Sea' and was to have two primary functions; firstly, operating 10 to 12 miles (16 to 19km) forward of the wing columns of the Grand Fleet, it was to attack the High Seas Fleet as it deployed and, secondly, any submarines that missed the German deployment were to press forward into the Heligoland Bight to make submarine interceptions of the Germans ships as they returned to harbour, or to undertake surface shadowings of German warships escaping laterally from the engagement. The German submarines had a similar function, and 18 boats were committed to the Jutland operation; three were submarine minelayers charged with laying fields off the Forth, the Moray Firth and to the west of the Orkney Islands, and the other 15 were tasked with the provision for reconnaissance and interception off the Grand Fleet's main harbours.

Below: The *U-31* was the lead boat of an 11-submarine class of sea-going submarines built by Germany and completed in 1914 and 1915. The *U-31* was itself lost in 1915, probably as a result of striking a mine in the North Sea. The basic details of the class included surfaced and submerged displacements of 685 and 878 tons respectively, a length of 212ft 4in (64.72m), a two-shaft propulsion arrangement with 1,850hp (1,380kW) diesel engines and 1,200hp (895kW) electric motors for surfaced and submerged speeds of 16.4 and 9.7 knots, a crew of 39, and an armament of four 19.7in (500mm) torpedo tubes and either one 4.1in (105mm) deck gun or two 3.4in (88mm) deck guns.

The last class of British submarines built in World War I was something of a departure from previous design concepts, for it was planned specifically for the hunter-killer role, seeking and destroying German submarines. Twelve of the class were ordered and 10 were completed to a very far-sighted design with a high length/beam ratio in a streamlined hull, single-shaft propulsion and enlarged battery capacity. This gave the boats the very high submerged speed of 14 knots, which was not exceeded by any submarine class until the closing stages of World War II, as well as longer submerged endurance at high speed: if a submarine detection system more effective than the hydrophone had been available, these 'R' class boats might very well have proved highly effective.

During this period German submarine construction had been proceeding apace. The well-established 'UB', 'UC' and 'Mittel-U' classes remained in production right to the end of the war, but further developments were increasing the capabilities of the German submarine arm. The first of these developments, ordered in January 1915, was the 'UE I' class of ocean minelayers, of which 10 were built with two longitudinal tubes (for 32 mines) rather than the vertically inclined tubes of the coastal minelayers. The class

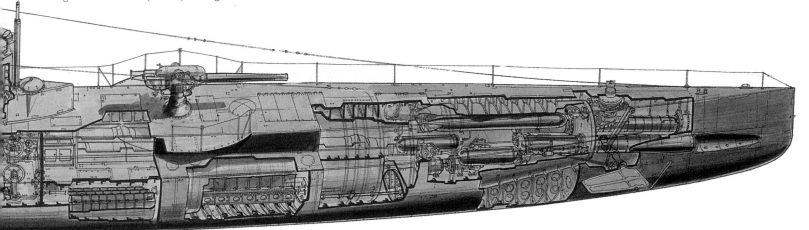

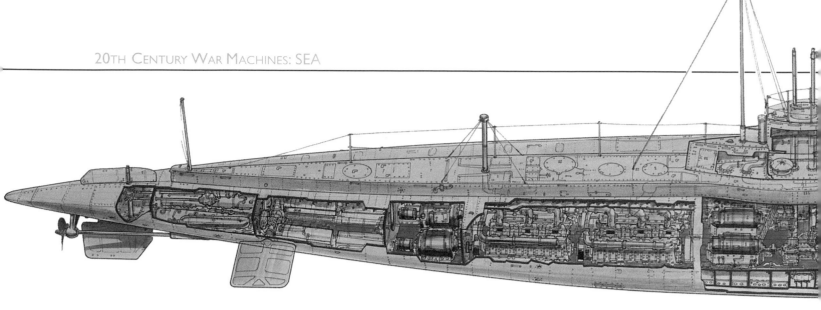

Above: Built in two four-boat subclasses constructed by the Germania and Danzig Dockyard during 1910 and 1911, the eight submarines of the 'U5' class were medium-size boats. All but one of the submarines were lost in World War I: the *U5* was mined off Zeebrugge in 1914, the *U6* was torpedoed off Stavanger in 1915 by the *E16*, the *U7* was erroneously torpedoed in the North Sea during 1915 by the *U22*, the *U8* was sunk in the Dover Strait during 1915 by British destroyers, the *U9* (illustrated) became a surface minelayer in 1915 and a training boat in 1916 before being scrapped in 1919. The *U10* was lost in the Baltic Sea during 1916 probably after hitting a mine, the *U11* was mined in the Dover Strait during 1914, and the *U12* was rammed and sunk off Fife Ness in 1915 by the British destroyer *Ariel*. The most successful of the boats was the *U9*, which sank the elderly British armoured cruisers *Hogue*, *Aboukir* and *Cressy* in a single engagement.

also possessed a lower length/beam ratio to allow a significant increase in bunkerage for considerably greater range. Although nicknamed the 'Children of Sorrow' and losing five of their number during the war, the boats of the 'UE I' class proved moderately effective and were followed by a further 10 boats of the improved 'UE II' class with the capability to operate off the eastern coast of the USA. These boats were considerably larger than their predecessors, and could carry 48 mines, no fewer than 24 torpedoes (12 internally and 12 externally) for the four 19.7in (500mm) tubes in the bows, and a gun armament of one 5.91in (150mm) or two 4.13in (105mm) weapons. Another eight of the class were scrapped late in the war before being completed, and it is possible to see in these boats the origins of the German submarines that proved so effective in World War II.

Although the success of the minelaying submarines was considerable, it was a success that did not directly seize the imagination of the naval authorities, and therefore greater attention was paid to the 'U-Kreuzer' types designed as submarine cruisers for long-range offensive operations against Allied shipping. This class resulted from the German realisation late in 1915 that it was often wasteful to use a torpedo against a target that could just as effectively be destroyed by surface gunfire, and the result was an initial order placed in May 1916 for the four boats of the 'U135' class; complemented in August of the same year by three boats of the generally similar but considerably larger 'U139' class. The 'U135' class had a submerged displacement of 1,535 tons and carried an armament of four

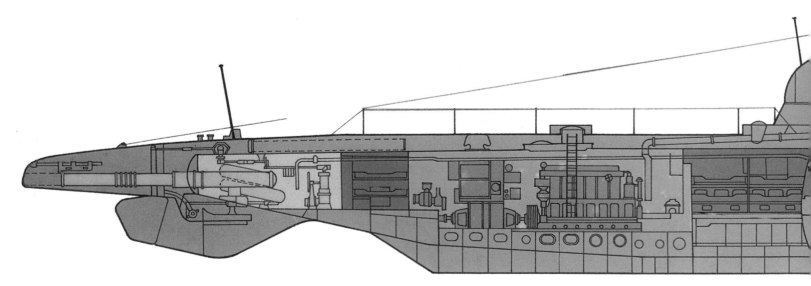

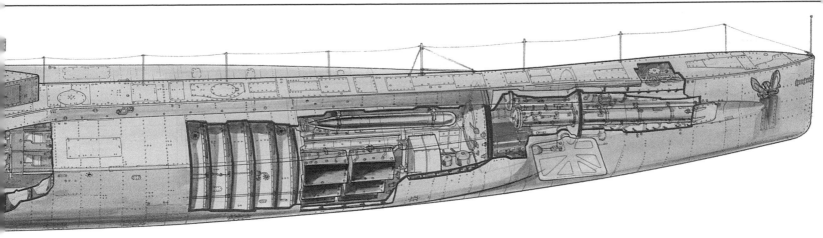

19.7in (500mm) bow torpedo tubes complemented, according to some sources, by two stern tubes of the same calibre, and also one 5.91in (150mm) deck gun, while the 'U139' class had a submerged displacement of 2,485 tons and an armament of six 19.7in (500mm) torpedo tubes (one bow and two stern) as well as two 5.91in (150mm) deck guns. An order was later placed for nine of the even larger 'U142' class with a submerged displacement of 2,785 tons and the same armament as the 'U139' class, but only one of these was completed, and it was scrapped in 1919.

The problem with these submarine cruisers was the fact that their greater size and armament were not really needed, for smaller submarines armed with a 3.465 or 4.13in (88 or 105mm) gun could achieve basically the same results on a hull that was cheaper and quicker to build, and which offered greater manoeuvrability. It might have been different if the additional size of the submarine cruisers had been used for significantly increased bunkerage for greater range, but as it was, the agility-sapping extra size was required mainly for the larger number of heavier guns and ammunition magazines.

It is worth noting that, as a result of the ever-tightening British naval blockade of her ports, which effectively halted all her maritime trade, Germany turned to the concept of the cargo-carrying submarine as a means of maintaining a trade in high-value freight. The first of these mercantile submarines was the *Deutschland*, which sailed from Kiel in June 1916 with a cargo of dyes, precious stones and mail. The submarine reached Baltimore

Below: The *U-26* was one of the 64-strong 'UC II' class of submarine minelayers completed in 1916 and 1917. The *U-26* was built by Vulkan in Hamburg, and was lost to British destroyer attack in the Thames estuary during 1917 while on a minelaying sortie. This inboard view reveals how much of the boat's forward section was occupied by the minelaying installation, which comprised six inclined tubes each carrying three mines. The rest of the armament comprised three 19.7in (500mm) torpedo tubes (one under the waterline at the stern and two above the waterline in the bow casing), and one 3.4in (88mm) deck gun. Other details of the class included surfaced and submerged displacements of 400-434 and 480-511 tons respectively depending on specific subvariant, a length of between 162ft (49.4m) and 173ft (52.7m) depending on specific subvariant, a two-shaft propulsion arrangement with 500-600hp (373-447kW) diesel engines and 460-620hp (343-462kW) electric motors for surfaced and submerged speeds of 11.5-12 and 6.6-7.4 knots respectively, and a crew of 26-28.

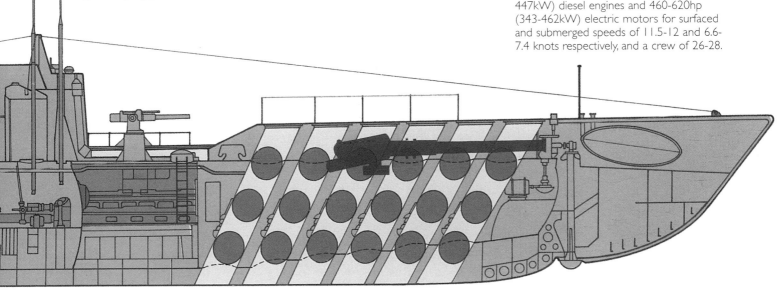

Completed in 1917 after being built by Weser at Bremen, the *UB-86* was one of the prolific 'UB III' class of coastal submarines of which 85 were completed up to the end of World War I. The *UB-86* survived the war and was surrendered to the British, who sold the boat for scrapping in 1921. Details of the 'UB III' class included surfaced and submerged displacements of 508-520 and 639-650 tons, a length of 182ft (55.5m), a two-shaft propulsion arrangement with 1,100hp (820kW) diesel engines and 788hp (588kW) electric motors for surfaced and submerged speeds of 13.5 and 7.5 knots respectively, a crew of 34, and an armament of five 19.7mm (500mm) torpedo tubes (four in the bows and one in the stern) together with one 4.1 or 3.4in (105 or 88mm) deck gun. The serrated structure over the bow was designed to facilitate the penetration of anti-submarine nets.

in the American state of Maryland just over two weeks later and, as it was entirely unarmed, it had to be treated as an otherwise conventional merchant vessel. After discharging the outward-bound load, the submarine took on a cargo of nickel, silver and zinc for the return voyage, which was achieved without incident. A second vessel of the second type, namely the *Bremen*, left on a similar voyage to Norfolk in the state of Virginia, but was lost without trace probably as the result of hitting a mine off the Orkney Islands.

The *Bremen*'s voyage had been planned in concert with a more offensive sortie towards the USA by the *U53*, which reached Newport, Rhode Island, in October 1916 to the great discomfiture of the Americans. The submarine later departed, and after leaving US territorial waters but within sight of an

American lightship began to attack Allied shipping. The Americans were furious, but were powerless to intervene before the submarine, after sinking five ships, finally headed for Germany. The whole escapade had been planned to frighten the USA into a retreat to strict neutrality, but signally failed to achieve this objective. The whole plan had been conceived within the concept of an all-out submarine offensive along the American east coast, but Kaiser Wilhelm II had refused to allow the implementation of the plan, and the whole concept of the mercantile submarine was therefore nullified. The Germany navy consequently ordered the conversion of the *Deutschland* into a submarine cruiser, and in February 1917 ordered another six boats with the standard armament two 19.7in (500mm) bow torpedo tubes, and two 5.91in (150mm) and two 3.465in (88mm) deck guns.

German submarine developments in World War I were completed by the small 'UF' and vast 'UD' class designs. The 'UF' class was designed for coastal operations in the Strait of Dover. With a submerged displacement of slightly under 300 tons and an armament of two 19.7in (500mm) bow torpedo tubes, the type was ordered to the extent of 92 units between December 1917 and July 1918, but none had been completed before Germany's defeat. The 'UD' class had a displacement of 4,000 tons and was intended for the submarine cruiser role with the same armament as the 'U151' class (converted mercantile submarines), but the type was cancelled as impractical. The only other type of submarine to enter service in World War I was the 'UΛ' class, which comprised a single small boat originally ordered by Norway.

Before the end of World War I in November 1918, Germany had ordered 811 submarines, 768 of this total resulting from orders placed during the war. More than 400 of this total were cancelled or scrapped while still uncompleted, and 178 other boats were lost. This represented some 47 per cent of the submarine arm's boats, and with the boats were killed 515

A member of the large 'UC II' class of German coastal minelayers, the *UC-71* was built by Blohm und Voss and completed in 1916. The boat saw considerable service in World War I, but sank in 1919 when on its way to surrender.

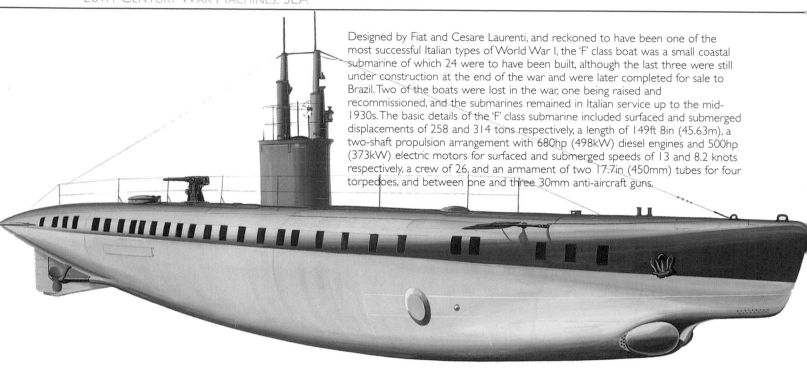

Designed by Fiat and Cesare Laurenti, and reckoned to have been one of the most successful Italian types of World War I, the 'F' class boat was a small coastal submarine of which 24 were to have been built, although the last three were still under construction at the end of the war and were later completed for sale to Brazil. Two of the boats were lost in the war, one being raised and recommissioned, and the submarines remained in Italian service up to the mid-1930s. The basic details of the 'F' class submarine included surfaced and submerged displacements of 258 and 314 tons respectively, a length of 149ft 8in (45.63m), a two-shaft propulsion arrangement with 680hp (498kW) diesel engines and 500hp (373kW) electric motors for surfaced and submerged speeds of 13 and 8.2 knots respectively, a crew of 26, and an armament of two 17.7in (450mm) tubes for four torpedoes, and between one and three 30mm anti-aircraft guns.

officers and 4,849 of other ranks (40 per cent of the submarine arm's personnel strength) in return for the sinking of more than 11 million tons of Allied shipping, including British losses of more than 2,000 ships with more than 14,000 merchant mariners.

The critical point in the submarine campaign came in February 1917, when the Kaiser reluctantly agreed to the launch of a campaign of unrestricted submarine warfare against the shipping which plied between the Allied nations. This campaign came as an enormous blow to the Allies in Germany and the UK in particular, and during April 1917 the merchant shipping tonnage lost to submarine attack increased to 881,000 tons, representing one ship in every four bound for a British port. The effect of the campaign was so profound that it was calculated at this time that the UK had food reserves for only six weeks, and the country therefore faced the prospect of starvation or an accommodation with the Germans.

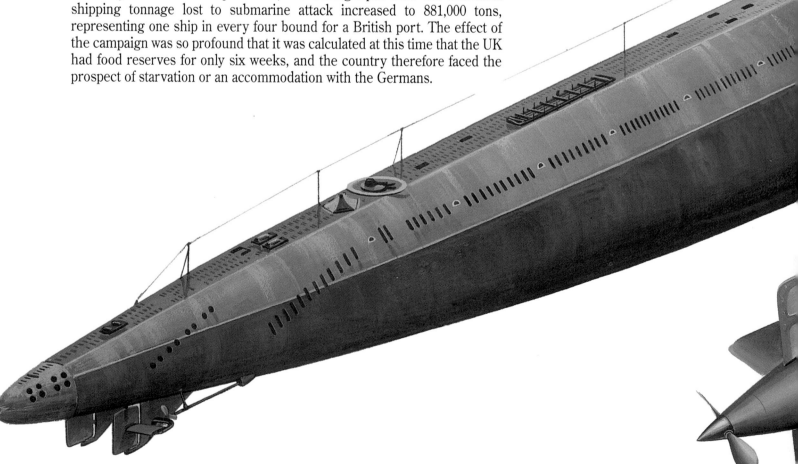

In the event, the launch of the unrestricted submarine warfare campaign was the fact that finally sealed Germany's defeat. Long exasperated by Germany's attitude, which included an apparent attempt to foment an anti-American revolution in Mexico, the start of the new campaign was the final straw for the USA, which declared war on Germany in April 1917. There was little that the USA could achieve in the short term to aid the European Allies except to increase the flow of food and other supplies, and to undertake limited anti-submarine measures in the western half of the Atlantic, but this coincided with the belated British introduction of the convoy system, which rapidly proved itself the best method of defence against submarine attack. Although the Admiralty had long argued against the system, on the grounds

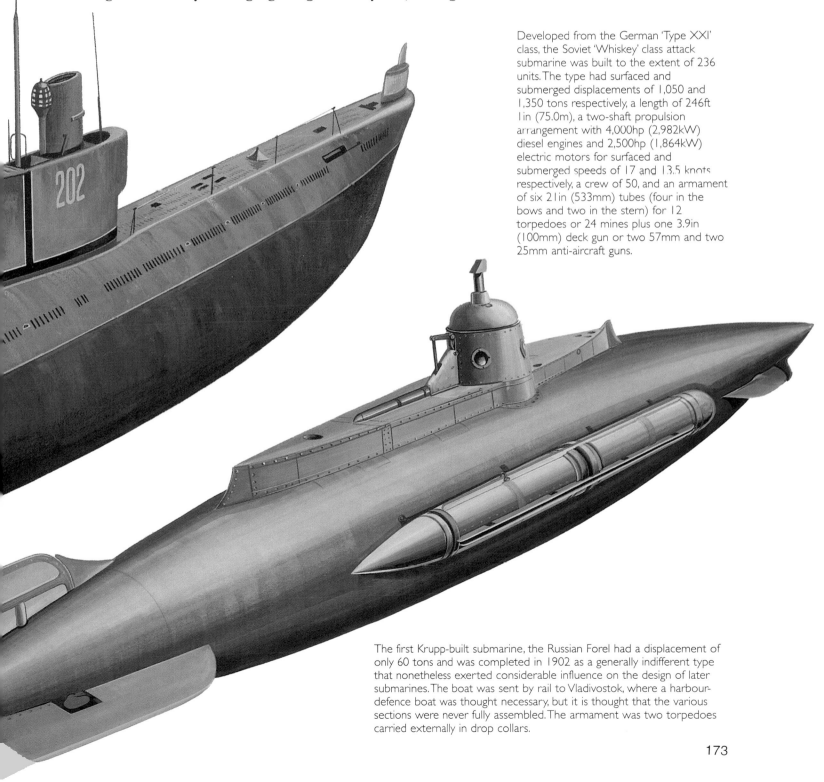

Developed from the German 'Type XXI' class, the Soviet 'Whiskey' class attack submarine was built to the extent of 236 units. The type had surfaced and submerged displacements of 1,050 and 1,350 tons respectively, a length of 246ft 1in (75.0m), a two-shaft propulsion arrangement with 4,000hp (2,982kW) diesel engines and 2,500hp (1,864kW) electric motors for surfaced and submerged speeds of 17 and 13.5 knots respectively, a crew of 50, and an armament of six 21in (533mm) tubes (four in the bows and two in the stern) for 12 torpedoes or 24 mines plus one 3.9in (100mm) deck gun or two 57mm and two 25mm anti-aircraft guns.

The first Krupp-built submarine, the Russian Forel had a displacement of only 60 tons and was completed in 1902 as a generally indifferent type that nonetheless exerted considerable influence on the design of later submarines. The boat was sent by rail to Vladivostok, where a harbour-defence boat was thought necessary, but it is thought that the various sections were never fully assembled. The armament was two torpedoes carried externally in drop collars.

that it concentrated targets for submarine attack, it was soon proved that the concentration of defence provided by the escort warships was greater than the concentration of opportunity offered to the German submarines, and sinkings soon declined to a significant degree (257 out of 84,000 convoyed ships, or 0.4 per cent, compared with 2,616 independently sailed ships), especially after the Americans were able to provide a measure of protection on their side of the Atlantic ocean.

The failure of the unrestricted submarine warfare campaign coincided with the threatened arrival of vast American armies, in France to bolster the steadily growing Allied offensive capability. This persuaded the German armies to launch their final desperate offensives during the spring of 1918, just before the main weight of the American forces began to make its presence felt, and the failure of these offensives sealed Germany's ultimate defeat.

The world's first submarine minelayer, the Russian *Krab* was built at Nikolayev on the Black Sea. Although laid down in 1908, the boat was not completed until 1915, when it had been rendered obsolete by more recent German submarine minelayer developments. The boat had two long ducts along the length of the upper casing, and the mines were moved to the rear along these ducts by a conveyor belt system that dropped the mines over the stern through a pair of hatches. The boat encountered many teething problems but nonetheless managed to lay some successful fields in the Black Sea before being scuttled by the British in 1919. The wreck was raised by the Soviets in 1935 and then scrapped.

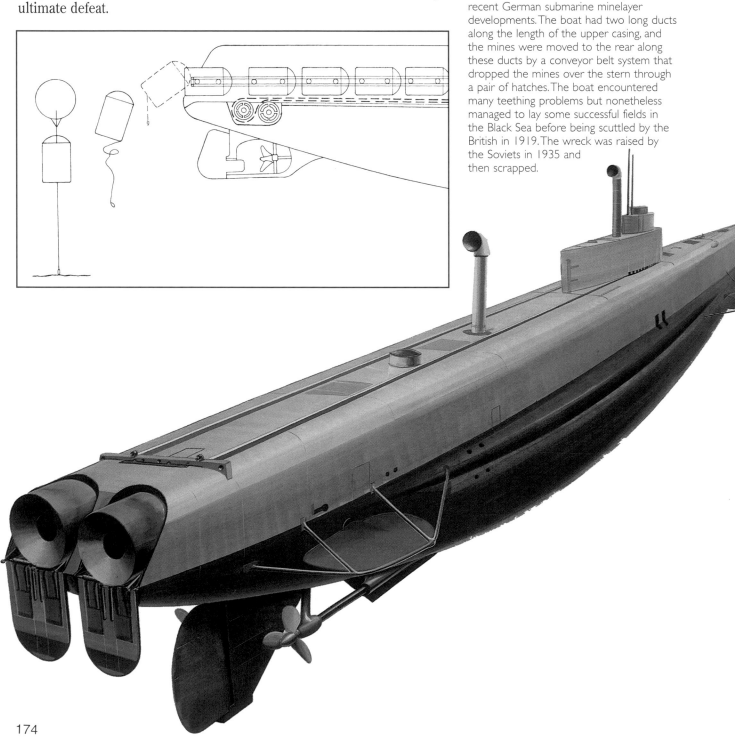

Lessons Forgotten – The Submarine Between the World Wars

Designed as a portly ocean-going replenishment type to supply operational boats with oil fuel and torpedoes in mid-Atlantic, the 'Type XIV' was built to the extent of six boats by Deutsche Werke at Kiel. All six boats were lost to Allied attack in 1942 (one boat) and 1943 (five boats). The basic specification included surfaced and submerged displacements of 1,688 and 1,932 tons respectively, a length of 220ft 3in (67.1m), a two-shaft propulsion arrangement with 2,800hp (2,088kW) diesel engines and 750hp (559kW) electric motors for surfaced and submerged speeds of 14.5 and 6.25 knots respectively, a crew of 53, an armament of two 37mm and one 20mm anti-aircraft gun, and provision for a cargo that included 432 tons of oil fuel and four torpedoes, the latter carried as deck cargo.

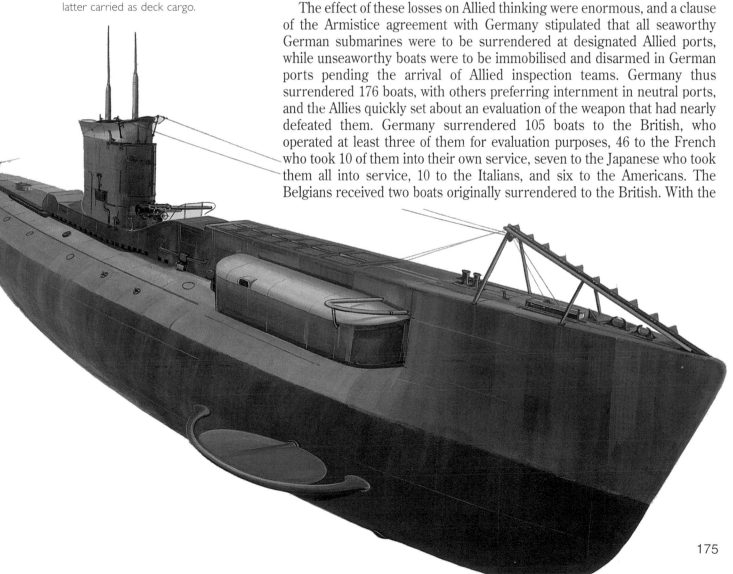

A s the major powers emerged from World War I in the last months of 1918, most of them were exhausted both financially and spiritually, and were determined to ensure that nothing of a similar magnitude could occur again. One of the major factors they had to take into consideration was the submarine, and evidence of its importance in World War I was provided by the revelation that the UK, the world's major maritime power, had lost more than 9 million tons of mercantile shipping, representing some 90 per cent of its pre-war tonnage, within the context of total Allied losses of more than 13 million tons.

The effect of these losses on Allied thinking were enormous, and a clause of the Armistice agreement with Germany stipulated that all seaworthy German submarines were to be surrendered at designated Allied ports, while unseaworthy boats were to be immobilised and disarmed in German ports pending the arrival of Allied inspection teams. Germany thus surrendered 176 boats, with others preferring internment in neutral ports, and the Allies quickly set about an evaluation of the weapon that had nearly defeated them. Germany surrendered 105 boats to the British, who operated at least three of them for evaluation purposes, 46 to the French who took 10 of them into their own service, seven to the Japanese who took them all into service, 10 to the Italians, and six to the Americans. The Belgians received two boats originally surrendered to the British. With the

exception of the French boats, all of these surrendered craft were destroyed by inter-Allied agreement in 1922 and 1923, but by this time all possible implications of German design practices had been gleaned.

Oddly enough, given the fact that its general clumsiness and overgunning were readily apparent, the major Allied powers decided that the German submarine cruiser concept had considerable merit and therefore started on the development of such boats for their own submarine arms. This tendency was exacerbated by the fact that the two navies that received more than their 'share' of the German spoils, namely those of the USA and Japan, were expanding rapidly and considered the submarine cruiser ideal for operations in the vast oceans that were their primary theatres of operation. The Americans incorporated many features of the U140 in their 'V' class boats, which comprised the three boats of the 'Barracuda' subclass and the six other boats that constituted four subclasses. All these boats were notable for their very long range, considerable complements of 21in (533mm) torpedoes, and large-calibre deck gun comprising one 5in (127mm) weapon in all but the *Narwhal* and *Nautilus*, which each carried two 6in (152mm) weapons. Among the last six boats was the *Argonaut*, which was a further development incorporating the type of minelaying capability (60 mines) of which the Americans learned from another German submarine, the 'UE II' class *U117*.

The Japanese moved into the submarine cruiser field with the *I-52*, derived from the 'UE II' class boat *U125* which the Japanese had placed in service as the *O-1*. The Japanese followed the *I-52* with the four submarines of the 'Type J1' class, each of which had a submerged displacement of 2,790 tons, a range of 24,400 miles (39,265km), and an armament of six 21in (533mm) tubes with 20 torpedoes, and two 5.5in (140mm) deck guns. Although derived from the 'UE II' class, these boats had no minelaying capability, which was then incorporated in the succeeding but

somewhat smaller 'Type KRS' class, of which four were built with provision for 42 mines as well as a standard armament of four 21in (533mm) tubes with 12 torpedoes, and one 5.5in (140mm) deck gun.

The British also acquired an interest in the submarine cruiser, and moved into this area of operation with the *X1*, a further development of the Germans' uncompleted 'U173' class of very large submarine cruisers, which was armed with four 5.2in (132mm) guns in two paired mountings as well as six 21in (533mm) tubes for 12 torpedoes. The British even went so far as to adopt a pair of German diesel engines for surface running, but these proved to be plagued by unreliability and other problems, and the *X1* was scrapped after only five years, taking with it British interest in the submarine cruiser concept.

Of the European nations, this left only France as an adherent of the submarine cruiser concept. The French opted for a boat built with the largest-calibre gun permitted by the Washington Naval Treaty of 1922, namely 8in (203mm). The result was the large *Surcouf*, which carried two 8in guns in a trainable turret, eight 21.7in (550 mm) tubes for 18 torpedoes, and a mounting for four 15.7in (400mm) tubes for eight specialised anti-ship torpedoes. The boat also had provision for a small scouting floatplane, which could be dismantled for carriage in a small watertight hangar, and provision for the incarceration of 40 prisoners.

The French *Surcouf* was the greatest of all the submarine cruisers, and was notable for its great endurance, turreted pair of 8in (203mm) guns, and accommodation for the crews of captured ships.

In the early 1920s serious consideration was given in the Washington Naval Treaty to the banning of the submarine, and this was a notion that the British, with their losses to submarine attack in World War I still fresh in their minds, fully approved. The French and Italians, on the other hand, saw the submarine as a comparatively cheap yet effective weapon with which they could come to rival the larger powers, and therefore pressed for the type's retention. So too did the Japanese, who saw in the type a means of offsetting the Americans' superiority in large surface warships. The result of these machinations was that the submarine was not banned, but merely limited to the same 8in (203mm) main gun calibre as the heavy cruiser. And as a result of French pressure, no limit was fixed on the numbers of submarines that each of the powers was allowed to build, and unrestricted submarine warfare was not outlawed. An immediate result was that the world's major navies, restricted by treaty in the numbers and sizes of the major warships they might build, turned their attentions to the large-scale manufacture of submarines, and the world's smaller navies also

stepped up the pace of their submarine programmes. Of these smaller navies, the most adventurous were the Danish, Dutch, Norwegian, Polish and Swedish, of which all but the Norwegians opted for indigenous as well as imported designs.

The most far-sighted of these nations, so far as technical innovation was concerned, were the Dutch. In 1937 their 'O21' class introduced a breathing mast so that the diesel engines could be run when the submarine was just below the surface of the water, thereby allowing the batteries to be charged. This important development received little acclaim, and indeed the masts were removed by the British when some of the boats escaped the defeat of the Netherlands in May 1940 and reached the UK. It was only later in the war, when the Germans discovered parts of such a mast in a Dutch shipyard, that its full value was appreciated: the Germans developed the concept into the *Schnorchel* that allowed their boats to travel just under the surface for protracted periods, therefore receiving less attention from the rampant Allied anti-submarine aircraft.

The exaggerated importance attached to the submarine as a major force in modern war is nowhere better attested than in the suggestion put before the French parliament in 1920; that the French navy procure a fleet of between 250 and 300 submarines not only to replace the navy's current force of battleships and cruisers, but also to expand France's overall naval capabilities. The submarine's popularity had suffered a severe reverse in the later stages of World War I, the French navy argued, and a balanced force of surface vessels and submarines was needed, and it was this reasoned view that prevailed. The French navy therefore started a major programme of submarine construction based on two core types, namely the first-class submarine with a displacement of about 1,000 tons for ocean and overseas offensive/defensive use, and the second-class submarine with a displacement of some 600 tons for home-based defensive use. The first-class submarines comprised the nine units of the 'Requin' class, and the 29 units of the '1,500-tonne' class in several subvariants that were to have been replaced in the early 1940s by the 14 units of the 'Roland Morillot' class. The second-class submarines comprised the 10 units of the 'Ariane' class in three subvariants, and the 22 units of the 'Amazone' class in five subvariants. Finally ,there were the six submarine minelayers of the 'Saphir' class.

A country that was left out of the international naval planning of the 1920s was the USSR, which emerged from the collapse of Russia with a considerable fleet of World War I submarines of which only a few were serviceable in the early 1920s (10 in the Baltic, one in the Arctic and five in

Built by Blohm und Voss in Hamburg, the *U-1407* was a 'Type XVIIB' class coastal submarine with Walther propulsion. The boat was scuttled in May 1945 but later raised for trials in Royal Navy hands as the N25 that later received the name *Meteorite*. The 'Type XVIIB' class had surfaced and submerged displacements of 312 and 357 tons respectively, a length of 136ft 3in (41.5m), a single-shaft propulsion arrangement with 2,500hp (1,864kW) Walther geared turbines for a speed of 21.5 knots together with a subsidiary plant of 210hp (156.5kW) diesel motor and 77hp (57.4kW) electric motor for surfaced and submerged speeds of 8.5 and 5 knots respectively, a crew of 19, and an armament of two 21in (533mm) tubes for four torpedoes.

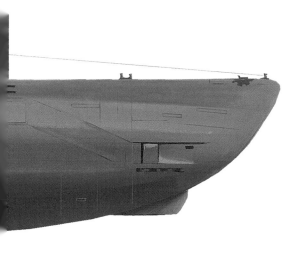

the Black Sea). Soviet military developments during the remainder of the 1920s were confined mainly to the army and air force, together with a limited refurbishment of existing naval units, and it was 1931 before the navy received any new submarines, in the form of the six units of the 'D' class based on an Italian design and then 24 units of the 'L' class based ultimately on the British 'L' class of World War I; one of these boats had been sunk during the Allied intervention in the USSR in 1919, was raised in 1928 and recommissioned into the Soviet navy in 1931. The last of the resulting 'L' class boats was not commissioned until 1942.

These two types were of moderately large size, and further capability was provided by smaller boats optimised for the coastal defence role. These boats included 90 units of the 'Shch' class commissioned between 1933 and 1942, 33 units of the 'Stalinets' class commissioned from 1936, and three units of the 'Pravda' class also commissioned from 1936. The 'Pravda' class boats were very good, possibly because the design was based on the German 'Type IA' class created by one of the clandestine teams that Germany established in the Netherlands, Spain and the USSR to maintain an uninterrupted submarine-designing capability despite the ban on such activities imposed by the Treaty of Versailles in 1919.

These boats represented the most important elements of the Soviet submarine fleet and occupied the intermediate-displacement sector of the size spectrum. The USSR also favoured smaller and larger submarines, however, the former represented by the 'Malyutka' class with a displacement of only 160 tons and an armament of two 21in (533 mm) torpedo tubes, and the latter by the 'Katyusha' class optimised for the submarine cruiser role with a displacement of 1,390 tons and an armament of ten 21in torpedo tubes plus two 3.93in (100mm) and two 45mm deck guns. Production of the 'Malyutka' class deck amounted to more than 50 boats in the period between 1933 and 1937, with more units of two later subvariants added between 1938 and 1944, and deliveries of the 'Katyusha' class amounted to at least 13 boats between 1940 and 1942.

Completed in September 1915 after being built by Electric Boat at Fore River, the M-1 was the first double-hull submarine, and survived to 1922 before being sold out of the service. The boat had surfaced and submerged displacements of 488 and 676 tons respectively, a length of 196ft 3in (59.82m), a two-shaft propulsion arrangement with 840hp (626kW) diesel engines and 680hp (507kW) electric motors for surfaced and submerged speeds of 14 and 10.5 knots respectively, a crew of 28, and an armament of four 18in (457mm) torpedo tubes and one 3in (76mm) deck gun.

Having failed in their attempt to have submarines banned by the Washington Naval Treaty in 1922, the British decided that they had to compete in this important field and in 1923 launched a major programme of design and construction based on the 'L' class of 1917. This resulted in the 'O' class that had greater length and beam than the 'L' class but the same primary armament of eight 21in (533mm) tubes located as six in the bows and two in the stern with a total of 16 torpedoes. Power remained essentially unaltered even though the size and displacement had increased, so the maximum attainable surfaced and submerged speeds were reduced, although this was offset by the greater range provided by enlarged bunkerage. Further development of the same basic design resulted in the slightly larger 'P' and 'R' classes.

The next British development was the 'River' class, of which six were built from 1929 and with a surfaced speed of 22 knots. This was made possible only by the introduction of larger diesel engines, which required the omission of the stern torpedo tubes, but it soon became clear that the boats, although successful in the technical sense, had been created to a flawed operational concept as there was really little need for a submarine with a high surfaced speed except for commerce-raiding sorties in the Pacific Ocean, in which the Royal Navy had little interest at the time.

Over much the same period, the British commissioned six 'Porpoise' class submarine minelayers each with a complement of 50 mines in an external casing. Again, these boats proved successful at the technical level but were in this instance rendered superfluous by the British development of a mine type that could be laid through the tubes of standard submarines. Even so, the 'Porpoise' class boats proved their worth in 1941 and 1942, when they were operated as supply submarines running essential equipment and food into the beleaguered island fortress of Malta.

By the late 1920s, the Royal Navy had decided that its current types of patrol submarines were basically too large for successful employment in European and Mediterranean waters, and therefore undertook the development of a new and smaller type as the 'S' class, of which some 60 units were subsequently completed with a standard armament of six 21in (533mm) torpedo tubes in the bows. Other than its reduction in size, the most important improvement in the 'S' class over the preceding classes was the incorporation of all bunkerage inside the pressure hull, thereby removing the type of 'telltale' oil leaks that had bedevilled the earlier classes with their external bunkerage.

A truly remarkable but generally unsuccessful type, the British 'M' class comprised two boats completed in 1918 by Vickers and a third unit completed in 1920 by Armstrong Whitworth. The M1 sank in 1925 after a collision at sea, the M2 was altered to carry a seaplane and foundered in 1932, and the M3 was altered to a minelayer and was sold in 1932.

The 'S' class, of which 62 were completed between 1932 and 1945, was one of the most successful British submarine types of World War II and was used for offensive operations in home waters, the Mediterranean and the Far East. The second group, to which all but the first 12 boats belonged, was characterised by surfaced and submerged displacements of 715 and 990 tons respectively, a length of 217ft 0in (66.14m), a two-shaft propulsion arrangement with 1,900hp (1,417kW) diesel engines and 1,300hp (969kW) electric motors for surfaced and submerged speeds of 14.75 and 9 knots respectively, a crew of 44, and an armament of seven 21in (533mm) torpedo tubes and one 3in (76mm) deck gun.

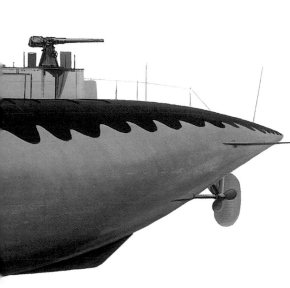

The 'S' class was too small for protected overseas work, however, and to provide this capability for its worldwide commitments, the Royal Navy developed the larger but otherwise similar 'T' class, which had no fewer than ten 21in (533mm) torpedo tubes located as eight in the bows (including two in the bulbous bow casing) and two amidships in the casing.

Throughout this period of considerable technical improvement in the design and construction of submarines, Germany had been prohibited by the terms of the Treaty of Versailles from any involvement in submarine development. Determined not to fall behind, however, the German authorities established a clandestine method of keeping abreast of developments, primarily through the agency of design offices in neutral countries such as the Netherlands, Spain and the USSR, where submarines were designed and built for local use as well as for the export market.

When the Nazi party came to power in 1933, therefore, Germany lacked submarines but was more or less conversant with the latest submarine designs. Thus, when it was decided in 1934 to resume the construction of submarines in Germany, considerable expertise was available for the rapid creation of an indigenous design capability. At this time, the German navy was considering five basic types of boat, in the forms of a coastal boat with a displacement of up to 500 tons, a coastal minelayer also with a displacement of up to 500 tons, a sea-going boat with a displacement of up to 750 tons, an ocean-going boat with a displacement of 1,000 tons, and a submarine cruiser with a displacement of 1,500 tons. The origins of the sea-going type were found in the *Gür*, which had been designed as the 'Type IA'

The 'Type A' midget submarine had a submerged displacement of 46 tons, a length of 78ft 6in (23.9m), a single-shaft propulsion arrangement with a 600hp (447kW) electric motor for surfaced and submerged speeds of 23 and 19 knots respectively, a range of only 80 miles (129km), a crew of two, and an armament of two 18in (457mm) tubes each carrying a single torpedo.

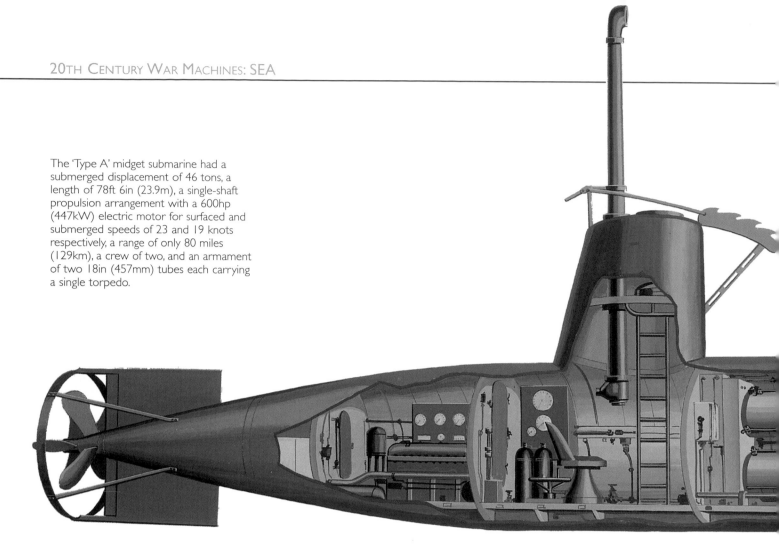

class by a German team and built in Spain for Turkey in the earlier 1930s, and which also formed the basis of the Soviet 'Stalinets' class, while three of the other types were based more loosely on the best German designs of World War I: the 'Type II' coastal type was modelled on the 'UB II' class, the 'Type VII' sea-going type was based on the 'UB III' class with a number of improvements developed for the Finnish 'Vetehinen' class, and the 'Type IX' ocean-going type was derived from the 'UE II' class. All three types proved successful, and were therefore built in large numbers through a succession of steadily improved subvariants which incorporated the lessons learned from their predecessors.

The most important of the types developed before the outbreak of World War II in September 1939 was possibly the 'Type VIIB', which was a slightly enlarged version of the 'Type VIIA' with higher-powered diesel engines and modified saddle tanks for improved seaworthiness; enlarged bunkerage ensured increased range despite the higher surfaced speed. The type had surfaced and submerged displacements of 753 and 857 tons respectively, a length of 218ft 3in (66.52m) and beam of 20ft 3in (6.17m), a two-shaft propulsion arrangement with 2,800hp (2,088kW) diesel engines and 750hp (559kW) electric engines for surfaced and submerged speeds of 17.25 and 8 knots respectively, surfaced and submerged ranges of 6,500 and 80 miles (10,460 and 129km) respectively at speeds of 12 and 4 knots, a crew of 44, and an armament of five 21in (533mm) tubes (four in the bows and one in the stern) for 12 torpedoes or 14 mines, plus one 3.465in (88mm) deck gun supplemented by one 20mm cannon for anti-aircraft use. The 'Type VII' submarine was easy to build and, by submarine standards, was decidedly useful but was not ideally suited to the type of submarine operations that Germany launched in World War II as its surfaced range was somewhat

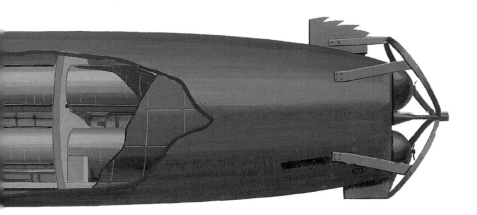

'Type A' midget submarine

DESIGNED to operate within the context of the Combined Fleet for the decisive conflict thought inevitable with the US Navy's Pacific Fleet in a war between Japan and the USA, the 'Type A' midget submarine was intended to penetrate American harbours and cripple major warships lying at anchor in them. The prototype boats were based on the shape of the torpedo, and therefore possessed no conning tower, and had all-electric propulsion based on a large battery capacity that had to be charged by a parent vessel as the boats themselves carried no charging equipment. The lack of a conning tower was deemed impractical for purposes of surfaced navigation, and the following *Ha 1* and *Ha 2* pre-production boats thus introduced a conning tower and a superimposed pair of torpedo tubes in the bows. These two boats were completed by Kure Navy Yard in 1936, and their success in trials led to the placement of orders for 11 production boats to be delivered by Ourazaki for deployment on adapted seaplane carriers such as the *Chitose*, *Chiyoda* and *Mizuho*, which carried out their first midget submarine trials in 1941; the 'Type C1' class attack submarine could also carry one 'Type A' midget boat on the deck casing abaft the conning tower. The initial 41 boats were complemented from 1942 by another 15 generally similar craft, which like their surviving predecessors were generally operated in the training and harbour defence roles as early operations with the first boats had revealed that lack of range was an intractable tactical limitation. The boats completed before the outbreak of war in December 1941 generally had free-flooding torpedo tubes, while those completed later had bow caps for the tubes as well as other improvements such as propeller guards, net cutters and jumper wires to facilitate penetration through anti-submarine nets.

limited and its internal volume too small for protracted patrols: such operations demanded that virtually every part of the space inside the submarine had to be packed with additional food and spare equipment, which had an adverse effect on habitability and therefore long-term operational capability.

It is worth digressing at this point to consider the nature of the anti-submarine capability that had been evolved in the period between the world wars. The most important single element of this capability was the ASDIC system that could both detect and secure the bearing and range of a submerged submarine. Named after the Allied Submarine Devices Investigation Committee that had been created in 1918 to look into the matter of combating German submarines, ASDIC (or more generally Asdic) was based on a sonic pulse transmitted through the water to create an echo that bounced off the target submarine, the bearing of the echo's maximum return being the bearing of the target, and the time between the despatch of the pulse and the receipt of the echo being used to calculate range. This was of major importance in the battle against the submarine, and by the outbreak of World War II some 200 British escort warships had been fitted with the device, which was thought to provide a decisive edge over the submarine. Asdic, or sonar (sound navigation and ranging) as it was known to the Americans, was certainly a vital element in the anti-submarine arsenal, but was dangerously over-emphasised in British tactical thinking in the period before the World War II.

Too few vessels were fitted with the equipment, and peacetime trials had failed to reveal the full extent of Asdic's limitations, especially against a surfaced submarine or when the Asdic-equipped warship passed over a submerged submarine, which allowed submarine captains to develop the tactic of changing course, speed and depth as the warship arrived overhead to attack with its depth charges, which could only be fired laterally and dropped over the stern on the target submarine's anticipated position.

At the start of World War II, the German navy had 56 operational submarines and another five were in the final stages of construction. This was a small number with which to start operations (the German navy had planned on the basis of a later war, as indicated by Germany's Nazi leadership), and 40 were already on their war stations off the UK, sinking the liner *Athenia* on the first day of hostilities despite Hitler's instructions that such targets were not to be attacked for fear of antagonising neutral opinion. Even so, the German submarine captains were very careful in their selection of targets, and up to the time of Germany's major assault in the west, which started in May 1940, the Germans had sunk only 199 merchant ships and in the process had lost 18 of their own submarines. The Germans had also enjoyed a considerable measure of success against warships, sinking the aircraft–carrier *Courageous* and the elderly battleship *Royal Oak* amongst others. Although in real terms it was the loss of the aircraft-carrier that was more important than the sinking of the battleship in its protected anchorage in Scapa Flow, it was the loss of the battleship that had the more profound effect on the British, who were still battleship- rather than carrier-minded and now felt compelled to relocate their major surface units to a number of secondary bases.

During this period the British, who had only 38 submarines available in home waters at the beginning of the war, used their boats in the manner that had become standard in the latter part of World War I, which was mainly reconnaissance off German ports to warn of any movement by Germany's major surface units. This activity was counterproductive, for the Germans were undertaking little in the way of such movements and were able to deal fairly harshly with the British submarines.

Built by Kure Navy Yard and completed in March 1927, the *I-53* was renumbered as the *I-153* in May 1942. The boat was one of the few Japanese submarines to survive World War II, and after the Japanese surrender was scrapped in 1946. The submarine is seen here running its Hiroshima Bay trials during 1927 in standard 'Type KD3A' class submarine cruiser configuration with surfaced and submerged displacements of 1,800 and 2,300 tons respectively, a length of 328ft 1in (100.0m), a two-shaft propulsion arrangement with 6,800hp (5,070kW) diesel engines and 1,800hp (1,342kW) electric motors for surfaced and submerged speeds of 20 and 8 knots, and an armament of eight 21in (533mm) tubes in the bows for 16 torpedoes plus one 4.7in (120mm) deck gun.

The oldest class of British submarines to see active service in World War II, the 'O' class comprised nine boats delivered in a three-boat first group and a six-boat second group with greater displacement and power. The first group, completed in 1926, lost one boat during the war and had its two survivors scrapped in 1945, while the second group, completed in 1928, lost four of its number during the war leaving two boats for disposal at Durban in 1946 (one scrapped and the other scuttled). Seen here leaving Valetta harbour in Malta is the first group's Otway, which was allocated to the Royal Australian Navy in 1927. The boat had surfaced and submerged displacements of 1,350 and 1,870 tons respectively, a length of 275ft 0in (83.82m), a two-shaft propulsion arrangement with 3,000hp (2,237kW) diesel engines and 1,350hp (1,007kW) electric motors for surfaced and submerged speeds of 15.5 and 9 knots respectively, a crew of 54, and an armament of eight 21in (533mm) torpedo tubes (six in the bows and two in the stern) and one 4in (102mm) gun.

The first opportunity for the British boats to shine came with the German invasion of Norway in April 1940, when British boats (supplemented by the French *Rubis*) started to lay major minefields off the Norwegian coast and to attack German shipping taking German troops into Norway and then supplying them during the following weeks: the *Spearfish* damaged the pocket battleship *Lützow* and the *Clyde* seriously hurt the battle-cruiser *Gneisenau*, and, in combination with other successes by the British surface and submarine forces during this period, hit the German navy so hard that it lacked the strength for the invasion of the UK planned for later in the same year.

Part of this success was attributable to the effectiveness of British torpedoes at this time: these impact-fused weapons proved generally successful while the Germans' theoretically more capable magnetically fused weapons were revealing great unreliability: the object of the magnetically fused torpedo was to detonate as the weapon passed under the keel of the target, thereby breaking the target's back rather than merely blowing a hole in the side as was the general result of an impact-fused detonation. In 30 attacks during the spring of 1940, 29 German torpedoes failed and the only successful detonation sank the submarine *Thistle*.

In June 1940, the whole tenor of the war changed with the defeat of France, and Italy's entry into the war on the side of Germany. The Royal Navy, now without French support, had thus to bear the whole burden of the naval war against an opponent whose strength had been considerably enlarged. Moreover, the German submarines were now relishing the prospect of operating from captured French bases with direct access to the South-Western Approaches and the North Atlantic, rather than from German bases that required the boats to pass right around the British Isles.

The Submarine in World War II – The Western Theatre

B Y the end of 1940, no fewer than 12 flotillas of German submarines had moved to the French bases of Brest, La Rochelle, La Pallice, St Nazaire, Lorient and Bordeaux, of which the last also accommodated flotillas comprising a maximum of 27 Italian submarines, which proved generally inferior to their German counterparts as a result of their large conning towers and relatively low surface speed but nevertheless managed to sink nearly one million tons of Allied shipping up to mid-1943 in their primary operational area off the Azores.

The majority of French bases were close tothe Germans' most important operational areas, through which the convoys carrying the UK's raw materials, food supplies and oil had to pass. Although the Admiralty had not made the same mistake as in World War I, and had instituted a major convoy system from the outbreak of hostilities, the system and the tactics of its escorts were still in their infancy and therefore offered the German submariners' superb opportunities.

In August 1940, Hitler finally permitted the start of unrestricted submarine warfare, but the German submariners did not at first achieve major successes. The British anti-submarine forces available in the South-Western Approaches had now developed considerable skill, and it was not until they had shifted their operational areas deeper into the Atlantic, mostly out of reach of British aircraft and short-range escorts, that the Germans began to achieve greater successes. This is reflected in the fact that between June and November 1940 the German submarines sank 1,600,000 tons of British shipping, mostly in the second half of the period.

Even so, the Germans realised that they faced a difficult task: the USA had exchanged 50 obsolete destroyers, capable of comparatively speedy conversion into effective anti-submarine vessels, for 99-year leases on British bases in the Caribbean, thereby signalling its intention to support Britain against Germany in the same way as it had in World War I; and the German navy, having been informed that the war would be of short duration, was now faced with an acute shortage of boats for operations in the North Atlantic. The production of new boats was accelerated as much as possible, so that while four new boats were delivered between September and December 1939, 60 more came off the slips between January and December 1940, at a steadily increasing rate that was nonetheless still inadequate to replace losses and allow a major expansion of the submarine campaign at a time when the Germans had suffered the loss of 34 boats. Some improvement in the Germans' position had resulted from the British

Based on a German design for the Finnish navy, and sized to the minimum possible sea-going displacement so that production could be maximised, the 'Type VII' submarine was built in very large numbers in a number of subvariants to become one of the German navy's most important types of World War II. The class is here represented by a 'Type VIIC' boat with surfaced and submerged displacements of 769 and 871 tons respectively, length of 220ft 3in (67.1m), a two-shaft propulsion arrangement with 2,800hp (2,088kW) diesel engines and 750hp (559kW) electric motors for surfaced and submerged speeds of 17 and 7.5 knots, a crew of 44, and an armament of five 21in (533mm) tubes (four in the bows and one in the stern) for 14 torpedoes or mines plus one 3.4in (88mm) deck gun and a combination of one 37mm and two 20mm anti-aircraft guns.

Inset: During World War II, the specialised anti-submarine aeroplane became as much of a threat to the German U-boats as the surface warship: this is a 'Type IX' submarine under attack by an aeroplane in June 1942.

reaction to the threat of German invasion after the evacuation from Dunkirk in May and June 1940, when most destroyers had been withdrawn from convoy escort duties, but as they could put only some 30 boats into action at any one time, the Germans were still unable to inflict a decisive blow. Even so, the great submarine 'aces' such as Otto Kretschmer and Günther Prien were able to exploit their skills to the maximum, and each sank more than 200,000 tons of shipping in this period.

The tactic evolved by men such as Kretschmer and Prien was the night attack on the surface: here the submarines could not be detected by the Asdic of the British escorts, and their very low silhouettes were virtually impossible to spot. Kretschmer took the concept to its ultimate limit by penetrating into the heart of the convoy before starting his attack, making it all but impossible for the escorts, which were generally operating in a ring outside the columns of the convoy, to launch a counterattack.

Admiral Karl Dönitz, commanding the submarine arm, took the concept of the night attack a step further by adding it to the 'wolf pack' concept. In this, as many submarines as possible were vectored into position to ambush a convoy discovered by a submarine or a long-range reconnaissance aeroplane: only when a large number of boats had been assembled were they released to make a concentrated night attack, swamping the defences (generally comprising converted trawlers, corvettes and sloops that could not match the 17-knot speed of surfaced submarines) and savaging the convoy in a tactic that was repeated on as many successive nights as possible as long as the pack could keep in contact with the luckless convoy. The nocturnal 'wolf pack' attack system was introduced between October 1940 and March 1941, and proved devastating.

The factors that now most limited the success of the German submarines were their lack of range and their relatively small number of reload torpedoes, and this particularly affected the 'Type VII' and 'Type IX' boats that formed the bulk of the flotillas' strength. A partial remedy was the introduction of the 'Type XIV' or 'milch cow' submarines, which were

Here represented by the *Aeneas* completed in October 1945 after construction by Cammell Laird, the British 'A' class submarine was designed for long-range operations in the Pacific Ocean but was completed too late for service in World War II. The class had surfaced and submerged displacements of 1,120 and 1,620 tons respectively, a length of 281ft 9in (85.88m), a two-shaft propulsion arrangement with 4,300hp (3,206kW) diesel engines and 1,250hp (932kW) electric motors for surfaced and submerged speeds of 18 and 8 knots respectively, a crew of 60, and an armament of no fewer than ten 21in (533mm) torpedo tubes, one 4in (102mm) gun and one 20mm anti-aircraft gun. The torpedo tubes were disposed as six (two external) in the bows and four (two external) in the stern.

Fighting the Submarine

THE standard weapon used the submarine in World Wars I and II was the depth charge, which was basically a weighted steel cylinder filled with high explosive and fitted with a hydrostatic pistol on which the desired detonation depth was set before the weapon was released: on landing in the water, the depth charge sank rapidly and on reaching the set depth was exploded to create an expanding spherical pressure wave designed to cause decisive damage to the target. The skill in using the depth charge lay in determining the target submarine's position, course, speed and depth, for only thus could the necessary depth settings be entered on the depth charges of the fired pattern of weapons to create the three-dimensional concussion with the target in it. This was a remarkably difficult thing to achieve, for on hearing the approaching attacker, the target submarine's commander would almost certainly order changes in his boat's course, speed and depth. In the days when depth charges were the only attack option and Asdic (or sonar) lost the submarine as the attacker passed over him, this gave the submarine commander valuable seconds in which to effect the changes and thus negate the intuition of the attacker's commander. In general, therefore, depth charge attacks were protracted and demanded both skill and endurance from the operating crews charged with loading the launcher equipment (one or more rails dropping depth charges over the stern together with two or more projectors firing depth charges laterally over each quarter) and setting the required detonation depth on the hydrostatic pistols. This situation was radically altered by the development of ahead-throwing weapons such as the initial 'Hedgehog' with its 24 impact-fused small bombs and the later 'Squid' and improved 'Limbo' with their three depth-fused large bombs, all of which were fired over the bows of the attacker against a target still held in the attacker's Asdic (or sonar).

By the middle years of World War II, the attentions of Allied bombers were becoming so devastating to the Germans' submarine bases in France that enormous resources, in terms of manpower and material, had to be expended on the creation of bomb-proof 'U-boat pens' that provided a safe lair for submarines between their sorties into the Atlantic. By 1944, however, even these pens were not immune to the latest British bomb, the 12,000lb (5,443kg) 'Tall Boy' dropped by the Avro Lancaster heavy bomber to reach transonic speed before impacting with its target and penetrating deep into it before the warhead was detonated.

produced in modest numbers to supply submarines at sea: each of these boats carried a cargo of 432 tons of oil fuel and four reload torpedoes. Some 10 of the boats were delivered in 1941 and 1942, and all were sunk as the Allies rightly considered them to be a greater threat than the theoretically more dangerous submarines they supported. Despite the importance of the type, another ten boats were cancelled because of their increasing vulnerability to attack and destruction as they transferred fuel whilst on the surface. The same thinking was responsible for the cancellation of the large 'Type XV' and 'Type XVI' submarines that had been planned.

Meanwhile the British had not been idle, and an early response to the surfaced submarine attack was the adoption of Type 271 radar, which could detect the conning tower of a surfaced submarine at a range of 2.5 miles (4km) and allow the escort commander to launch an attack while the submarine was still out of effective torpedo range of the target convoy. Introduced at almost the same time was 'Huff-Duff', which was the equipment not only to detect the high-frequency radio transmissions of Germans submarines making a convoy contact report, but also of fixing its location to within 440yds (400m).

The combination of these two weapons immediately swayed the balance back toward the British, and another factor that aided the British was their ability to read much of the ciphered German signal traffic. Thus March 1941 was a disaster for the Germans, who achieved some successes but also lost five boats including those of the 'aces' Kretschmer, Prien and Schepke.

In concert with their improved electronic 'weapons', the British were devising and introducing more-capable genuine weapons, including Hawker Hurricane fighters launched on a one-way mission from adapted merchant ships to intercept and destroy German reconnaissance aircraft before ditching in the sea close to a ship that could rescue the pilot. Greater long-term success was promised by two other developments that were not yet ready for service. These were the escort carrier, which was a simple conversion of a medium-sized merchant ship so that each major convoy could be provided with its own fighter and anti-submarine aircraft, and the projector type of weapon that could fire its bombs ahead of the ship against a target submarine still held in the Asdic's beam. The first of these projector weapons, appearing in 1941, was the 'Hedgehog', which was a spigot mortar firing a pattern of 24 small impact-fused bombs each carrying 32lb (14.5kg) of Torpex explosive sufficient to penetrate the hull of any submarine. Further development led to the 1943 appearance of the more powerful 'Squid', which fired three full-sized depth charges each containing 300lb (136kg) of explosive and therefore possessing the ability to cause catastrophic damage with a near miss as well as a direct hit.

In December 1941 the USA entered the war on the Allied side after the Japanese attack on the Hawaiian base of Pearl Harbor and Germany's subsequent declaration of war. This immediately eased the British task as the US Navy was now able to play a more active part than its previous patrolling on the western side of the Atlantic, and as American production facilities were more readily available to meet British needs. In the early part of 1942, therefore, six merchant hulls were converted into escort carriers and, of these, five were delivered to the UK, which had pioneered the escort carrier with great success with the *Audacity* that had proved its worth in 1941 before being sunk after a one-month career.

Named for one of Germany's greatest submarine 'aces' of World War I, Otto Weddigen, whose tiny U-9 had sunk the British armoured cruisers *Hogue*, *Aboukir* and *Cressy* in a single short engagement, this was the German navy's 1st Submarine Flotilla, complete with depot ship, seen at Kiel in 1937.

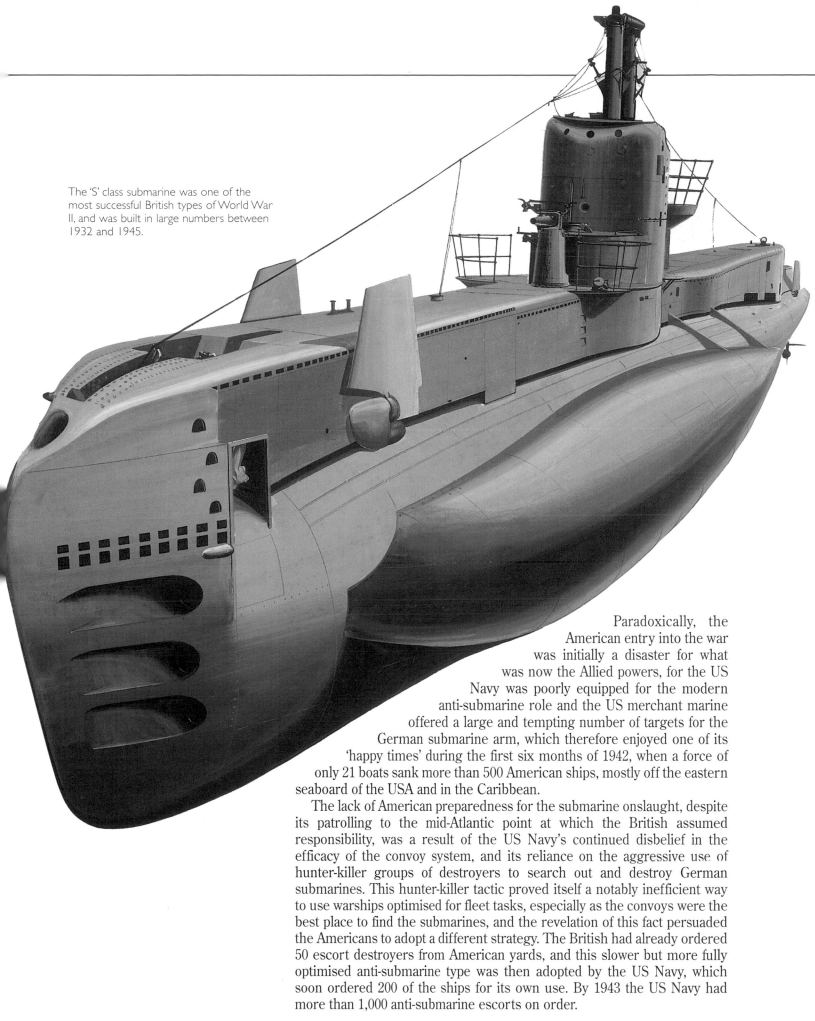

The 'S' class submarine was one of the most successful British types of World War II, and was built in large numbers between 1932 and 1945.

Paradoxically, the American entry into the war was initially a disaster for what was now the Allied powers, for the US Navy was poorly equipped for the modern anti-submarine role and the US merchant marine offered a large and tempting number of targets for the German submarine arm, which therefore enjoyed one of its 'happy times' during the first six months of 1942, when a force of only 21 boats sank more than 500 American ships, mostly off the eastern seaboard of the USA and in the Caribbean.

The lack of American preparedness for the submarine onslaught, despite its patrolling to the mid-Atlantic point at which the British assumed responsibility, was a result of the US Navy's continued disbelief in the efficacy of the convoy system, and its reliance on the aggressive use of hunter-killer groups of destroyers to search out and destroy German submarines. This hunter-killer tactic proved itself a notably inefficient way to use warships optimised for fleet tasks, especially as the convoys were the best place to find the submarines, and the revelation of this fact persuaded the Americans to adopt a different strategy. The British had already ordered 50 escort destroyers from American yards, and this slower but more fully optimised anti-submarine type was then adopted by the US Navy, which soon ordered 200 of the ships for its own use. By 1943 the US Navy had more than 1,000 anti-submarine escorts on order.

By this time the position of the Allies in the Atlantic was critical. During 1941 the Germans had sunk 4,328,000 tons of British shipping, of which about half had succumbed to the submarines and the remainder to a combination of mines and attacks by aircraft and surface raiders. In 1942, the German submarines were responsable for more than 6,000,000 tons of the 7,790,000 tons of Allied shipping lost. Moreover, whereas the German submarine force had amounted to 91 boats at the beginning of the year, by December 1942 it totalled 212 operational boats despite the loss of 87 submarines during the course of the year. This boded extremely well for the German war effort, which was now based largely on the need to secure victory in Europe before the Americans could bring their vast industrial and manpower resources to bear on the continent. The Germans calculated that they would have to sink at least 800,000 tons of shipping per month to achieve their object of starving the British into submission and preventing the arrival of substantial US forces, and during 1942 the Allied loss rate ran at 650,000 tons per month. This was an extremely parlous situation for the Allies, and the replacement of the sunk merchant tonnage became of paramount importance. The solution was found in the development of the 'Liberty' and 'Victory' class ships, which were standardised types that could be built quickly and economically, and in the fact that the British escort building programmes were beginning to bear fruit in this period with the delivery of an increasing number of 'River' class frigates and other ships, all equipped with increasingly sophisticated electronic systems to swell the number of German submarine losses.

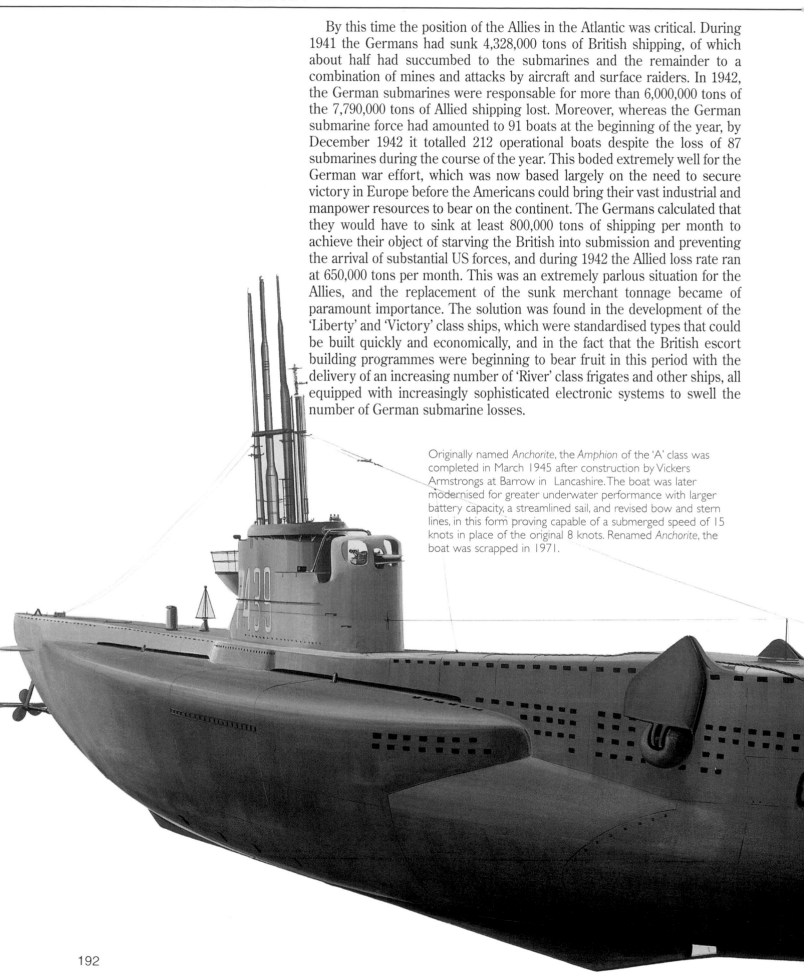

Originally named *Anchorite*, the *Amphion* of the 'A' class was completed in March 1945 after construction by Vickers Armstrongs at Barrow in Lancashire. The boat was later modernised for greater underwater performance with larger battery capacity, a streamlined sail, and revised bow and stern lines, in this form proving capable of a submerged speed of 15 knots in place of the original 8 knots. Renamed *Anchorite*, the boat was scrapped in 1971.

A German chart entitled 'England's Dead' shows the claimed (and indeed generally correct) sinkings of British ships round the British Isles in the period between September 1939 and September 1940.

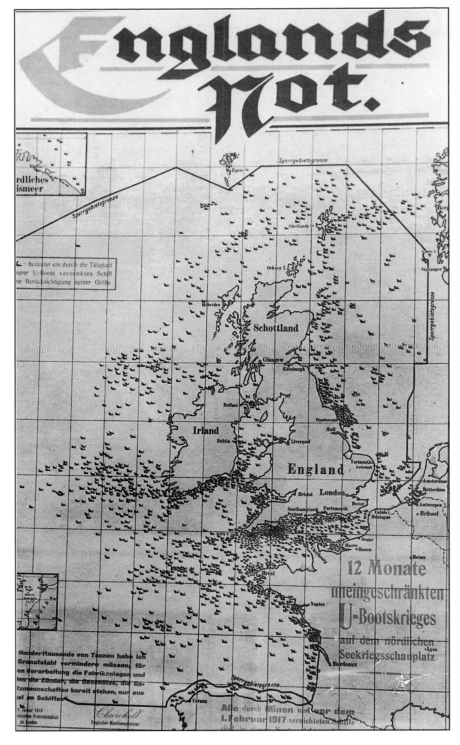

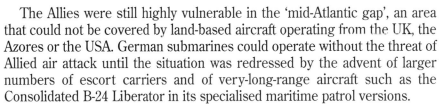

The Allies were still highly vulnerable in the 'mid-Atlantic gap', an area that could not be covered by land-based aircraft operating from the UK, the Azores or the USA. German submarines could operate without the threat of Allied air attack until the situation was redressed by the advent of larger numbers of escort carriers and of very-long-range aircraft such as the Consolidated B-24 Liberator in its specialised maritime patrol versions.

Overestimates of the tonnages its submarines were sinking persuaded the submarine arm's command that the target of 800,000 tons per month was on the verge of attainment, and the campaign against Allied merchant shipping was therefore maintained at as high a pitch as possible. The high command felt that two new developments would finally tip the balance

Seen while being moved to the water after construction at the Howaldtswerke yard at Kiel, the 'Type XVII' submarine was based on the Walther propulsion system and construction was based on the assembly of prefabricated sections to speed the process. These boats, whose high speed was partially offset by their short range and difficult propulsion system, could cover 114 miles (183km) at 20 knots on their Walther geared turbine propulsion system.

decisively in favour of the submarine. These developments involved the acoustically homing torpedo to increase the likelihood of securing a decisive hit, and the radar detector to reduce the likelihood of submarines being caught unawares on the surface by radar-fitted Allied warships (and, increasingly, specialised anti-submarine aircraft that could swoop down for the kill with little or no warning).

The advent of these two new devices coincided more or less with two Allied 'failures'. The first of these was the general withdrawal of American escort forces from the Atlantic in June 1942 for use in the Pacific, which at that time was considered the more dangerous theatre, and the second was the thinning of the surviving merchant convoy escort forces in the Atlantic to provide support for the military convoys preparing for the Allied invasion

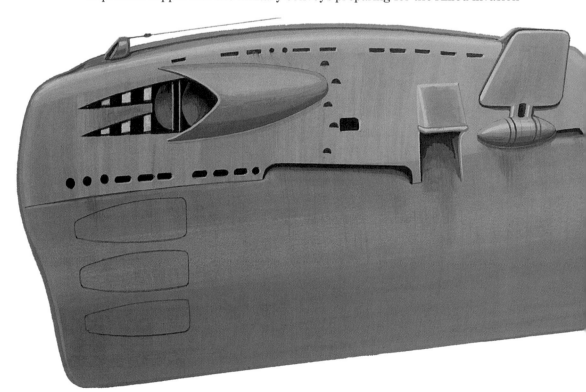

of French North-West Africa scheduled for November 1942. The effect of the German technical developments and Allied diminution was a tilt in the balance toward the Germans that was offset, only partially at first, by the advent of the first Allied support groups.

Made possible by the comparatively large number of new escort vessels that were now coming into service under increasingly experienced commanders, these groups were designed specifically for the hunting and killing of German submarines drawn to the magnet of the convoys and their close escort forces. These escort forces looked after the immediate protection of their convoys, leaving the support groups to operate on a longer leash to detect incoming submarine forces and prosecute their contacts over a protracted period without having to worry about convoy protection.

This meant that by the beginning of 1943, the sides were moderately well balanced and each in a relatively strong position with an increasing number of modern and well-equipped vessels manned by increasingly experienced and determined crews under capable captains. The one significant edge possessed by the Allies, however, was their possession of long-range aircraft fitted with progressively sophisticated radar. Despite this fact, it was the Germans who achieved the first major success of the year when, in March, they used intelligence information to ensure the interception by 39 submarines of 77 ships (52 in a slow convoy and 25 in a fast convoy). In the resulting battle, 21 ships totalling 140,000 tons were sunk for the loss of only three submarines. It was a major German victory, and had rightly come to be regarded as the high point in the German effort in the Battle of the Atlantic. The immediate results of this clash were a further strengthening of the German resolve to crush the UK by destroying the convoy system on which the nation was wholly reliant, and a wavering in the British naval high

The submarines of the 'T' class were among the most successful and widely deployed British boats of World War II, and substantial numbers were built in two main groups. Launched between 1937 and 1941, the 22 boats of the first group had surfaced and submerged displacements of 1,090 and 1,575 tons respectively, a length of 275ft 0in (83.82m), a two-shaft propulsion arrangement with 2,500hp (1,864kW) diesel engines and 1,450hp (1,081kW) electric motors for surfaced and submerged speeds of 15.25 and 9 knots respectively, a crew of 59, and an armament of ten (or eleven in the last seven boats) 21in (533mm) torpedo tubes located as six internal and two external bow tubes plus two (or three in the last seven boats) external stern tubes as well as one 4in (102mm) deck gun. The 30 boats of the second group differed in details such as their two-shaft propulsion arrangement with 2,500hp (1,864kW) diesel engines and 1,450hp (1,081kW) electric motors for surfaced and submerged speeds of 15 and 9 knots respectively, a crew of 65, and an armament of eleven 21in (533mm) torpedo tubes located as six internal and two external bow tubes plus three external stern tubes as well as one 4in (102mm) deck gun and one 20mm anti-aircraft gun.

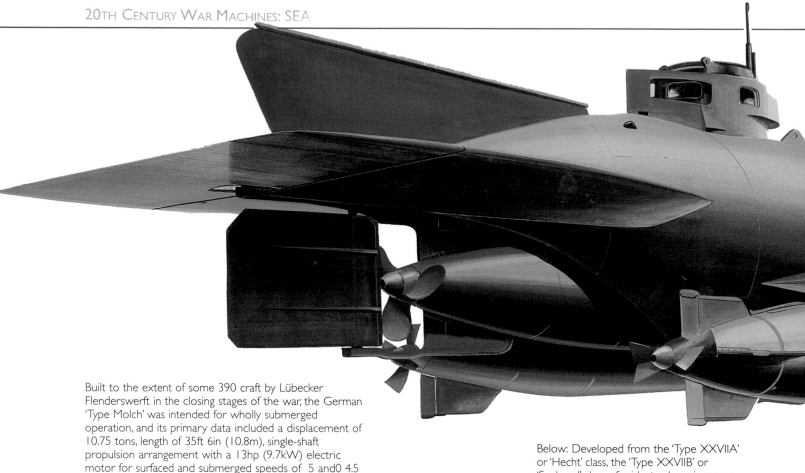

Built to the extent of some 390 craft by Lübecker Flenderswerft in the closing stages of the war, the German 'Type Molch' was intended for wholly submerged operation, and its primary data included a displacement of 10.75 tons, length of 35ft 6in (10.8m), single-shaft propulsion arrangement with a 13hp (9.7kW) electric motor for surfaced and submerged speeds of 5 and0 4.5 knots respectively, crew of one, and an armament of two 21in (533mm) torpedoes carried externally.

Below: Developed from the 'Type XXVIIA' or 'Hecht' class, the 'Type XXVIIB' or 'Seehund' class of midget submarines was built to the extent of some 252 boats with a displacement of 15 tons, length of 39ft 0in (11.9m), single-shaft propulsion arrangement with one 60hp (44.7kW) diesel engine and one 25hp (18.6kW) electric motor for surfaced and submerged speeds of 7.75 and 6 knots respectively, a crew of two, and an armament of two 21in (533mm) torpedoes carried externally.

command, which once again gave serious consideration to the termination of the convoy system in favour of independent sailings until new countermeasures could be introduced.

Fortunately for the Allies, the convoy system was not abandoned, and the March 1943 battle soon proved to be the worst encounter that might be expected with the Germans, principally because the escort carriers and support groups diverted to the Anglo-American landing in French North-West Africa were by now returning to their primary tasks of hunting and killing German submarines. Further impetus was given to the Allied fightback by the American provision of some 60 B-24 Liberator long-range bombers for adaptation as maritime patrol aircraft, and the British introduction of short-range radar for the air-to-surface vessel (ASV) role. This radar was notably important, for it possessed good performance, and was a very significant advantage that could not be detected by the Germans' current generation of radar warning systems. The result was a steep increase in the number of German submarines lost to British air attack, especially as they sortied toward their operational areas on the surface and under the imagined cover of darkness.

The shift in the balance became apparent in May 1943, when another great convoy battle occurred but resulted this time in the loss of only a few merchant ships against the sinking of eight out of 12 attacking submarines as the result of the intervention of aircraft and two support groups. This disaster forced the German submarine command into two errors. Still believing that ample warning of a radar-assisted air attack was provided by its radar warning systems, the command ordered that the submarines

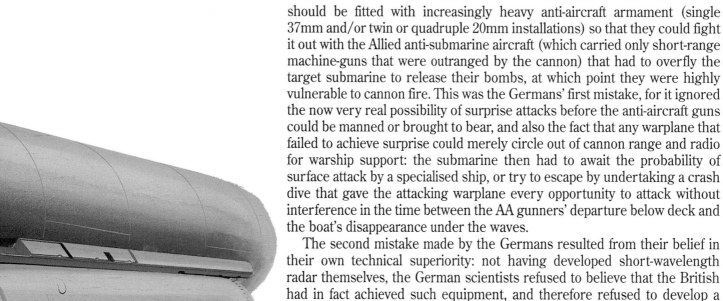

should be fitted with increasingly heavy anti-aircraft armament (single 37mm and/or twin or quadruple 20mm installations) so that they could fight it out with the Allied anti-submarine aircraft (which carried only short-range machine-guns that were outranged by the cannon) that had to overfly the target submarine to release their bombs, at which point they were highly vulnerable to cannon fire. This was the Germans' first mistake, for it ignored the now very real possibility of surprise attacks before the anti-aircraft guns could be manned or brought to bear, and also the fact that any warplane that failed to achieve surprise could merely circle out of cannon range and radio for warship support: the submarine then had to await the probability of surface attack by a specialised ship, or try to escape by undertaking a crash dive that gave the attacking warplane every opportunity to attack without interference in the time between the AA gunners' departure below deck and the boat's disappearance under the waves.

The second mistake made by the Germans resulted from their belief in their own technical superiority: not having developed short-wavelength radar themselves, the German scientists refused to believe that the British had in fact achieved such equipment, and therefore refused to develop a radar warning system capable of detecting such radar. This gave the British a decisive edge in making undetected radar-aided night and adverse-weather attacks, and the German ignorance of the British use of centrimetric-wavelength radar was compounded when a captured British airman revealed that the British could home on German submarines using equipment to detect their current generation of Metox radar warning receiver. Tests revealed that the Metox equipment did in fact produce emissions, and the British successes were therefore ascribed to this failure in the German equipment rather than to their considerable achievement in developing a new type of radar.

The effect of these two German errors combined with the development of anti-submarine warships and techniques by the British and Canadians, who were responsible for 98 per cent of the oceanic escort work, to shift the balance of the war against the Germans. In April 1943, the Germans had sunk 245,000 tons for the loss of 15 submarines, but in May the trend was reversed by the sinking of 165,000 tons for the loss of 40 submarines, and in the following two months the trend was continued by the sinking of 18,000 tons for the loss of 17 submarines during June and by the sinking of 123,000 tons for the loss of 37 submarines during July. Having been certain just a few months earlier that victory was just around the corner, Dönitz was now forced to concede that his boats had been defeated, and he called a temporary halt to the German offensive until better submarines and new weapons were available.

The devices now adopted as standard features for Germany's new submarines, and as retrofits whenever possible on existing boats, included the *Schnorchel* device to allow the submarine to replenish its air supply and run its battery-charging diesel(s) while operating just under the surface, the Pillenwerfer Asdic-spoofing chemical compound that could be fired into the water off the submarine, and the coating of periscopes and even the hull in

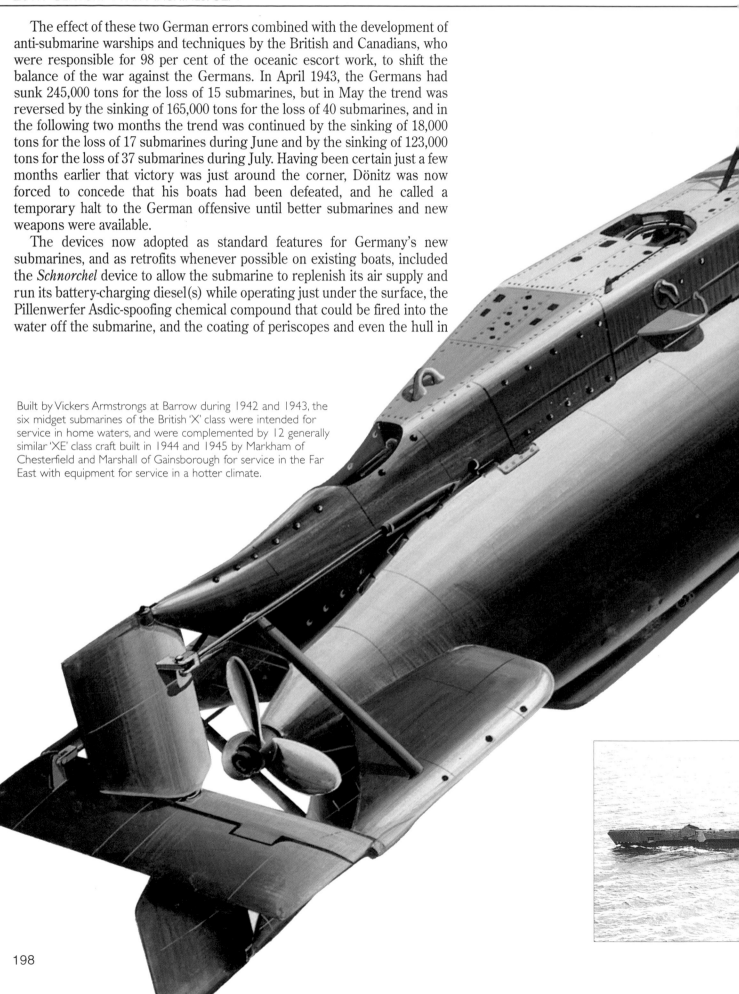

Built by Vickers Armstrongs at Barrow during 1942 and 1943, the six midget submarines of the British 'X' class were intended for service in home waters, and were complemented by 12 generally similar 'XE' class craft built in 1944 and 1945 by Markham of Chesterfield and Marshall of Gainsborough for service in the Far East with equipment for service in a hotter climate.

rubberised compounds which would, it was hoped, absorb rather than reflect electro-magnetic and acoustic energy.

These were considered to be palliatives at best, and the greatest hopes were built round the successful development and production of the Walther propulsion system, which was basically a closed-cycle turbine system which burned a mix of diesel oil and concentrated hydrogen peroxide to provide high power levels independent of atmospheric oxygen. This opened the possibility of true submarine rather than submersible operations, freeing the submarine from the chance of detection by radar and offering, when the system was installed in a streamlined hull, submerged speeds at least equal to surfaced speeds. The Walther propulsion system had first been tested in 1940, and made its production debut with the 'Type XVIIA' coastal submarines, of which four were completed in 1943 with a propulsion arrangement that geared two Walther turbine systems to one shaft for a submerged speed of 26 knots of 5,000hp (3,728kW), which was by far the highest underwater speed attained by any submarine up to that time. This type of surface-independent performance opened up the possibility of a totally revised capability against Allied convoys, so rapid production became the order of the day and designers revised the 'Type XVIIA' design into the 'Type XVIIB' and 'Type XVIIG' designs with only one Walther turbine for the still remarkable submerged speed of 21.5 knots on 2,500hp (1,864kW).

The problem for Germany, however, was the same as that presented by many of the country's other very advanced weapons introduced in this and later stages of World War II: firstly, in terms of money, time and resources, they were extremely expensive to develop, and secondly, they were pressed into production before all their problems had been eliminated, in an effort to stave off the defeat made that much more likely by the virtual nonexistence of Germany's long-term military planning and the frequent foolishness of its political leadership. So far as the Walther-powered submarines were concerned, the main problems that had not yet been overcome were the production and storage of the concentrated hydrogen peroxide oxidant, which was known as Ingolin: this was expensive to manufacture (about eight times as much as diesel oil), and for storage required exceptional cleanliness to prevent rapid decomposition and spontaneous combustion. Ingolin was also consumed at a prodigious rate by the Walther turbine: the 'Type XVIIB' submarine carried 55 tons of Ingolin, which provided a range of 114 miles (183km) at a speed of 20 knots. The submarine also possessed a secondary diesel and electric propulsion arrangement rated at 210 and 77hp (156.5 and 57.4kW) respectively for surfaced and submerged speeds of 8.5 and 5 knots, and surfaced and submerged ranges of 3,000 and 40 miles (4,828 and 64km).

These difficulties made the large-scale production and deployment of Walther-powered submarines problematic, a fact fully appreciated by Dönitz, who in July 1943 advised Hitler that it would be better to concentrate on an interim type known as the 'Electro' boat that could bridge the gap between the standard Schnorchel-equipped submarines and the planned Walther-powered boats. The first of this interim series was the 'Type XXI' class, which was an ocean-going submarine of the conventionally powered type with a number of improved features designed to offset the several advantages that the Allies had recently come to enjoy. The improved features were a very well-streamlined hull and conning tower to reduce submerged drag, and trebled battery capacity for greater underwater endurance at higher speed.

Such a development had been conceptually available for some time, and the availability of submarines of this type in substantial numbers during

Intended mainly for service in the Mediterranean, the 'U' class was built to the extent of 49 boats between 1937 and 1943. The boats were produced in two subclasses as the 15 boats of the first group and the 34 boats of the second group with very slightly greater length and displacement. There followed the similar 'V' class of 34 boats built in 1943 and 1944. Seen here is the 'V' class Upshot, which was completed in 1944 after construction by Vickers Armstrongs at Barrow.

1944 would have given the Germans enormous tactical advantages. The submarine 'Type XXI' class design had surfaced and submerged displacements of 1,621 and 1,819 tons, a crew of 57, a propulsion arrangement that combined two 2,000hp (1,491kW) diesel engines and 2,500hp (1,865kW) electric motors for surfaced and submerged speeds of 15.5 and 16 knots, surfaced and submerged ranges of 11,150 and 285 miles (17,945 and 460km) respectively at speeds of 12 and 6 knots, and an armament of six 21in (533mm) tubes in the bows for 23 torpedoes (or 12 torpedoes and 12 mines) complemented by four 30mm anti-aircraft cannon in two remotely controlled twin mountings faired into the front and rear upper corners of the conning tower. Other major improvements were all-welded construction from eight prefabricated sections, an upgraded *Schnorchel* system that allowed unlimited submerged running of the diesels for a speed of 12 knots, provision of two 113hp (84.25kW) creeper electric motors for silent running at a maximum of 5 knots, and a powered torpedo reload system to speed this all-important process and allow the implementation of saturation attacks.

Dönitz assured Hitler that the existing production system could start deliveries of these improved submarines from November 1944, but the German leader was insistent that earlier deliveries would be possible if the Nazi production system took over, and as a result production of the 'Type XXI' was entrusted to a system that ran construction of the obsolete 'Type VIIC' class in parallel with that of the magnificent 'Type XXI', whose building was thus undertaken by teams that combined one-third of skilled personnel with two-thirds of unskilled labour including old men, women and even children not required for conscription into the armed forces.

This insanely run system could not succeed, however, for the German air force had overriding priority for many of the required strategic materials, and the German army had priority for the manpower which would have been required to crew the new submarines, whose production Dönitz

Operated in home, Mediterranean and Far Eastern waters, the 'T' class was built to the extent of 52 boats between 1937 and 1944. The boats were completed in two subclasses as the 22 boats of the first group and the 30 boats of the second group with minor improvements. The boat illustrated is the *Thunderbolt*, built by Cammell Laird in 1938 and initially commissioned as the *Thetis*. The boat sank in Liverpool Bay during June 1939 and was renamed after being salvaged and refurbished, but was sunk by Italian warships in March 1943.

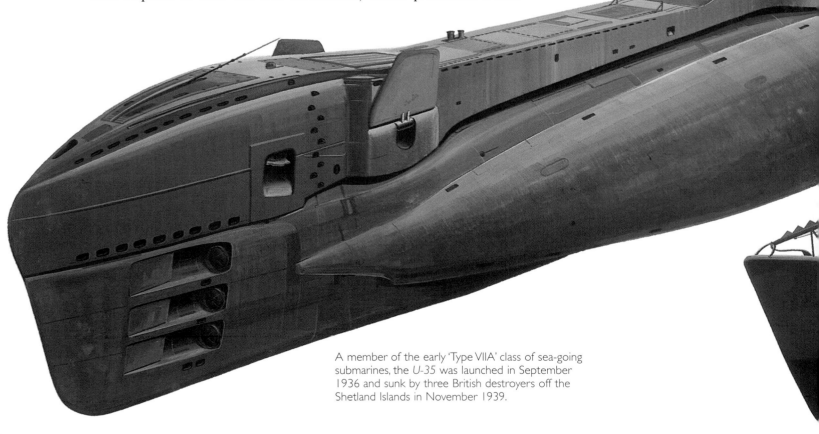

A member of the early 'Type VIIA' class of sea-going submarines, the *U-35* was launched in September 1936 and sunk by three British destroyers off the Shetland Islands in November 1939.

estimated at 27 boats per month in the second half of 1943 rising to 30 boats per month in 1945. In the event, additional manpower was later provided by transfers from the army and air force, but the shortages of steel required for submarine construction could never be overcome.

The effect of all these changes was a diminution of the submarine arm's overall efficiency and determination, and even the availability of the *Schnorchel* was in many ways detrimental, for its ability to provide comparatively safe underwater progress removed the chance for the high-speed surface manoeuvring that had often given the German submarines an edge in their battles with convoys and their escorts. Further Allied developments also resulted in radar that could detect a *Schnorchel* in smooth conditions, and the 'Foxer' towed decoy for acoustic homing torpedoes. From the middle of 1943 the invasion of Italy by the Allies and then their slow progress northward along the peninsula gradually deprived the Germans of the bases they needed for submarine operations in the eastern Mediterranean, and the invasions of north-west and southern France in July and August 1944 removed the bases that had provided the strongpoints for German operations in the Atlantic and western Mediterranean respectively.

The Mediterranean became an Allied 'lake' from this time forward, and in northern waters the submarines were forced back to their original German bases, which meant that they had once again to undertake the long and dangerous trip round the north of Scotland before they could reach their operational areas or return home. Thus the only area in which the German submarines continued to enjoy a measure of success was that offered by the Norwegian Sea and Arctic Ocean, where they encountered the Allied convoys plying the route to the ports of the northern USSR.

The Germans were therefore compelled to turn their attention to a number of midget submarine classes that could only operate in sheltered waters, but although built in large numbers, these 'Molch', 'Hecht', 'Seehund', 'Biber', 'Marder' and 'Neger' types proved almost wholly ineffective in real terms. The 'Type XXIII' coastal and 'Type XXI' ocean submarines with Walther propulsion began finally to reach service from the last weeks of 1945, but despite their technical sophistication, became available too little and too late to have any effect on the final outcome of the submarine war.

Thus the German submarine effort, which had been so close to success in May 1943, ended in total decline during May 1945, when the German

Built to the extent of four boats in 1938, the Italian 'Brin' class had a displacement of 1,000 tons, surfaced and submerged speeds of 17.4 and 8.7 knots respectively, and an armament of eight 21in (533mm) torpedo tubes and one 3.9in (100mm) deck gun. Two of the boats were transferred to the Spanish Nationalist navy in 1938-39 and replaced by two similar submarines.

surrender at the end of World War II compelled all submarines at sea to surface, fly a black flag, and then search out the Allied warships that would accept their surrender. The surrendered submarines were then concentrated at Lisahally in Northern Ireland, just as they had been at Harwich in 1919, and were then taken for disposal.

This is not the whole story of the submarine war in the west, however, for mention should also be made of the British midget submarine effort in northern waters, and of the exploits of British and Italian 'chariots' and submarines in the Mediterranean.

Although they were beaten into the field by the Italians and Japanese, the British emerged from World War II as the most successful protagonists of the midget submarine, which was built in two closely related forms for European and Far Eastern operational service. The European type, of which six were built in 1942-43 and complemented by six generally similar but less well-equipped training boats, had a crew of four, surfaced and submerged displacements of 37 and 40 tons respectively, a propulsion arrangement of one 42hp (31.3kW) diesel engine and one 30hp (22.4kW) electric motor for surfaced and submerged speeds of 6.5 and 5.5 knots respectively, and an armament comprising two side cargoes each containing 4,480lb (2,032kg) of explosive for release under the target and subsequent detonation by a time fuse.

The 12 boats built for Far Eastern service in 1944-45 were quite similar except for their slightly increased length, which resulted in surfaced and submerged displacements of 30 and 34 tons respectively with a crew of four or five, and surfaced and submerged speeds of 6.5 and 6 knots respectively. Other changes were air-conditioning, an airlock so that a diver could exit the boat and attach limpet mines to the target, and spring-loaded legs that helped to stabilise the boat on the seabed.

The most important raids and missions undertaken by these important little craft included the attack on the German battleship *Tirpitz* in a Norwegian fjord during September 1944, reconnaissance of the Normandy beaches and service as navigation markers during the invasion over these beaches in June 1944, and attacks on Japanese cruisers in Singapore harbour in 1945.

The 'Saphir' class of French submarine minelayers, here represented by the *Rubis* that made 22 minelaying sorties in the North and Norwegian Seas before being laid up in January 1945, was notably successful.

Opposite: A 'Type IXC' submarine leaves its base at Kiel in northern Germany for a sortie in the earlier part of World War II. The ocean-going 'Type IX' design was developed from the 'U-81' class of World War I with higher surfaced speed, longer range and provision for a larger number of reload torpedoes.

Following the Italian lead, the British also developed the 'chariot' or human torpedo, which was an evolution of the torpedo with provision for a crew of two to ride on the weapon, penetrate to the target and attach the warhead with cables, and then depart before the timed detonation of the warhead. Efforts were made to employ the 'chariot' around Norway, but the water was too cold for the exposed crewmen, and the type was therefore employed more profitably in the Mediterranean, where craft of this type sank the Italian cruisers *Bolzano*, *Gorizia* and *Ulpio Traiano*.

The Mediterranean was vital to British war plans, and when Italy entered the war in June 1941, the British immediately feared a major outbreak of German and Italian submarine attack on their naval units and convoy routes all along the Mediterranean. The British were fortunate, however, for the best of the Italian submarines and commanders were despatched through the Strait of Gibraltar to operate in the central Atlantic from a base at Bordeaux, and the Germans decided not to weaken their North Atlantic offensive by diverting boats to the Mediterranean.

This left the British with a relatively free hand to use their own submarines in a highly effective manner for the interception and destruction of Italian shipping, which was moving men, equipment and supplies from Italy to North Africa, where a major land campaign erupted between the British and their imperial allies on the one side, and the Italians and then the Germans on the other. Despite the operational difficulties of the theatre, in which aircraft were seldom far from the scene of any naval activity and could detect a submarine down to about 50ft (15m) depth in virtually all conditions (compared with only periscope depth in the North Sea and 30ft (9m) in the north Atlantic), the British submarines exacted a very high toll from the Italians.

The British submarines initially used in the Mediterranean were the boats of the 'O', 'P' and 'R' classes, which were easy to identify not only because of their comparatively large size but also by the fact that their external bunkers tended to leak oil; despite these factors, the success rate of the boats was high. By May 1941, British submarines operating from Gibraltar, Malta and Alexandria had sunk more than 100,000 tons of Italian shipping, and in the middle months of the year the boats disposed of another 150,000 tons using torpedoes or, whenever possible, their more economical deck guns that were also employed for the shelling of coastal targets such as railway lines and bridges.

The British success rate imposed a very severe strain on the relations between the Italians and Germans, for the latter blamed the former for the fact that wholly inadequate quantities of equipment and supplies reached their joint forces operating in North Africa. It seemed that the British were within an ace of securing a major and relatively bloodless triumph over the Axis naval and land forces operating in the Mediterranean and on its southern shore, but it was at this point that the Germans decided to intervene more forcefully by introducing some of their own submarines into the theatre.

The effects of this change in Axis deployment was rapid: in November 1941, German submarines torpedoed and sank the aircraft carrier *Ark Royal* and battleship *Barham*, and in the following month sank the

cruiser *Galatea*. Further misery was added by the activities of Italian human torpedoes; in December 1941 two of these craft penetrated into Alexandria harbour and succeeded in inflicting severe damage on the battleships *Queen Elizabeth* and *Valiant*.

The events of 1941 in the Mediterranean coincided with the start of the Japanese onslaught through the Pacific and into South-East Asia, and an immediate British response was the despatch to this theatre of most of the surviving surface warships from the Mediterranean, leaving the initiative in the Mediterranean to the Germans and Italians. British strength in the theatre now rested almost entirely with the surviving submarines, which continued to wreak havoc on Axis supply convoys and occasional surface warships, despite the fact that submarine activities were severely hampered by the large number of German warplanes now operating over the Mediterranean. Even so, the British boats achieved wonders not only in their primary offensive role, but also in the increasingly important secondary task of running essential supplies into Malta, which was now under tight Axis blockade. By the middle of 1942, the submarines had run some 65,000 tons of fuel, food, equipment and medical supplies in to the island. Thereafter the situation eased as the Axis forces in North Africa finally went over to the strategic defensive after September 1942 and were defeated in May 1943.

Only one of the 'L'Aurore' class of French sea-going submarines, of which 15 had been ordered in 1938, was completed before World War II. The Germans took over three incomplete boats and actually finished only one of them, and several of the others were completed after the war to an improved standard. The baseline configuration included surfaced and submerged displacements of 893 and 1,170 tons respectively, a length of 241ft 3in (73.50m), a two-shaft propulsion arrangement with 3,000hp (2,237kW) diesel engines and 1,400hp (1,044kW) electric motors for surfaced and submerged speeds of 14.5 and 9 knots respectively, a crew of 44, and an armament of nine 21.7in (550mm) torpedo tubes and one 3.9in (100mm) deck gun.

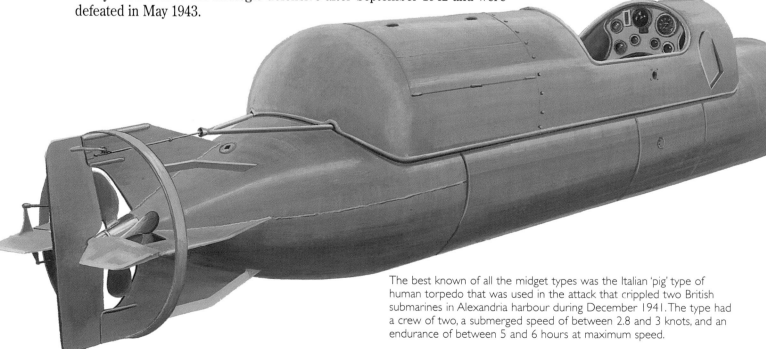

The best known of all the midget types was the Italian 'pig' type of human torpedo that was used in the attack that crippled two British submarines in Alexandria harbour during December 1941. The type had a crew of two, a submerged speed of between 2.8 and 3 knots, and an endurance of between 5 and 6 hours at maximum speed.

The Submarine in World War II – The Eastern Theatre

Japanese thinking in the 1920s and 1930s about the task of the submarine in a future war with the USA in the Pacific Ocean emphasised the laying of major submarine traps into which the US Pacific Fleet could be lured. This demanded submarines large and powerful enough to make long passages on the surface at high speed, the installation of a large battery of torpedo tubes, the carriage of a sizeable number of reload torpedoes and, in an increasing number of the boats, provision for a reconnaissance floatplane carried in a watertight hangar outside the pressure hull.

WHEN Japan entered World War II in December 1941 with its virtually simultaneous attacks on the Americans in Hawaii and the Philippines and on the British in Hong Kong and Malaya, is primary blow was directed against the ships of the US Pacific Fleet in Pearl Harbor. This attack wrought such devastation on the Pacific Fleet's primary surface warships in the theatre that the Americans were forced to revise their strategic thinking to capitalise on their only surviving major assets, namely three large aircraft carriers and a substantial number of the 113 submarines possessed by the US Navy at this time. Unfortunately for the Americans, however, 64 of these were obsolete boats built in World War I and therefore capable of undertaking only training work with a limited degree of operational capability in coastal waters, and nine others were large submarine cruisers whose mechanical unreliability made them ill-suited to

Pacific operations. This left the Americans with 40 modern boats, although the situation was not as bad as this limited total would suggest, for the construction of another 73 submarines had already been authorised, and of these, 32 were currently under construction. Given the fact that the Americans were disposed to leave operations in the Atlantic, where there were few German and Italian targets for submarine attack, this meant that the considerable majority of these new boats were earmarked for the Pacific Fleet.

The number of yards capable of building submarines had declined to three during the period between the world wars, but this number was rapidly doubled as two commercial builders and one navy yard developed submarine-building capability, and deliveries of diesel engines and/or electric motors was assured by the general strength of American industry, which could deliver the required engines and motors without any major difficulty.

With the Pacific clearly the theatre for which the submarines would be required, it was possible to standardise a number of features for the new boats, which were required to possess good habitability, considerable surface range, and volume for a large number of reload torpedoes. This was a philosophy which followed that of the 1920s and 1930s to produce the 10 boats of the 'P' class launched between 1935 and 1937, the 16 boats of the 'S' class launched between 1937 and 1939, and the 12 boats of the 'T' class launched between 1939 and 1941. The last of these classes included the *Tautog*, which was the most successful American submarine of World War II with a record that included the sinking of no fewer than 26 Japanese ships, and its general specification included a crew of 85, a submerged displacement of 2,370 tons, a propulsion arrangement that paired two

The Japanese submarine which sank the American aircraft carrier *Yorktown* during the Battle of Midway in the summer of 1942, the I-68 was the lead boat of the eight-strong 'Type KD6' class of ocean-going submarines. Built by Kure Navy Yard and completed in July 1934, the submarine was torpedoed and sunk by the American submarine *Scamp* in July 1943. The basic details of the 'Type KD6' class included surfaced and submerged displacements of 1,785 and 2,440 tons respectively, a length of 343ft 6in (104.7m), a two-shaft propulsion arrangement with 9,000hp (6,710kW) diesel engines and 1,800hp (1,342kW) electric motors for surfaced and submerged speeds of 23 and 8.25 knots respectively, a range of 14,000 miles (22,530 km) at 10 knots surfaced, and an armament of six 21in (533mm) tubes for 14 torpedoes, and one 3.9in (100mm) deck gun supplemented in later boats by one 4.7in (120mm) deck gun.

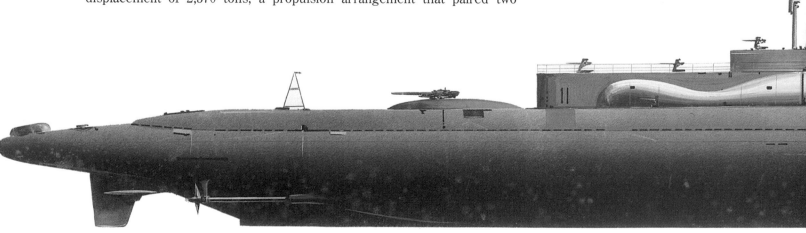

2,700hp (2,013kW) diesel engines and two 1,370hp (1,021.5kW) electric motors for surfaced and submerged speeds of 20 and 8.75 knots, an armament of ten 21in (533mm) tubes (six bow and four stern) for 24 torpedoes complemented by one 5in (127mm) gun and four machine-guns.

Experience with the ocean-going submarines of modern design allowed the creation of a basically standardised design for large-scale production from a time early in 1941. This design was based on a diesel-electric propulsion arrangement (diesel generators driving electric motors coupled to the two shafts through reduction gearing) and a hull of all-welded construction allowing a maximum diving depth of 300ft (91m), and was produced in three very closely related subvariants as the 'Gato', 'Balao' and 'Tench' classes (73, 132 and 30 boats respectively), some of the last being completed after the end of the war. The basic design used a double hull (of strengthened construction in the 'Balao' and 'Tench' classes for a maximum diving depth of 400ft/122m) divided into eight watertight compartments, and had four fuel tanks and eight ballast tanks. The primary data for the 'Balao' class included a submerged displacement of 2,425 tons, length of 311ft 9in (95.02m) with a beam of 27ft 3in (8.31m) and draught of 15ft 3in (4.65m), a two-shaft propulsion arrangement that combined General Motors or Fairbanks Morse diesel engines for 5,400hp (4,026kW) and two General Electric or Elliot Motor electric motors for 2,740hp (2,043kW), surfaced and submerged speeds of 20.25 and 8.75 knots respectively, a crew of 85, and an armament of ten 21in (533mm) tubes (six forward and four aft) for 24 torpedoes complemented by one deck gun, which was variously a 5in (127mm) weapon, 4in (102mm) weapon or a 3in (76.2mm) AA weapon supplemented during the course of the war by AA weapons up to 40mm calibre.

The submarine strength eventually offered by the later pre-war boats and the units of the 'Gato', Balao', and 'Tench' classes was very considerable, but was offset in the first two years of the Pacific war by defects in their torpedoes' magnetic fuses, which was basically the same difficulty that had been encountered by the Germans earlier in the war.

The factor that most characterised the American approach to submarine building in World War II was virtually complete standardisation, which facilitated training and equipment of the boats as well as their production on a production-line basis. The same was certainly not true of the Japanese, who had devoted a considerable part of their pre-war production capacity to several classes of submarine cruisers of the type that seemed to fascinate the Japanese naval high command. What became evident in the late 1940s, however, was the Japanese navy's lack of medium-sized submarines for oceanic duties, and this deficiency was first addressed in 1940 with an order for the first nine of a planned 88 but actual 18 'Type K6' class boats.

For their time, the Japanese 'Type STo' class submarines were the largest boats in the world, and were true ocean-going monsters designed to combine in one hull all the attributes and operational capabilities of the preceding classes as well as the capability to attack and destroy major targets, such as the lock gates in the Panama Canal, with their complement of three high-performance floatplanes. Only three boats were finished, two others being 90 per cent or more complete at the end of World War II, and another 12 boats were cancelled in March 1945. The basic details of this class included surfaced and submerged displacements of 5,223 and 6,560 tons respectively, a length of 400ft 3in (122.0m), a two-shaft propulsion arrangement with 7,700hp (5,741kW) diesel engines and 2,400hp (1,789kW) electric motors for surfaced and submerged speeds of 18.75 and 6.5 knots, a range of 30,000 miles (48,280km) at 16 knots surfaced, a crew of 144, and an armament of eight 21in (533mm) tubes for 20 torpedoes, one 5.5in (140 mm) deck gun, ten 25mm anti-aircraft guns, and three floatplanes.

Although rather small and therefore cramped, the boats were considered to be highly successful, and may be likened to the first units of the 'Gato' class in range capability. The basic designs for the 'Type K6' included a crew of 62, surfaced and submerged displacements of 1,115 and 1,447 tons, a length of 264ft 1in (80.5m) with a beam of 22ft 11.5in (7.0m) and a draught of 13ft 1.5in (4.0m), a two-shaft propulsion arrangement that paired diesel engines for 4,200hp (3,131.5kW) and electric motors for 1,200hp (895kW) for surfaced and submerged speeds of 19.75 and 8 knots respectively, surfaced and submerged ranges of 11,000 miles (17,700km) at 12 knots and 45 miles (52km) at 5 knots respectively, and an armament of four 21in (533mm) tubes in the bows for 10 torpedoes and complemented by one 3in (76.2mm) anti-aircraft gun and two 25mm cannon.

In the same year the Japanese ordered the first nine of a planned 27 but actual 18 boats of the 'Type KS' class, which was a somewhat smaller scouting submarine with a submerged displacement of 782 tons and an armament of four 21in (533mm) tubes for eight torpedoes. It is hard to imagine how these small submarines could ever have been of any real utility except for patrol around Japanese-held islands, for their surfaced range was a relatively indifferent 3,500 miles (5,635km) at 12 knots, which was hardly adequate for the type of grandiose oceanic warfare that the Japanese navy was planning.

These two classes, one possessing a genuine ocean-going capability and the other little more than a coastal type, were something of an oddity in Japanese thinking at this time, and in 1941 the Japanese navy returned to the concept of the very large ocean-going submarine with considerable range and endurance, heavy armament and, in most cases, provision for a small reconnaissance/spotter floatplane that could be dismantled for accommodation in a watertight hangar. These classes comprised the planned 14 but actual six units of the 'Type B2' class with a submerged displacement of 3,700 tons and an armament of six 21in (533mm) tubes for 17 torpedoes, the planned 10 but actual three units of the 'Type C2' class with a submerged displacement of 3,564 tons and an armament of eight 21in (533mm) tubes for 20 torpedoes but no seaplane, the single 'Type A2' class unit that was a virtual copy of the three 'Type A1' class boats of 1937 with a submerged displacement of 4,172 tons and an armament of six 21in (533mm) tubes for 18 torpedoes, the planned 32 but actual three units of the 'Type B3' class with a submerged displacement of 3,688 tons and an

This photograph reveals the Japanese submarines *I-402*, *I-36* and *I-47* at their moorings after they had been surrendered to the Americans. All of the boats were scuttled in April 1946. The *I-402* was a 'Type STo' class long-range attack submarine, the I-36 was a 'Type B1' class scouting submarine, and the I-47 was a 'Type C2' class attack submarine.

armament of six 21in (533mm) tubes for 19 torpedoes, and the planned 45 but actual three units of the generally similar 'Type C3' class with a submerged displacement of 3,644 tons and an armament of six 21in (533mm) tubes for 19 torpedoes.

The basic operational thinking that lay behind the design and construction of these classes was the long-cherished desire of the Japanese navy to seek out and destroy the US Navy's Pacific Fleet in a titanic Pacific battle. The large submarines were created within this overall scheme with the object of reconnoitring for the Combined Fleet and picking off any of the American warships on which they could achieve a firing solution. It was also appreciated that the Combined Fleet's surface and underwater units might not be able to bring the Pacific Fleet out to fight, especially after the attack on Pearl Harbor, and to provide an alternative capability to attack the American warships in harbour, the Japanese created a number of midget submarine classes that could be carried by large submarines or seaplane carriers to points off the major American bases and there launched to penetrate the harbour defences and attack the American warships lying at anchor.

The first of these midget submarine designs was the 'Type A' that appeared in 1936 as a development of an experimental boat built two years earlier. The 'Type A' design had a two-man crew, a submerged displacement of 46 tons, a 600hp (447kW) electric motor for surfaced and submerged speeds of 23 and 19 knots respectively, a range of 160 miles (257km) at 6 knots submerged, and an armament of two 18in (457mm) tubes for two torpedoes. Production totalled 41 boats, and after their failure in the Pearl Harbor operation, in which one boat was lost before the main attack was launched, the surviving units were relegated to the harbour defence role.

Further development of the midget submarine concept led in 1942 to the sole 'Type B' class unit that was an improved version of the 'Type A', and the success of this unit led to the construction of 15 'Type C' class units with slightly greater length and displacement to allow the incorporation of a 40hp (29.8kW) diesel engine that provided surfaced propulsion as well as battery recharging capability for surfaced and submerged ranges of 300 and 120 miles (485 and 195km) respectively. The 'Type C' was no more successful in operational terms, however, than the pioneering 'Type A'.

The main encumbrance with Japanese submarines did not tie in their technical features, but rather in the type of employment that was planned for them by the Japanese naval high command. This was beset by the desire for the Combined Fleet to better the Pacific Fleet in open battle, and therefore ignored the operational and strategic possibilities offered by attacks on targets other than warships (which would soon greatly exceed the numbers of American warships in the Pacific), and which were absolutely vital to the prosecution of the long-range amphibious warfare with which the Americans first checked and then rolled back the Japanese after their runaway victories up to the middle of 1942.

Conversely, the Japanese compounded this offensive error with the defensive mistake of thinking that their own shipping would not become a target for American submarine attack. The US Navy fully appreciated, though, that initially unescorted and then only indifferently escorted shipping was Japan's 'Achilles heel': the Japanese war effort was almost wholly reliant on the inward flow of raw materials and oil, and on the outward flow of finished weapons, equipment and men. From the beginning of the war, therefore, the Americans determined to cut the Japanese maritime lines of communication, starving the war industries in the home islands of the wherewithal to make weapons, and cutting off the Japanese

US Submarine Gun Armament in the Pacific

ALTHOUGH both the Americans and the Japanese relied on the torpedo as their principal weapon in the submarine campaign in the Pacific Ocean during World War II, they each appreciated that the torpedo was not a cost-effective weapon for use against smaller targets. The expenditure of such a weapon, of which only a comparatively small number of reloads could be carried even in the larger boats, was therefore avoided when the shell fire of a deck gun would suffice. The standard deck gun carried by American submarines of the 'Balao' and 'Tench' classes was the 25-calibre 5in (127mm) Gun Mk XIII using the same well-proved and readily available ammunition as used by the primary armament of American destroyers and the secondary armament of many larger American warships. On the 'Tench' class as designed, the gun mounting was installed on the after casing abaft the conning tower, and was operated by a two-man crew (elevation and laying numbers) on the mounting with support from a four man loading crew on the casing. The mounting weighed 5,940lb (2,694kg), and the gun fired a 53lb (24kg) shell to a range of 14,500 yards (13,260m) at an elevation of 40 degrees. The rest of the gun armament for the 'Tench' class, as it was designed, included an anti-aircraft fit of one 40mm and one 20mm guns on the forward and after parts of the lower conning tower structure. Wartime developments, however, often meant that the 'Tench' class boats had two 5in (127mm) guns on the forward and after casings, and two 40mm guns on the conning tower.

island bastions from all effective means of reinforcement and resupply. The threat posed by such a campaign becomes readily apparent from the fact that Japan relied on sea transport for 20 per cent of its food, 24 per cent of its coal, 88 per cent of its iron ore, 90 per cent of its oil, and 100 per cent for items such as rubber, tin and commodities essential for the maintenance of modern industry and transport.

The effect of the American campaign to sever Japan's maritime lines of communication was enormous, and it is arguable that Japan had been

Opposite: In the later stages of World War II, the Japanese placed increasing reliance on suicide weapons to offset the ever-increasing qualitative and quantitative superiority of the Allies' weapons, and in the naval arena this included the 'Kaiten' type of kamikaze submarine. Seen here in the course of a test launch from the obsolete light cruiser Kitakami in February 1945, this is a 'Kaiten I' class submarine based on the design of the Type 93 torpedo. Large numbers of these weapons were produced to a design that included a submerged displacement of 18.33 tons, a length of 48ft 6in (14.8m), a single-shaft propulsion arrangement with one 550hp (410kW) engine for a speed of 30 knots, a range that could be varied between 85,300yds (78,000m) at 12 knots to 25,100yds (22,950m) at 30 knots, a crew of one, and a warhead comprising 3,417lb (1,550kg) of high explosive.

effectively beaten but refused to concede the fact before the dropping of the atomic bombs on Hiroshima and Nagasaki in August 1945: in 1939, before the outbreak of the Pacific war, Japan had possessed 2,337 merchant ships, but by August 1945 this total had been reduced to 231. Some of the 4,000,000 tons of shipping succumbed to air attack, but the majority of losses were the victims primarily of American, and to a lesser extent British and Dutch, submarine attack directly with torpedoes or indirectly with mines. The Americans lost 60 submarines during the war, although the Japanese had claimed 486 – the true figure may be accounted a relatively small price to have paid for so magnificent a victory.

The American submarines did not limit their attacks to the vital Japanese merchant marine, but supplied scouting and aircrew recovery lines for the major offensive operations of the Pacific fleet, and also played a major part in sinking Japanese warships, including eight aircraft carriers and 12

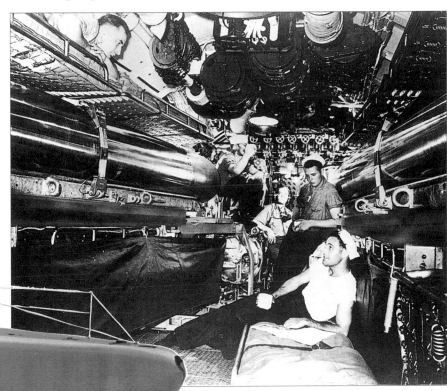

By comparison with their counterparts in the western theatre, both German and British, and with their Japanese opponents in the eastern theatre, the crews of American submarines enjoyed a fairly high level of habitability despite the general accolade of 'pig boats' for their submarines. This habitability factor combined with good food to maintain the morale and fighting efficiency of American submarines at a high pitch throughout their patrols.

Left: Built by the Portsmouth Navy Yard and launched in May 1941, the Drum was a typical member of the 'Gato' class and survived World War II. The boat was finally stricken in June 1968 and hulked as a naval monument at Mobile, Alabama. The basic details of the 'Gato' class included surfaced and submerged displacements of 1,526 and 2,424 tons respectively, a length of 311ft 9in (95.02m), a two-shaft propulsion arrangement with 5,400hp (4,026kW) diesel engines and 2,740hp (2,043kW) electric motors for surfaced and submerged speeds of 20.25 and 8.75 knots respectively, a crew of 85, and an armament of ten 21in (533mm) tubes for 24 torpedoes plus one 3in (76mm) deck gun that was later replaced by a 5in (127mm) weapon and supplemented by one 40mm and two 20mm anti-aircraft guns.

cruisers. The most telling of the former was the sinking of the huge *Shinano* by the *Archerfish* in November 1944, and a classic example of the latter was the destruction of the heavy cruisers *Atago* and *Maya* in October 1944 in an ambush by the *Dace* and *Darter*, which also severely damaged a third cruiser in the same action.

The Americans introduced the 'wolf pack' concept to their Pacific submarine operations during 1943, but by this time were so rampant that three-boat groups were deemed adequate to overwhelm even convoys supported by the indifferent escort vessels that the Japanese had started to build too late and in wholly inadequate numbers.

The complete superiority of the American submarine arm in the Pacific should not be allowed to disguise the fact that the Japanese submariners also had their moments of triumph, most notably in August 1942 when the *I-26* torpedoed and severely damaged the aircraft carrier *Saratoga*, and in September 1942 when the *I-15* torpedoed and severely damaged the battleship *North Carolina* and the *I-19* sank the aircraft carrier *Wasp*. These were relatively isolated instances, however, for in general the size of the Japanese submarines and the relative lack of tactical guile displayed by their commanders played into the hands of the American escort forces, of which one of the stars was the escort destroyer *England* that sank six Japanese submarines in the course of 12 days during May 1944.

Throughout the war, Japanese submariners urged on their high command the paramount importance of attacking targets other than the Pacific fleet's primary warships, but these pleas fell on deaf ears until a time late in 1942, when the import of the first American amphibious assaults on island groups in the Central Pacific finally sank into the minds of the Japanese naval high command. Even then, the response of these senior officers was ill-considered: realising the importance of these American assaults, they ordered virtually suicidal submarine attacks on the very well-protected ships of the landing forces, and also the use of submarines to transport men and equipment into bases that might become the next targets for American attack.

This use of attack submarines for the transport role was hardly a cost-effective method, as the British had realised during their supply runs to

Completed to the extent of 115 out of a planned 406 boats, the 'Type D Koryu' class of midget submarines had a submerged displacement of 59.33 tons, a submerged speed of 16 knots, a crew of five, and an armament of two 18in (457mm) tubes for two torpedoes.

The officer of the deck scans the horizon for ships and, perhaps more crucially, attacking warplanes, from his position on the conning tower of the *Batfish* during May 1945. A submarine of the 'Gato' class, the *Batfish* was built by the Portsmouth Navy Yard and launched in May 1943. The boat survived World War II, and was stricken in November 1969 before being hulked as a naval monument.

The boats of the 'Gato' (illustrated) and closely related 'Balao' classes bore the brunt of the US Navy's submarine warfare effort in the Pacific during World War II, and proved highly successful in the interdiction of the Japanese seaborne lines of communication, both naval and mercantile.

Malta in 1942, which were most effectively undertaken by a converted minelayer supported by a number of other boats. The Japanese response was therefore the construction of specialised transport submarines. The first of these were the 12 out of a projected 104 units of the 'Type D1' class. These boats had surfaced and submerged displacements of 1,779 and 2,215 tons respectively, a considerable range, armament limited to one 5.5in (140mm) deck gun and two 25mm cannon, and provision for a payload that could comprise 82 tons of freight or 110 men landed with the aid of two 14ft 6in (4.4m) boats.

Given the intense rivalry between itself and the Japanese navy, which it felt never gave adequate consideration to army demands, the Japanese army paralleled the navy move into transport submarines and commissioned its own type as the 'Yu 1' class, of which 12 were built. These were smaller boats, with a submerged displacement of 370 tons, and could carry 40 tons of freight.

Japan built a number of other submarine classes later in World War II, but the only two worthy of mention here are the huge 'Type STo' and midget 'Kaiten' types. Ordered in 1942 as the largest submarines envisaged up to that time, the 'Type STo' class was proposed at more than 18 units of which only three were completed with a crew of 144 men, a submerged displacement of 6,560 tons, the phenomenal surfaced range of 37,500 miles (60,350km) at 14 knots, and an armament that included eight 21in (533mm) tubes for 20 torpedoes, one 5.5in (140mm) deck gun, ten 25mm anti-aircraft cannon in two triple and four single mountings, and, most impressively of all, three special attack seaplanes (for which four torpedoes and 15 bombs were carried) that were designed specifically for attacks on the lock gates in

Opposite top: The 'Type STo' class submarine *I-400* comes alongside the US Navy's submarine tender Proteus to surrender in August 1945. After a thorough examination and evaluation, the submarine was scuttled off the US coast in 1946.

Opposite bottom: The fact that Germany was still planning to prosecute the submarine war at the time of her defeat is highlighted by this scene in Hamburg during May 1945, when large numbers of incomplete 'Type XXI' class submarines were discovered.

Below: A standard unit of the 'Tench' class, the *Torsk* was built by the Portsmouth Navy Yard and launched in September 1944.

the Panama Canal, whose destruction would have required American ships to round Cape Horn as a means of transiting between the Pacific and Atlantic Oceans.

The 'Kaiten' classes, of which four types were built, were designed for the *kamikaze* role, and were therefore suicide craft based on the design of the Japanese torpedo. The only operational model was the 'Kaiten 4' class, of which 419 were completed with a conventional torpedo motor rather than the hydrogen peroxide motors of the experimental 'Kaiten 2' and 'Kaiten 3' classes. Considerable effort was expended on these essentially defensive craft, which achieved no successes.

During the course of World War II, the Japanese submarine arm lost 149 of its 245 major boats excluding midget types and the German and Italian boats that were taken over in very small numbers.

By a quirk typical of history, it was the Americans' feeling that Japan's submarine arm had failed to live up to its real potential and was therefore a negligible risk, that was responsible for the last US catastrophe of World War II and its worst naval disaster of all time. The heavy cruiser *Indianapolis*, having delivered the first atomic bomb to the Mariana Islands, was steaming for Leyte in the Philippines. Believing that there was no real threat from the Japanese, the ship was neither escorted nor zigzagging and passed straight through the patrol line of the *I-58*, which fired a full spread of six torpedoes. Two of these hit, and the *Indianapolis* sank in a mere 12 minutes. It was three days later before anyone in the Philippines realised that the cruiser was overdue, and the belated rescue attempt meant that many of the men who had survived the sinking had meanwhile succumbed to wounds, the weather condition and sharks. The total loss of American life in this last Japanese submarine victory of the war was 883.

The Post-War Submarine

EVEN as the final defeat of Japan was being encompassed, teams of technical officers from the victorious Allied powers were scouring German ports, research centres and manufacturing facilities for information about the German submarines that had so nearly proved decisive. The boats in which the Allies were most interested were the conventionally powered 'Type XXI' class and the Walther-powered 'Type XVII' and 'Type XXIII' classes. With the immediate pressure of war lifted, the Allied powers concentrated their attention initially on the 'Type XXI' class design that was currently the most advanced conventionally powered submarine in the world. The main concepts learned from examination of these boats was the desirability of a highly streamlined hull with the minimum number of protuberances (including the deck gun), the streamlining of the conning tower with its platforms and periscope standards into a long sail, and the adoption of the *Schnorchel* as a standard feature that became known to the Americans as a snorkel and to the British as a snort.

The adoption of these features allowed the creation of new classes of submarine notable for underwater performance that was faster, quieter and longer-ranged, and the introduction of these new classes bought time for the primary submarine-building nations (the UK, USA and USSR) to consider their next moves. These included a practical investigation of the Walther system, although the USA soon dropped out of the running because of the dangers of the system, and by the mid-1950s all three nations had decided that the adoption of the Walther system was not a satisfactory solution to the question of how to produce true surface-independent submarines to replace the surface-reliant submersibles, which is what virtually all underwater vessels had been up to this time.

The solution, as the Americans had already realised, was the adoption of a nuclear propulsion arrangement in place of the diesel and electric or diesel-electric systems used in most recent submarines. This involved the creation of a shielded nuclear reactor whose controllable heat output could be used for the generation within a closed-cycle system of the steam that would power turbines for propulsion and/or the generation of electricity before being condensed back into water for return to the heat exchanger attached to the reactor. This would obviate the need for large batteries, although a number would be retained for emergency use, and though the system presented no major technical difficulties at the conceptual level, its development to a practical level demanded the injection of considerable capital and resources before a safe and usefully compact system could be prepared for submarine use.

While this longer-term solution to submarine propulsion and power was being planned and prepared, submarine designers continued to develop

A member of the 'Benjamin Franklin' class, the *George Bancroft* was originally armed with Poseidon submarine-launched ballistic missiles but was later modified to carry the considerably more capable Trident I missile. The boat was built by Electric Boat between August 1963 and December 1964, and was commissioned in January 1966.

conventionally powered boats. The US Navy's immediate response to the implications of the German submarines of World War II was the 'GUPPY' (Greater Underwater Propulsive Power) programme in which many surviving units of the 'Gato', 'Balao' and 'Tench' classes, together with the uncompleted units of the last class, were revised or completed with a lengthened and more streamlined hull/sail combination, larger batteries and a snorkel. Others of these boats were revised for experimental purposes, including the evaluation of the submarine for underway replenishment of oil and supplies at sea, and as the launch platform for guided missiles.

This last plan was of greater long-term importance, and started with the conversion in 1948-49 of the *Carbonero* and *Cusk* to carry and launch the 'Loon' surface-to-surface missile, which was an American development of the Fieseler Fi 103 weapon better known in the West as the V-1 of World War II. The trials confirmed the feasibility of the system, and the US Navy then authorised the development of the Regulus I, which was a substantial turbojet-powered missile intended for the anti-ship role, and the *Barbero* and

A member of the definitive 'Tench 'class of fleet submarines completed late in World War II the USS *Amberjack* was launched in July 1944. and the boats features included an armament of ten 21in(533nn) tubes (six forward and four stern) for 24 torpedoes, one 5in (127mm) deck gun, one 40mm ant-aircraft gun and one 20mm anti-aircraft cannon.

The GUPPY Programme

IN 1945 the US Navy found itself with a large force of related 'Gato', 'Balao' and 'Tench' class fleet submarines that had proved very successful against the Japanese in the Pacific war but had now been rendered technically obsolete by the advent of the German 'Type XXI' class submarine. For the longer term the US Navy was planning the introduction of nuclear-powered submarines, but now required a short-term expedient to maintain a credible submarine force at a time of worsening relations with the USSR, which was known to be developing a major submarine capability based on the 'Type XXI' design. The US Navy's solution was therefore the GUPPY (Greater Underwater Propulsive Power) programme in which four reload torpedoes, part of the fresh water tankage and deck gun magazine volume were used for increased battery capacity for greater submerged speed and endurance in concert with an exterior that was streamlined by the deletion of all guns, the remodelling of the casing, and the fairing of the conning tower into a low-drag 'sail'. The two 'GUPPY I' class prototype conversions had no snorkel, but this was added in the following 12 'GUPPY II' class conversions that introduced a higher-power but very expensive type of battery. The next 12 'GUPPY IA' conversions (two of them for the Dutch navy) therefore reverted to the original type of battery even though this meant a sacrifice of 1 knot of submerged speed; at the same time 16 boats were converted to the more austere Fleet Snorkel standard with a GUPPY-type sail and snorkel but without the remodelled hull. Finally there came 16 'GUPPY IIA' class conversions with one main engine removed to allow the relocation of some secondary machinery as a means of optimising sonar performance. The 'GUPPY' classes were now taken in hand under the FRAM (Fleet Rehabilitation And Modernization) programme, nine 'GUPPY II' class boats being revised to 'GUPPY III' class standard with the hull lengthened by 10ft (3.05m) to allow the incorporation of a plotting room and a longer sail as well as a new fire-control system that would allow use of the Mk 45 Astor nuclear anti-submarine torpedo. Further development of the concept introduced a sail of plastic construction, and a number of existing fleet boats were upgraded to an improved Fleet Snorkel standard with the plastic sail. Once the US Navy had started to introduce nuclear-powered attack submarines, many of the 'GUPPY' boats were transferred to friendly navies, some of which still operate the submarines in limited numbers.

The *Skate* was the lead boat of the four-strong 'Skate' class of attack submarines, which were the first 'production line' submarines of the nuclear-powered type. The boats were commissioned between December 1957 and December 1959 after construction by four yards (one commercial and three navy) to provide experience in the building of such submarines. The basic details of the class included surfaced and submerged displacements of 2,550 and 2,848 tons respectively, a length of 267ft 8in (81.6m), a two-shaft propulsion arrangement with a single nuclear reactor supplying steam to 6,600hp (4,921kW) geared steam turbines for a submerged speed of about 20 knots, a crew of 84.

Intended for the coastal role, the *U-29* of the 18-strong West German 'Type 206' class was built by Howaldtswerke at Kiel and launched in November 1973. The basic details of the class, which is typical of the high-performance conventionally powered submarines of the period, include surfaced and submerged displacements of 456 and 500 tons respectively, a length of 159ft 6in (48.6m), a single-shaft propulsion arrangement of the diesel-electric type with a 1,500hp (1,118 kW) electric motor and 1,200hp (895kW) diesel engines for surfaced and submerged speeds of 10 and 17.5 knots respectively, a crew of 21, and an armament of eight 21in (533m) tubes for 16 wire-guided torpedoes or mines, supplemented as required by a further 24 mines in external containers.

Tunny were later adapted to carry two of these missiles in cylindrical hangars. Further development of the Regulus concept resulted in the considerably larger Regulus II with strategic capability, and as this more massive weapon could only be carried by larger submarines, the US Navy ordered the *Grayback* and *Growler*, which were built in the period between 1952 and 1958 with two large cylindrical hangars built into the forward casing. The Regulus II system was abandoned after only five years, but the submarines associated with it were retained in service after conversion as transports for amphibious warfare and special forces teams.

The USA's last series-built submarines of the conventionally powered type were the 'Tang' class of attack submarines of which six were completed in the period between 1949 and 1952, and finally the 'Barbel' class of attack submarines of which just three were built between 1956 and 1959. The design of the 'Darter' class was based on that of the 'Type XXI' submarine, and the design may therefore be compared with the Soviet 'Whiskey' class, which was built in very large numbers although it was in no way as

A conventionally powered patrol submarine, the *Ghazi* is one of the Pakistani navy's four French 'Daphné' class boats bought as one ex-Portuguese and three new-build vessels. The type has surfaced and submerged displacements of 869 and 1,043 tons respectively, a length of 190ft 0in (57.8m), a two-shaft propulsion arrangement with 1,300hp (969kW) diesel engines and a 1,600hp (1,193kW) electric motor for surfaced and surfaced speeds of 13.5 and 16 knots respectively, a crew of 45, and an armament of 12 21.7in (550mm) torpedo tubes located as eight in the bows and four in the stern.

sophisticated a type as the American design. Although obsolescent by American standards at the time of its appearance, the 'Barbel' class design nonetheless remains interesting as that in which a number of hitherto experimental features were combined for the first time in an operational series. These features included the type of low-drag 'teardrop' hull first tested in the US Navy's experimental *Albacore* launched in 1953, a single large propeller turning comparatively slowly for a reduced noise 'signature', all the control systems centralised in an 'attack centre' for fully optimised operational capability and, as a retrofit, the diving planes on the bows replaced by planes on the sides of the sail.

This period after the end of World War II was characterised by a rapid decline in relations between the USA and the USSR, now indisputably the world's two superpowers, and the equally rapid development of a 'cold war' between these superpowers and their allies. The USSR had quickly followed the USA's lead into nuclear weapons capability, and the USA feared a major air assault with such weapons. Early warning was therefore of paramount importance for defence, and the USA made extensive use of ships and submarines fitted with long-range surveillance radar for timely warning of any imminent Soviet attack on the continental USA. One of the most fascinating of these boats, most of which were converted from conventionally powered attack submarines, was the *Triton*, which was built in 1959 as one of the first nuclear-powered boats and was for its time the largest submarine in the world, with a submerged displacement of 7,773

Built by Electric Boat between November 1962 and June 1968 for a commissioning date in August 1969, the US Navy's conventionally powered *Dolphin* was designed and built as a research submarine with a perfectly cylindrical hull 18ft 0in (5.49m) in diameter closed off at each end with a hemispherical bulkhead. Extensive use was made of alloys and plastics, and the boat was used mainly for deep-diving and acoustic work as well as oceanographic research.

tons and a two-shaft nuclear propulsion arrangement for surfaced and submerged speeds of 27 and 20 knots respectively, the former allowing rapid transit between operational areas.

Throughout this period, little was known about the development of Soviet submarines. It gradually became clear, however, that Soviet developments from the mid-1940s had resulted in delivery in the early 1950s of the 'Whiskey' class conventionally powered submarine in large numbers for the attack role, to which were later added the radar picket and, from 1961, missile launch roles in four and 12 boats respectively. Production of this class eventually amounted to 236 boats, and from 1961 a considerable number of these useful submarines were transferred to the navies of friendly nations.

The next major type to appear was the 'Zulu' class, whose operational capability with a conventional propulsion arrangement was confirmed in 1952, after early attempts to create an effective version of the Walther propulsion system had failed. Some 26 of the type were built as longer-ranged equivalents of the medium-range 'Whiskey' class, and of these boats six were completed or converted as strategic missile submarines, with the rear part of their sails adapted for the vertical launch of two ballistic missiles. Built at about the same time to a total of 22 units, the 'Golf' class was basically an enlarged version of the 'Zulu' class design with a longer sail carrying three vertically launched missiles.

The development of Soviet conventionally powered submarines continued with the 'Romeo' class of which 17 were built between 1958 and

Lead submarine of the five-strong 'George Washington' class and commissioned in December 1959, the *George Washington* was the US Navy's first nuclear-powered ballistic missile submarine and as such opened a new era in strategic warfare. The class was typified by surfaced and submerged displacements of 5,959 and 6,709 tons respectively, a length of 381ft 8in (116.4m), a single-shaft propulsion arrangement with one reactor supplying steam to 15,000hp (1,118kW) geared steam turbines for a submerged speed of about 20 knots, a crew of 112, and an armament of 16 vertically launched Polaris missiles and six 21in (533mm) torpedo tubes.

Whereas the 'George Washington' class had been produced by adapting 'Skipjack' class attack submarines already under construction with a lengthened hull to accommodate the missile section, the following 'Ethan Allen' class of nuclear-powered missile submarines was designed specifically for its task although it drew considerably from the 'Thresher' class attack submarine in features such as its stronger hull material and improved silencing features. The boats also introduced passive towed-array sonar for improved defensive capability. The basic details of the 'Ethan Allen' class, here exemplified by the *Ethan Allen* that was built by Electric Boat between September 1959 and November 1960 for commissioning in August 1961, included surfaced and submerged displacements of 6,946 and 7,884 tons respectively, a length of 410ft 5in (125.1m), a single-shaft propulsion arrangement with one reactor supplying steam to 15,000hp (1,118kW) geared steam turbines for a submerged speed of about 20 knots, a crew of 110, and an armament of 16 vertically launched Polaris missiles and four 21in (533mm) torpedo tubes.

Right: Built by Nackums and the Karlskrona Navy Dockyard between 1976 and 1981, the three conventionally powered attack submarines of the Swedish navy's 'Näcken' class of attack submarines have a teardrop-shaped hull.

1961 as successors to the 'Whiskey' class with two more torpedo tubes together with greater range and diving depth, the 'Quebec' class of which 30 were built between 1954 and 1957 to replace the pre-war 'M' class boats in the coastal role and fitted with a closed-cycle propulsion arrangement, and the 'Foxtrot' class of which 76 were built between 1958 and 1967 as successors to the 'Zulu' class with reduced surface range but significantly improved underwater speed.

The USSR followed the USA's lead into the development of nuclear-powered submarines, but unlike its ideological foe did not entirely abandon the conventionally powered submarine. Between the early 1970s and 1982, therefore, the Soviet navy received 18 'Kilo' class submarines to replace the units of the 'Foxtrot' class with an improved type whose larger internal

The *Thresher* was lead boat of the US Navy's second full class of nuclear-powered attack submarines, which was built to the extent of 14 boats with a modified teardrop-shaped hull with the torpedo tubes relocated to the amidships position thereby leaving the bow entirely clear for the advanced sonar that was the core of the class's anti-submarine capability. The *Thresher* was lost in the Atlantic in April 1963, and the class was later renamed as the 'Permit' class after its second boat. The details of the class included surfaced and submerged displacements of 3,705 and 4,311 tons respectively, a length of 278ft 6in (84.9m) increased in some of the later boats, a single-shaft propulsion arrangement with one reactor supplying steam to 15,000hp (11,118kW) geared steam turbines for a submerged speed of 30 knots, a crew of 94, and an armament of four 21in (533mm) tubes for 22 torpedoes.

volume is used for improved habitability, greater battery capacity, and a larger weapon load. The final development of Soviet conventional submarine thinking was the 'Kilo' class, which entered production in 1978 or 1979 with a considerably better hull form than the 'Tango' class for improved underwater speed.

Although the USA and the USSR have largely dominated the technological and constructional aspects of submarine development in the period since World War II, a number of other countries have contributed and in the process have created or maintained significant submarine warfare capabilities.

At the end of World War II, the UK's most important submarines were those of the 'S' and 'T' classes, complemented during the late 1940s by a number of 'A' class boats designed in World War II for long-range operations in the Pacific but completed too late for this campaign. The 'S' and earlier 'T' class boats were of riveted rather than welded construction, and were therefore deemed unsuitable for major development after the war even though five 'T' class boats were given a more streamlined casing, but eight of the later 'T' class boats and 14 of the 18 'A' class boats were taken in hand

Opposite: The Italian navy's *Romeo Romei* was built as the US Navy's *Harder* of the six-strong 'Tang' class, which was the American attempt to exploit the concept of the German 'Type XXI' class submarine and thereby match the capabilities of the Soviet 'Whiskey' class that was in the event built in much larger numbers. The basic details of the design included surfaced and submerged displacements of 1,560 and 2,260 tons respectively, a length of 287ft 0in (87.5m), a two-shaft propulsion arrangement with 4,500hp (3,355kW) diesel engines and 5,600hp (4,175kW) electric motors for a surfaced and submerged speed of 16 knots, a crew of 83, and an armament of eight 21in (533mm) torpedo tubes located as six in the bows and two in the stern.

Built to the extent of 23 boats, the 'Golf' class was the USSR's first attempt to create a submarine with vertically launched ballistic missile capability, in this instance with only three tubes for SS-N-4 missiles that could be launched only after the submarine had surfaced, and a conventional propulsion arrangement with three shafts driven by 6,000hp (4,474kW) diesel engines and 5,300hp (3,952kW) electric motors for a submerged speed of 12 knots.

during the 1950s for modernisation along the lines of the American 'GUPPY' programme, with a lengthened and more streamlined hull containing an uprated propulsion arrangement and more battery cells for a doubled submerged speed. This provided the Royal Navy with a useful attack submarine capability into the late 1950s, but further development was centred on new construction in the form of the eight boats of the 'Porpoise' class built between 1956 and 1961, making use of the lessons learned from captured German data and British post-war developments in the creation of a type notable for its generally good performance and exceptional quietness. Further development of the concepts embodied in the 'Porpoise' class, individually small but collectively large, resulted in the 'Oberon' class, of

The *Seawolf*, built between September 1953 and July 1955 by Electric Boat for commissioning in March 1957, was in essence a prototype attack submarine with a nuclear powerplant based on a sodium- rather than pressurised water-cooled reactor. There were considerable problems with this powerplant, however, and the US Navy therefore decided to concentrate of pressurised water-cooled reactors.

which 13 were built for the Royal Navy between 1957 and 1967, with another 14 delivered to export customers. To complete the story of British conventional submarine design, mention must be made of the superb 'Upholder' class ordered in the early 1980s to replace the 'Oberon' class. Notably quiet and equipped with anti-ship missiles as well as advanced torpedoes all controlled for a high-quality fire-control system, production and operational service have been truncated as a result of the 'peace dividend' accruing from the collapse of the USSR in the late 1980s and the effective end of the 'cold war'.

In 1945, France was faced with the immense task of rebuilding not only the country's armed forces but also the industrial base required to equip these forces with weapons of indigenous design and manufacture. So far as its navy's submarine arm was concerned, a start was made with the receipt of four British 'S' class boats for training purposes and the completion to a modernised standard of five 'La Creole' class submarines from incomplete 'L'Aurore' class hulls that had survived the war. This bought time for French

The *Nautilus* was the world's first nuclear-powered submarine, and with its pressurised water-cooled reactor proved considerably more successful than the slightly later Seawolf with its sodium-cooled reactor.

designers to assimilate the latest thinking in submarine concepts, and the result comprised the six boats of the 'Narval' class of ocean-going submarine, all completed in the period between 1957 and 1960, and the four boats of the 'Aréthuse' class of sea-going submarine, completed between 1957 and 1958 after design as the world's first dedicated hunter-killer submarines. Between 1964 and 1970, the 'Aréthuse' class was supplemented and finally supplanted by the slightly larger 'Daphné' class, of which 11 were completed as smaller counterparts to the ocean-going 'Narval' class boats. Several more 'Daphné' class boats were built in France for Pakistan (three boats), Portugal (four boats) and South Africa (three boats), and an additional four were produced under licence in Spain as 'S 61' class units.

The three other northern European countries that have designed and built their own submarines are the Netherlands, Sweden, and Germany. Dutch design and production have been responsible for the four-strong 'Dolfijn' class with a unique triple hull design, the 'Zwaardvis' class of two attack submarines, and the 'Walrus' class of four improved attack submarines. Swedish design and construction have yielded the six boats of the 'Hajen' class based on the 'Type XXI' design, the six boats of the 'Draken' class, the five boats of the 'Sjöormen' class of teardrop-hulled attack submarine with an X-shaped arrangement of surfaces at the stern, the three boats of the smaller 'Näcken' class of attack submarines, and the four advanced boats of the 'Västergötland' class of attack submarines.

Once allowed to re-arm in the mid-1950s as part of the North Atlantic Treaty Organization (NATO), which was faced with the threat of Soviet-led aggression by the forces of the Warsaw Pact countries, West Germany started to rebuild its armed forces with emphasis on the ground and air elements that would have to play a key part in the defence of West Germany, the most likely avenue for a communist

The British moved into nuclear-powered submarine construction somewhat later than the Americans, and therefore placed greater initial reliance on updated versions of the conventionally powered types that had done well in the later stages of World War II. One of the classes that received a modernisation was the 'T' class of ocean-going submarines, of which five were moderately improved with a streamlined casing and sail as the 'T Streamline' class and eight were more significantly upgraded with the same improve-ments as well as a lengthened hull, two more electric motors and increased battery capacity as the 'T Conversion' class. The boat illustrated is the *Thrasher*, which was not used for either of the programmes and was therefore scrapped in 1947.

offensive. The navy was not neglected, however, and plans were laid for the creation of small but high-quality elements responsible for operations in the western end of the Baltic Sea and in the southern part of the North Sea. Part of this capability was inevitably vested in a new submarine arm, and to provide an initial training capability the new West German navy raised two 'Type XXIII' and one 'Type XXI' submarines for reconstruction with the type of electric propulsion (the diesels being used only as generators) that has been used for all subsequent German submarine classes: the boats became the two 'Hai' and one 'Wilhelm Bauer' class submarines.

The new navy's first operational submarines were the three (originally 12) units of the 'Type 201' coastal boat with a submerged displacement of only 433 tons, the high submerged speed of 17.5 knots and the heavy armament of eight 21in (533mm) tubes for eight torpedoes, but only limited range and indifferent habitability for the crew of 21. Further development of the same basic concept led to the 11 units of the slightly larger 'Type 205' class, which was not notably successful, and then the successful 'Type 206' class of which 18 units were completed with features to reduce underwater noise and a capability that allows the use of advanced torpedoes which

The Soviet submarine type known in the West as the 'Whiskey Twin Cylinder' class was a conversion of the standard 'Whiskey' class conventionally powered attack submarine with a side-by-side pair of cylindrical container-launchers abaft the sail for two SS-N-3 'Shaddock' nuclear-tipped cruise missiles.

Le Redoutable is the lead submarine of France's five-strong first class of nuclear-powered ballistic missile submarines built by the Arsenal de Cherbourg between 1964 and 1982.

receive their guidance commands via a wire system from the submarine's fire-control computer. Germany's latest submarine class is the highly advanced 'Type 212' with hybrid fuel cell/battery propulsion for considerably extended underwater endurance.

The design of these boats was the responsibility of IKL (Ingenieurkontor Lübeck), which has become a world leader in the design of conventionally powered submarines that have secured considerable success in the export and licence-built markets. Among IKL's designs are the 'Type 207' class used by Denmark and Norway and the 'Type 209' used in a number of differently sized subvariants by Argentina, Brazil, Chile, Colombia, Ecuador, Greece, India, Indonesia, Israel, Peru, South Korea, Taiwan, Turkey and Venezuela.

The only other European country to have designed and built advanced conventionally powered submarines is Italy, whose post-war career in this field began with the four 'Toti' class attack submarines optimised for the coastal role and then progressed, via the four larger 'Sauro' class and four 'Sauro (Improved)' class attack submarines optimised for the sea-going role, to the 'S 90' class modern type with excellent capabilities.

Laid down in the early 1950s and all commissioned by 1960, the six boats of the 'Narval' class, here exemplified by the *Narval*, were the first French submarines designed to incorporate the concepts first revealed in the German 'Type XXI' class of World War II.

The helmsman's position in *Le Redoutable* reveals how modern submarines are controlled in a manner similar to that used for aircraft although there is, of course, no exterior view!

This view of the US Navy's *Nautilus* under way reveals that the core design was derived from that of the 'Type XXI' adapted for a nuclear powerplant. The teardrop-shaped hull characteristic of most modern submarines was adopted only later.

The only other country in the world to have designed and built advanced conventionally powered submarines is Japan, whose first post-war boat was the *Oyashio*, completed in 1960 with a submerged displacement of 1,420 tons, a submerged speed of 19 knots, and an armament of four 21in (533mm) torpedo tubes in the bows, and a wholly conservative design based on a whale-shaped hull. There followed the four submarines of the two-boat 'Hayashio' and 'Natsushio' classes with a shorter and fuller hull for good safety features and excellent habitability, but with submerged displacements of only 800 and 850 tons respectively, they were limited in capability to coastal work. The size was nearly doubled in the five submarines of the 'Oshio' class that followed between 1965 and 1969 as Japan's first post-war

The 'Type 209' class submarine designed in Germany has become the most common type of conventionally powered submarine in the world, helped considerably by its high performance and availability in several forms allowing any navy to choose a model ideally suited to its requirements. This is the *Islay* of the Peruvian navy, which operates six of the boats, and is an example of the 'Type 209/1' or 'Type 1200' class with surfaced and submerged displacements of 1,185 and 1,285 tons respectively, a length of 183ft 5in (55.9m), a single-shaft propulsion arrangement of the diesel-electric type with 9,440hp (7,040kW) diesel engines and 4,960hp (3,700kW) electric motor for surfaced and submerged speeds of 10 and 22 knots respectively, a crew of 31, and an armament of eight 21in (533mm) tubes in the bows for 14 wire-guided torpedoes or 28 mines.

The *Huancavilca* is one of two 'Type 209/2' or 'Type 1300' class submarines operated by the Ecuadorian navy with details that include surfaced and submerged displacements of 1,285 and 1,390 tons respectively, a length of 195ft 2in (59.5m), a single-shaft propulsion arrangement of the diesel-electric type with 9,440hp (7,040kW) diesel engines and 4,960hp (3,700kW) electric motor for surfaced and submerged speeds of 11 and 21.5 knots respectively, a crew of 33, and an armament of eight 21in (533mm) tubes in the bows for 16 torpedoes or 32 mines.

attack submarines of the ocean-going type, but Japanese submarine concepts finally began to reach maturity in 1971 with the delivery of the first of seven 'Uzushio' class boats with a teardrop-shaped hull, a displacement of 3,600 tons, a submerged speed of 20 knots, and an armament of six 21in torpedo tubes located amidships to leave the optimum bow location for the sonar. From 1980 there followed the 10 boats of the 'Yuushio' class developed from the 'Uzushio' class with deeper diving capability and improved electronics, and the most modern of the Japanese submarine classes, entering service from 1990, is the six-strong 'Harushio' class with a

The *Enrico Toti*, completed in January 1968, was the name boat of the Italian navy's four 'Toti' class conventionally powered submarines with surfaced and submerged displacements of 460 and 585 tons respectively, a length of 151ft 6in (46.2m), a single-shaft propulsion arrangement of the diesel-electric type with two diesel engines and 2,200hp (1,640kW) electric motor.

Many submarines surplus to the requirements of the UK and USA in the period after the end of World War II were passed or sold to the navies of friendly nations seeking to develop their navies. Typical of this tendency was this boat, the ex-British *Truncheon* of the 'T' class, which was sold to the Israeli navy in the mid-1960s as the *Dolphin* together with two similar boats.

submerged displacement of 2,750 tons, a submerged speed of more than 20 knots, and an armament of six 21in tubes for wire-guided torpedoes as well as underwater-launched Harpoon anti-ship missiles.

As these conventionally powered developments were under way, the USA was pressing ahead with the development of the nuclear-powered submarine initially for the attack role and then, in a considerably larger form, for the ballistic missile launch role. The starting point for the concept of the dedicated attack (hunter-killer) submarine combined high underwater performance (especially in speed and endurance/range) offered by the nuclear propulsion arrangement, after effective quietening features had been developed, and the much-enhanced ability to detect

---

The Sinking of the *Belgrano*

It is believed that the only time a nuclear-powered attack submarine has been used to sink an enemy warship was in May 1982, when as part of the naval operations concerned with the British recapture of the Falkland Islands from an Argentine invasion force, the attack submarine Conqueror of the 'Churchill' class torpedoed and sank the Argentine heavy cruiser General Belgrano, an ex-American ship of the 'Brooklyn' class with a displacement of 13,645 tons and an armament of fifteen 6in (152mm) guns in five triple turrets. Although the Argentine ship, escorted by two ex-American destroyers, was slightly outside the total exclusion zone declared by the British, she remained a distinct threat to the British naval forces preparing for the landings on the Falklands, and the decision was taken at the highest level to sink her. The *Conqueror* had been shadowing the *General Belgrano* with passive sonar, and on receipt of the 'sink' order from London, the captain of the *Conqueror* ordered the start of the attack plot on the DCB wire-control system and decided to use the elderly Mk 8** torpedo, designed in the period before World War II, rather than the more modern Mk 24 Tigerfish wire-guided torpedo, as the older weapon's 750lb (340kg) warhead was better suited to the destruction of a large surface vessel than the 331lb (150kg) warhead of the Mk 24, and as the Mk 8** could be fired in a salvo of four while the Mk 24 could be fired only in a salvo of two. The four torpedoes were fired from a range of about 1,400yds (1,280m) with their gyros set to generate a curved course and so confuse the Argentines about the position of the attacker. As soon as the torpedoes had been fired, the *Conqueror* dived to 985ft (300m) and soon heard two large explosions: the first torpedo detonated on the port side of the hull under the after 5in (127mm) secondary gun director and the second just forward of 'A' turret. The ship sank in about 45 minutes, taking with her the bodies of 321 Argentine sailors, the vast majority of them killed in the initial explosions. Some 880 other men were later rescued from the water by other Argentine ships.

Opposite: To provide industry and the navy with experience in the design and operation of a submarine capable of carrying vertically launched ballistic missiles, the French navy commissioned the Gymnote as an experimental conventionally powered boat with four of the M-1 missiles planned for the country's first nuclear-powered missile submarines, together with the associated fire-control and inertial navigation systems. The boat was launched in March 1964 and commissioned in October 1966.

Thought to be the fastest boats currently in service, the attack submarines of the Soviet (now Russian) 'Alfa' class can reach a submerged speed of 45 knots with a single-shaft propulsion arrangement based on two liquid metal-cooled reactors supplying steam to two sets of turbo-alternators generating the current for a 46,940hp (35,000kW) electric motor. The 'Alfa' class is also based on a hull of high-strength titanium for a maximum diving depth of 3,280ft (1,000m) although the normal operating limit is 1,970ft (600m).

and track enemy submarines provided by modern sonar (sound navigation and ranging).

These features became feasible in the early 1950s, and resulted in two pioneering boats, namely the *Nautilus* and the *Seawolf* as the world's first nuclear-powered submarines, in each case with an armament of six 21in (533m) tubes in the bows for the targets whose presence, bearing and range were indicated by the advanced BQS-4 sonar. The first and more successful of the submarines was the *Nautilus*, which was commissioned in April 1955 with a Westinghouse S2W pressurised water-cooled reactor powering two sets of geared steam turbines delivering some 13,400hp (9,990kW) to two propellers for a submerged speed of 23 knots. The *Seawolf*, which was finally commissioned in March 1957, was less successful as a result of the poor performance of the General Electric S2G liquid sodium-cooled reactor, powering two sets of geared steam turbines delivering some 13,000hp (9,693kW) to two propellers for a submerged speed of about 20 knots.

It was the *Nautilus* and its water-cooled reactor system that paved the way for succeeding generations of American nuclear-powered submarines. It is worth noting here that this pioneering boat retained the type of hull/sail shape

introduced by the 'Type XXI' class although on a somewhat larger scale, as indicated by the submerged displacement of 4,092 tons. This greater size was dictated largely by the volume of the reactor system and its associated shielding, and meant that the boat was not as agile under the surface as its predecessors, but experience soon showed that the extra interior volume provided by the additional cross-section right along the hull was vital to the success of the protracted underwater sortie made possible by the nuclear powerplant. The length of the sortie in a nuclear-powered boat was now limited not by energy and/or air considerations, but rather by the quantity of food that could be carried and by the habitability of the crew accommodation: both of these factors were improved by the greater internal volume now available.

The first nuclear-powered production boats were the four units of the 'Skate' class of attack submarines built between 1955 and 1959. These were

The Submarine-Launched Ballistic Missile

ABLE to operate as a mobile entity in any area within range of the target, the ballistic missile submarine is a far harder target than any missile-launch site in a fixed location on the Earth's surface, especially as in its definitive form with a nuclear powerplant and submarine- rather than surface-launched missiles such a submarine is independent of the sea's surface for the full length of its patrol. This makes it very difficult for any possible opponent to detect and track such a submarine as it patrols quietly in a very large volume of water. The nature of this submerged patrol made it essential from the beginning of these strategic activities that effective means were found for the submarine to receive messages from its national command authorities, and to know with very great precision its exact geographical location at any moment. The communications capability was provided initially by the release of an antenna lifted to the surface by a small buoy and then by the development of extremely low frequency (ELF) radio waves able to penetrate to the submerged submarine, and the navigational capability was provided by the ship's inertial navigation system (SINS). The latter is an extremely sophisticated equipment into which the ship's position is loaded at the beginning of the patrol: the submarine's three-dimensional movements (in terms of direction and acceleration) are then measured by highly precise gyroscopic systems and integrated with a time function in the SINS's computer to produce a highly accurate plot of the submarine's position, which is required not only for navigation but also for accurate targeting of the missiles. The primary generations of this type of inertially guided missile in American service have been four types designed and built by Lockheed as the UGM-27 Polaris, UGM-73 Poseidon, UGM-96 Trident I and UGM-133 Trident II. The Polaris entered service in 1960 with a warhead yielding 0.5 megatons (later replaced by three 200-kiloton warheads), and in three variants increased in weight from 28,000lb (12,701kg) to 35,000lb (15,876kg) and in length from 28ft 0in (8.53m) to 32ft 3.5in (9.85m) for a range increased from 1,380 miles (2,221km) to 2,880 miles (4,635km). From the 1970s the Polaris was complemented and then replaced by the Poseidon with a warhead bus carrying between 10 and 14 multiple independently targeted re-entry vehicles (MIRVs) each carrying a 40-kiloton warhead delivered with a mean accuracy of 605yds (553m), a weight of 64,000lb (29,030kg), a length of 34ft 0in (10.36m), and a range variable between 2,485 miles (4,000km) increasing to 3,230 miles (5,600km). The Trident I entered service in 1979 after development as a longer-ranged weapon whose availability would increase the size of the deeper-water patrol areas that could be used by American missile submarines. With eight MIRVs each carrying a 100-kiloton warhead delivered with a mean accuracy of 600yds (549m), the Trident I weighs 70,000lb (31,751kg), has a length of 34ft 0in (10.36m), and possesses a range of 4,230 miles (6,808km). The current weapon is the Trident II that entered service in the late 1980s with considerably improved targeting accuracy for its larger number of more powerful warheads. The Trident II thus has a weight of 130,000lb (58,968kg), a length of 44ft 6.6in (13.58m), and a range of 7,500 miles (12,070km) with ten 335-kiloton warheads delivered with an accuracy of 130yds (120m), although a maximum of 15 similar warheads can be fired over a shorter range.

A member of the 'Thresher' (later 'Permit' class) of nuclear-powered attack submarines, the *Whale* here surfaces through the ice of the polar regions, which the essentially unlimited endurance of nuclear propulsion made fully accessible to modern submarines for a significant extension of their operating areas.

smaller boats, similar to the conventionally powered 'Tang' class in overall dimensions, and had a smaller Westinghouse S3W or S4W reactor powering two sets of geared steam turbines delivering 6,600hp (4,921kW) to two propellers for a submerged speed of about 20 knots. The boats had the same BQS-4 sonar, but the armament was increased to eight 21in (533mm) tubes by the addition of two in the stern. The success of the 'Skate' class paved the way for the US Navy's comprehensive move into nuclear propulsion for its submarines, and further development into larger and steadily more capable classes was based on the combination of the nuclear powerplant, in progressively powerful and reliable forms and generally driving a single propeller, with the 'teardrop' hull pioneered by the *Albacore*, and evermore sophisticated computer-assisted sonar systems relying increasingly on the passive mode for the detection and tracking of target submarines, whose

The Wire-Guided Torpedo

WITH the original type of locomotive torpedo based on a gyroscopically controlled unit for guidance, the weapon was committed once it had left its tube with the data (either straight or curved course, depth and speed/range parameters) inputted before launch on the basis of the solution to the fire-control problem worked out in the submarine's control spaces on the basis of variables such as target bearing, course, range and speed (plus anticipated changes in these factors) derived from acoustic and optical observation. Any unexpected changes in the target's data therefore nullified the results of the fire-control calculation. With the development of the wire-guided torpedo, however, the torpedo is launched on the basis of the original fire-control solution but its guidance package can then be provided, throughout its attack, with an updated fire-control solution processed by the submarine's fire-control computer on the basis of changed data. This allows constantly improvement of the fire-control solution, and in the event of a break in the guidance wire link, the torpedo can continue the attack on the basis of the data currently stored in the computer of its guidance package.

Typical of the older submarines maintained in first-line service virtually up to the present is the *Papanikolos* of the Greek navy, a 'GUPPY IIA' conversion of a 'Balao' class fleet submarine dating from World War II.

Designed specifically for the submarine hunter-killer role, the *Rubis* is the lead boat of the French navy's sole nuclear-powered attack submarine class. These eight boats are currently the smallest submarines of their type in operational service.

range is acquired only at the last minute by the active 'ping'.

The first of these new classes was the 'Skipjack' class of six boats with a submerged speed of about 30 knots and an armament of six 21in (533mm) bow tubes for 24 torpedoes, followed by the 'Thresher' (later 'Permit') class of 11 boats with a submerged speed of about 27 knots and an armament of four 21in amidships tubes for 22 Mk 48 wire-guided torpedoes (or 18 torpedoes and four UUM-44 SUBROC underwater-launched rockets each carrying a small homing torpedo as payload) to allow the incorporation of larger and more sophisticated passive/active sonar in the optimum bow position. This class paved the way for the first very large class, which was the 'Sturgeon' class of 42 boats characterised by a submerged speed of about 26 knots and an armament of four 21in amidships tubes for 23 Mk 48 torpedoes or 19 torpedoes and four SUBROC weapons.

These boats were completed between 1966 and 1975, and were the mainstay of the US Navy's hunter-killer submarine capability until the later 1970s, when the first of an eventual 62 'Los Angeles' class boats entered service. Completed between 1976 and 1987, these boats each have a submerged displacement in the order of 6,925 tons, a submerged speed of 32 knots on the 35,000hp (26,095kW) supplied to one propeller by the two geared steam turbines powered by one S6G reactor, and an armament of four 21in amidships tubes for a total of 26 weapons, whose versatile fit can include Mk 48 torpedoes, UGM-84 Harpoon submarine-launched anti-ship missiles and BGM-109 Tomahawk cruise missiles in a typical mix of 14, four and eight respectively: the later boats also have vertical launch tubes for 12 Tomahawk missiles, allowing the weapons launched through the amidships tubes to be concentrated on the Mk 48 and Harpoon types, although these can be replaced by up to 78 mines for further expansion of the submarine's operational capabilities.

From the mid-1990s, the 'Los Angeles' class boats are to be supplemented and eventually replaced by the 'Seawolf' class with a submerged displacement of 9,150 tons, a submerged speed of 35 knots driven by a single pumpjet propulsor powered by the 60,000hp (44,735kW) provided by the S6W reactor.

In the period after World War II, the Royal Navy modernised a number of its submarines to conform more closely with the design details that had made the German 'Type XXI' class submarines such a potential threat. This programme included the conversion of 14 'A' class boats, such as the *Alaric* illustrated here, to the 'A (Modernised)' class configuration with a lengthened hull, streamlined forward and after casings, the conning tower replaced by a sail, and the four external torpedo tubes (two in the bows and the other two in the stern) removed to leave a total of six 21in (533mm) tubes in the bows for 18 torpedoes.

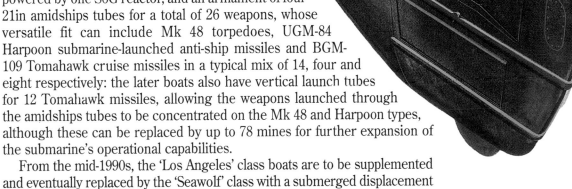

The armament of these boats is eight 25.6in (650mm) tubes for a total of about 50 tube-launched weapons or a larger number of mines.

The American lead into nuclear-powered attack submarines was followed with as little delay as possible by the USSR, whose first class of this type was the 'November' class, of which 12 were delivered between 1958 and 1964. The type had a submerged displacement of 5,300 tons, a submerged speed in the order of 30 knots on the 30,000hp (22,370kW) delivered to two propellers by the geared steam turbines powered by a single reactor, and an armament of eight 21in bow tubes for 24 torpedoes. The type was not notably successful because of its high levels of underwater noise, and it also suffered from the unreliability of its nuclear reactor, which was poorly shielded and therefore exercised a distinctly malign influence on its crews.

In 1968 there appeared the first of the succeeding 'Victor' class, which

The *Ethan Allen* was the lead boat of the five-strong class that was the US Navy's first purpose-designed ballistic missile submarine class, and was completed in August 1961 with the flat-topped missile compartment for 16 UGM-27 Polaris missiles, in two longitudinal rows of eight missiles, abaft the sail.

Completed in December 1960, the *Dolfijn* was the lead boat of the Dutch navy's four-strong 'Dolfijn' class of conventionally powered attack submarines with a triple hull arrangement with the three pressure cylinders disposed in a triangular pattern.

Hunter-killer Armament

DESIGNED for the detection and destruction of other boats, the nuclear-powered hunter/killer submarine was initially armed with torpedoes (replaceable by tube-launched mines) for attacks on targets identified and tracked with the aid of increasingly sophisticated sonar of the active and, increasingly, the passive types. The longer range and accuracy of these detection and tracking systems then led to the development of the wire-guided torpedo for long-range engagements. The wire-guided torpedo lacks the range of its launch submarine's sensors, however, and this led to the concept of the submarine-launched rocket, which was an encapsulated weapon fired from an otherwise standard torpedo tubes to reach the surface, break open and release a ballistic rocket that flew to the vicinity of the target and there released into the water either a homing torpedo or a nuclear depth change. Typical weapons of this type include the Honeywell UUM-44 SUBROC introduced to American service in 1965 with a 5 kiloton depth charge delivered over a range of 35 miles (56km), the SS-N-15 'Starfish' introduced to Soviet service in 1972 with a 5 kiloton depth charge delivered over a range of 23 miles (37km), and the SS-N-16 'Stallion' introduced to Soviet service in the mid-1970s with a homing torpedo or nuclear depth charge delivered over a range of 34 miles (55km). From these weapons it was only a short conceptual step to the tube-launched encapsulated anti-ship and cruise missiles (typically the McDonnell Douglas UGM-84 Harpoon and General Dynamics BGM-109 Tomahawk respectively) used by several Western navies to increase the operational versatility of their hunter/killer submarines.

The emergence of a submarine-launched ballistic missile from the water is always a highly impressive sight as the weapon seems to shake itself free of the water, straighten itself, accelerate and then turn onto the desired climb angle. This is a Trident test launch from a submarine of the US Navy.

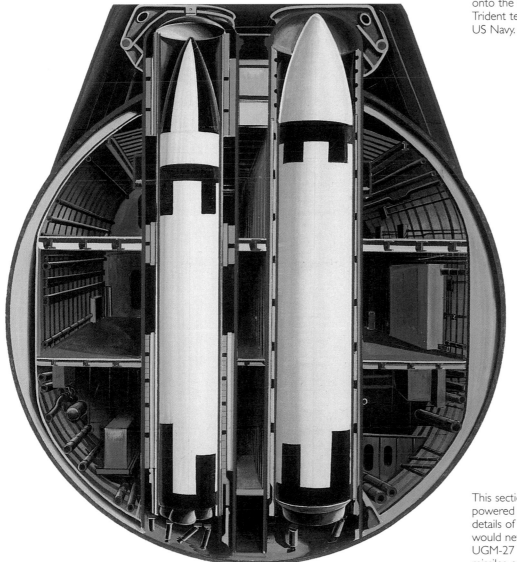

This section through an American nuclear-powered ballistic missile submarine shows details of a side-by-side installation (that would never have been made in reality) of UGM-27 Polaris and UGM-73 Poseidon missiles on the left and right respectively.

239

This view of part of the interior of the *Repulse*, a 'Resolution' class nuclear-powered ballistic missile submarine of the Royal Navy, reveals the considerably greater volume and efficiency-generating comfort of modern submarines by comparison with the cramped interiors of their diesel-electric predecessors in World War II.

The *Repulse* seen on the surface gives a good impression of the whale-like proportions of modern submarines.

was developed through three main variants in a programme that lasted to 1991 and was the first Soviet submarine with a 'teardrop' hull. The first variant was the 'Victor I' class that was delivered to the extent of 15 submarines up to 1974, with a submerged displacement of 5,300 tons, a submerged speed of 32 knots on the 30,000hp (22,370kW) delivered to one propeller by the geared steam turbine powered by two reactors, and an armament of six 21in bow tubes for either 24 torpedoes or 22 torpedoes and two SS-N-15 'Starfish' anti-ship missiles. There followed the 'Victor II' class of which seven were delivered up to 1978, with a longer hull to provide improved torpedo reload facilities, a submerged displacement of 5,800 tons and a submerged speed of 30 knots. Finally there was the 'Victor III' class of which 26 were delivered up to 1991 to an improved 'Victor II' class design with a submerged displacement of 6,000 tons, a submerged speed of 30 knots, and an armament of two 21in and four 25.6in tubes all in the bows for up to 24 torpedoes, or for a reduced number of torpedoes to allow carriage of SS-N-15 'Starfish' and/or SS-N-16 'Stallion' anti-submarine missiles and SS-N-21 'Samson' cruise missiles.

Whereas these four classes were each based on a nuclear reactor with pressurised water cooling, the following two types switched to a reactor

Lead boat of the Dutch navy's two-strong 'Zwaardvis' class of conventionally powered submarines, the *Zwaardvis* was completed in August 1972 after construction between July 1966 and July 1970 by Rotterdam Dry Dock, and the details of the class include surfaced and submerged displacements of 2,350 and 2,640 tons respectively, a length of 219ft 6in (66.9m), a single-shaft diesel-electric propulsion arrangement with three diesel engines and one 5,000hp (3,728kW) electric motor for surfaced and submerged speeds of 13 and 20 knots respectively, and an armament of six 21in (533mm) tubes in the bows for 20 torpedoes.

cooled by a liquid metal, probably sodium. The first of these was the 'Alfa' class with a hull made of a titanium alloy rather than steel for the extreme diving depth of 2,295ft (700m) and a submerged speed of 45 knots on the 47,000hp (35,045kW) supplied to one propeller by two steam turbo-alternators powered by two reactors. The armament is six 21in bow tubes for 20 weapons including two SS-N-15 'Starfish' anti-submarine missiles.

The six 'Alfa' class boats were built between 1979 and 1983, and were then followed by the first of six 'Sierra' class submarines with a slightly reduced diving depth, a submerged displacement of 8,200 tons, and a submerged speed of about 34 knots on the 40,000hp (29,825kW) supplied to one propeller by two steam turbo-alternators powered by two reactors. The armament is four 21in and four 25.6in tubes for 22 weapons including a

The *Humaita* is one of three 'Oberon' class conventionally powered submarines bought from the UK by the Brazilian navy in the 1970s. The type has surfaced and submerged displacements of 2,030 and 2,410 tons respectively, a length of 295ft 3in (90.0m), a two-shaft diesel-electric propulsion arrangement with 3,680hp (2,745kW) diesel engines and 6,000hp (4,475kW) electric motor for surfaced and submerged speeds of 12 and 17 knots respectively, a crew of 69, and an armament of six 21in (533mm) tubes in the bows for 20 Mk 24 Tigerfish wire-guided torpedoes or 50 mines.

The *Arica*, last of the Peruvian navy's six-strong 'Type 209/1' class of conventionally powered submarines, is seen leaving Kiel after completion by Howaldtswerke in January 1975.

Although planned to a total of 180 units, the Soviet 'Foxtrot' class of conventionally powered submarines was in fact built to the extent of 'only' 62 boats between 1958 and 1971.

The Italian navy's *Leonardo da Vinci* was originally the US Navy's Dace of the 'Gato' class, and was transferred in December 1954 for service up to 1973.

variable number of SS-N-15, SS-N-16 and SS-N-21 missiles. The last type of nuclear-powered attack submarine developed in the USSR and still in very low rate production for the Commonwealth of Independent States is the 'Akula' class with a submerged displacement of 9,100 tons, a submerged speed of 32 knots on the power delivered to one propeller by the steam turbines driven by two pressurised water-cooled reactors; the armament is basically identical to that of the preceding 'Sierra' class.

These Soviet boats do not match the quietness of the American submarines they were built to rival, and also lack the sophistication of the American vessels in their sonar and fire-control systems.

The 'Charlie' class submarine, of which 21 were built for the USSR in three subclasses, was a nuclear-powered type optimised for the carriage and launch of nuclear-armed cruise missiles.

Although China has pretensions to nuclear-powered submarine capability, having produced four or five operational 'Han' class boats, the only other two countries that can genuinely be regarded as members of this exclusive club are the UK and France. The first of the British boats was the *Dreadnought* that was commissioned in 1963 with what was virtually the after end and propulsion arrangement of the American 'Skipjack' class submarine grafted onto a British forward end with British equipment and weapons. The following 'Valiant' class, of which five were built between 1962 and 1971, was a slightly larger and bulkier development incorporating a British reactor system for a submerged displacement of 4,900 tons, a submerged speed of 28 knots on the 15,000hp (11,185kW) supplied to one propeller by a geared steam turbine powered by a pressurised water-cooled reactor, and an armament of six 21in tubes for 26 torpedoes. Further development of the British concept of attack submarines resulted in the 'Swiftsure' and 'Trafalgar' classes. The 'Swiftsure' class, of which six were delivered between 1973 and 1980 with a shorter and fuller hull for increased diving depth, has a submerged displacement of 4,500 tons, a submerged speed of 30 knots, and an armament of five 21in bow tubes for 25 torpedoes or a mix of torpedoes and Harpoon anti-ship missiles. The 'Trafalgar' class, of which seven were delivered from 1983, is a quietened version of the

The *Flasher* was a standard member of the US Navy's 'Sturgeon' class of nuclear-powered attack submarines optimised for the hunter-killer role with considerable underwater speed, advanced BQQ-2 sonar in the optimum bow position, and four 21in (533mm) tubes amidships for wire-guided torpedoes.

244

The Italian navy's second submarine named *Leonardo da Vinci* is one of the four-strong 'Sauro' class. Built by CRDA in the period between June 1978 and October 1979, the boat was completed in 1981 with details that included surfaced and submerged displacements of 1,456 and 1,641 tons respectively, a length of 209ft 7in (63.9m), a single-shaft diesel-electric propulsion arrangement with 3,210hp (2,394kW) diesel engines and a 3,650hp (2,721kW) electric motor for surfaced and submerged speeds of 12 and 20 knots respectively, a crew of 45, and an armament of six 21in (533mm) tubes in the bows for twelve A 184 wire-guided torpedoes. Notable features are the cruciform of control surfaces on the stern, and the large seven-bladed propeller located at the extreme stern.

'Swiftsure' class with an improved reactor and pumpjet propulsion for a submerged speed of 32 knots at a displacement of 5,200 tons.

France has produced only one class of nuclear-powered attack submarine, the eight very small units of the 'Rubis' class delivered from 1983 and still in production. The type has a submerged displacement of 2,670 tons, a submerged speed of 25 knots on the 9,500hp (7,085kW) delivered to one propeller by an electric motor drawing current from two steam turbo-alternators driven by one pressurised water-cooled reactor, and an armament of four 21in tubes for 18 weapons including torpedoes and missiles.

As noted above, the primary attraction of the nuclear propulsion arrangement for underwater craft is that it turns these boats from mere submersibles into true submarines that can operate for very long periods in a fashion wholly independent of the surface. This has allowed nuclear-powered submarines to submerge on leaving base and to surface only when returning to base after a patrol of typically 60 days, and has adversely

Built in larger numbers than any other conventionally powered submarine of Western origins in the period after World War II, the German-designed 'Type 209' offers its potential customers full optimisation for specific roles through the highly adaptable features that permit the completion of the boat to any of several basic sizes with a choice of several weapon and electronic features. Seen left is a view typical of the interior of a 'Type 209' submarine, and below is the *Salta*, one of the Argentine navy's two 'Type 209/1' class boats commissioned in May 1974. A total of 20 such boats has been sold to five countries including Peru and Turkey, whose navies each operate six of the class.

The *Aréthuse* was one of the French navy's four 'Aréthuse' class conventionally powered hunter-killer submarines optimised for operations in the Mediterranean, and was deleted in April 1979.

The *Hyatt* is one of two 'Oberon' class conventionally powered submarines bought from the UK by the Chilean navy.

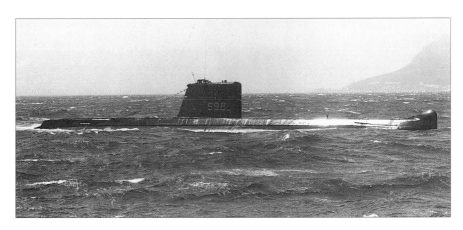

The *Emily Hobhouse* was one of three 'Daphné' class conventionally powered submarinse bought from France by the South African navy.

The *Amazonas* was one of two 'GUPPY III' class conventionally powered submarines secured from the USA by the Brazilian navy.

The *Tireless* was one of five 'T' class submarines of riveted rather than welded construction that were modified between 1950 and 1956 to the 'T (Streamline)' configuration with all guns removed, the casing streamlined, the conning tower streamlined into a sail, but with no modifications made to the propulsion arrangement. The details of the streamlined class included surfaced and submerged displacements of 1,090 and 1,424 tons respectively, a length of 273ft 6in (83.4m), a tow-shaft propulsion arrangement with 2,500hp (1,864kW) diesel engines and 1,450hp (1,081kW) electric motors for surfaced and submerged speeds of 15.25 and 9.5 knots respectively, a crew of 50, and an armament of six 21in (533mm) tubes for 11 torpedoes. This adapted type was not as effective in operational terms as the 'T (Conversion)' class, but was very useful for anti-submarine warfare training as it was faster and quieter than before. The five boats were all retired and scrapped between 1965 and 1970.

affected the ability of aircraft and surface warships, even when fitted with advanced sonar and magnetic-anomaly detection (MAD), to detect and track such submarines, especially when submarines could achieve unprecedented underwater speeds and were capable of diving to considerable depths. The former resulted in a dramatically increased search area to be covered by aircraft and surface warships, and the latter opened the possibility of using the different salinities and temperatures of greater volumes of water to help degrade the ability of searching sonar systems to acquire and track the submarine.

All these factors combined with development of the ship's inertial navigation system (SINS) and the nuclear-tipped ballistic missile to create one of the ultimate strategic weapons of the present day, namely the submarine-launched ballistic missile submarine that lurks in its patrol area for a long period, ready at command to unleash a devastating salvo of missiles which, as a result of the extremely accurate launch position inputted from the SINS, can be targeted with incredible accuracy. The submarine-launched ballistic missile (SLBM) has three primary advantages over the land-launched equivalent: firstly, its mobile launching point, which renders virtually impossible the chances of any pre-emptive attack by enemy missiles; secondly, its comparatively small size in relation to its land-launched counterpart, a fact made possible by the fact that virtually no point on Earth is more than 1,700 miles (2,735km) from the sea whereas

Left: The *Arashio* was the fifth and last unit of the Japanese navy's 'Oshio' class of conventionally powered submarines, which were the first fleet boats built in Japan after World War II. The submarine was completed in July 1969 after construction by Mitsubishi between July 1967 and October 1968. The details of this class included surfaced and submerged displacements of 1,650 and 2,150 tons respectively, a length of 288ft 8in (61.0m), a two-shaft propulsion arrangement with 2,300hp (1,715kW) diesel engines and 6,300hp (4,697kW) electric motor for surfaced and submerged speeds of 14 and 18 knots respectively, a crew of 80, and an armament of eight 21in (533mm) torpedo tubes located as six in the bows and two in the stern.

Below: The *Nazario Sauro* is the lead boat of the Italian navy's four-strong 'Sauro' class of conventionally powered submarines. Considerable delay in construction was caused by Italian financial problems between the mid-1960s and early 1970s, and then technical problems with the Italian batteries required the purchase of Swedish batteries.

The *Ouessant* was the fourth and last unit of the French navy's 'Agosta' class of conventionally powered submarines delivered in 1977 and 1978 with design emphasis placed not on range but rather on reduced noise, increased diving depth and greater submerged speed.

The *Okanagan* is one of three 'Oberon' class conventionally powered submarines operated by the naval element of the Canadian Armed Forces.

Opposite: The *Renown* is the third of the four 'Resolution' class nuclear-powered submarines that formed the backbone of the UK's strategic deterrent force until the advent of the 'Vanguard' class in the early 1990s.

Le Redoutable is the name boat of the class of nuclear-powered submarines that provides France with its primary nuclear deterrent capability.

Increased Versatility for the Missile Submarine

WITH the exception of China's single such boat, the nuclear-powered ballistic missile submarines placed in service by the world's other major nuclear powers (the USA, USSR, UK and France) were planned within the context of a possible World War III resulting from an armed confrontation between the two superpower blocs. This called for the use of increasingly sophisticated missiles that could penetrate high-grade physical and electronic defences to hit ever increasing numbers of military targets with pinpoint accuracy. When the 'Cold War' between the superpower blocs ended in the late 1980s with the economic and political collapse of the USSR, there were suggestions that the missile submarine was now superfluous. It soon became clear, however, that the world faces a crisis in the proliferation of nuclear weapons capability to countries of doubtful political stability, and with agendas driven as much by tumultuous political and religious antipathies as by rational thought. None of these 'loose pistol' members or would-be members of the nuclear club has a large or even very sophisticated nuclear capability, but all seem more disposed than any of the club's longer-term members to exert 'blackmail' pressure or even to use their weapons. This has given the missile-armed submarine a renewed life, for all of these countries can be watched from space and targeted by submarines with missiles carrying not MIRVed warheads but one or two medium-yield weapons that could be used for the excision of 'loose cannon' nuclear (or for that matter biological and/or chemical) warfare capability should the situation demand.

Opposite top: The *Sjöhästen* is one of the five 'Sjöormen' class conventionally powered attack submarines operated by the Swedish navy. Features of the class include a teardrop-shaped hull, an X-shaped configuration of the control surfaces at the stern, the forward set of hydroplanes located on the sail rather than the forward part of the hull, and a slow-turning five-blade propeller at the extreme stern for the quietest possible operation.

Right: The *Onondaga* is one of three 'Oberon' class submarines operated by the naval branch of the Canadian Armed Forces.

Opposite bottom: The 'Type 207' class of coastal submarine was designed in Germany for Norway on the basis of the 'Type 205' class operated by the German navy, and in the late 1980s Norway transferred three of its boats to Denmark. The basic specification for the class includes surfaced and submerged displacements of 370 and 435 tons respectively, a length of 149ft 0in (45.4m), a single-shaft diesel-electric propulsion arrangement with 1,210hp (900kW) diesel engines and one 1,710hp (1,275kW) electric motor for surfaced and submerged speeds of 12 and 18 knots respectively, a crew of 18, and an armament of eight 21in (533mm) tubes in the bows for eight Tp61 wire-guided anti-ship and NT 37C wire-guided anti-submarine torpedoes. Illustrated here is the Norwegian *Skolpen*, which was commissioned in August 1966 after construction by Rheinstahl. The Danish boats and six of the surviving Norwegian boats have been lengthened to 154ft 3in (47.0m) to allow the incorporation of updated fire-control and navigation electronics.

The *Triaina* was a 'Balao' class submarine transferred on loan from the USA to Greece in February 1965 and bought by the Greek navy in April 1976. The boat still existed into the mid-1980s but was confined to alongside training.

land-launched strategic missiles generally have to be launched from considerably greater ranges and must therefore be larger to carry more fuel; and thirdly, that countermeasures against nuclear-powered submarines are made very difficult by reason of the factors mentioned above. It is worth noting, moreover, that while first-generation SLBMs such as the Lockheed UGM-27 Poseidon were indeed comparatively small weapons of the intermediate-range type with a range in the order of 2,750 miles (4,425km) and the ability to carry one warhead, later weapons such as the second-generation Lockheed UGM-73 Poseidon were larger and were capable of a range in the order of 3,250 miles (5,230km) with a payload of 10 or 14 warheads; third-generation weapons such as the Lockheed UGM-96 Trident I were even larger for a range of some 4,250 miles (6,840km) with slightly fewer but independently and more precisely targeted warheads; and fourth-generation weapons such as the Lockheed UGM-133 Trident II are larger still for a range of 7,500 miles (12,070km) with between 10 and 12 independently and more precisely targeted

Still a Case for the Conventionally Powered Submarine

ALTHOUGH the nuclear-powered submarine offers far higher overall capabilities in terms of speed, endurance, weapons load and electronic sophistication in comparison with the conventionally powered submarine, it is also considerably more expensive and, for some specialised applications, not as effective as the conventionally powered boat. The factor of expense, in the development, construction and running of the boats, puts the nuclear-powered submarine out of the running for many navies, most of which do not in any event require the long endurance and deep oceanic capabilities that are the forte of such boats. For these smaller navies, therefore, the conventionally powered submarine provides more than adequate capabilities, especially in the shallower waters typical of coast-defence operations. Here the smaller size of the conventionally powered submarine is a decided asset, as is its propulsion arrangement, which is generally quieter than that of nuclear-powered boats which on a regular basis need to run the pumps associated with their reactor coolant systems. It has to be admitted, of course, that conventionally powered submarines are still not independent of the surface for purposes of refilling their air tanks and charging their batteries, but the submerged endurance of such boats is now significantly better than that of their counterparts in World War II, as a result of the widespread use of snorting and fairly radical improvements in chemical and physical technologies. The disparity between submarines with conventional and nuclear propulsion is being further narrowed, at least in tactical terms, by current developments in fuel cell and closed-cycle engine technologies, both of which offer higher and longer-endurance submerged power as well as the possibility of oxygen as a by-product.

The *Narval* was the last of the four 'S 60' class submarines constructed in Cartagena for the Spanish navy between August 1968 and November 1975 as licence-built versions of the French 'Daphné' class design.

The *Mochishio* is the second of the 10 'Yuushio' class conventionally powered submarines operated by the Japanese navy.

warheads. The Soviets sought to emulate the technological steps that allowed the Americans to develop and build these more advanced weapons, but they never managed to achieve the targeting accuracies of the American weapons, whose longer range meant that the launch submarines could operate in larger patrol areas in the deeper waters farther offshore, thereby reducing the chances of detection and destruction.

The first nuclear-powered ballistic missile submarines were the five units of the 'George Washington' class, which were built for the US Navy in the period between 1957 and 1961. The design was basically that of the 'Skipjack' class nuclear-powered attack submarine with the hull cut in half for the insertion of a constant-section missile compartment, some 130ft

(39.6m) long, immediately to the rear of the sail. This carried 16 vertical container/launcher tubes for the Polaris missile, and the result was a vessel with a submerged displacement of 6,710 tons and a submerged speed of about 20 knots.

The first American SLBM submarines designed as such were the five boats of the 'Ethan Allen' class, which were built between 1959 and 1963 to a design that was equivalent to the 'Thresher' class of attack submarines but with a hull of stronger alloy for the ability to dive deeper, improved quietening features, a towed-array passive sonar for defensive purposes, a submerged displacement of 7,885 tons, a submerged speed of about 20 knots, and a primary armament basically similar to that of the 'George Washington' class, namely 16 Polaris missiles as well as four rather than six 21in torpedo tubes.

Further development resulted in the somewhat larger 'Lafayette' class boat with a submerged displacement of 8,250 tons, a submerged speed of about 25 knots, and an armament of 16 missiles (originally Polaris but later Poseidon weapons) together with four 21in torpedo tubes. Construction of these 19 submarines was undertaken between 1961 and 1964, with the generally similar but quieter 'Benjamin Franklin' class of 12 submarines following between 1963 and 1967. As well as their improved quietening,

The *Splendid* was the last of six 'Swiftsure' class nuclear-powered attack submarines built for the Royal Navy in the period between June 1969 and January 1980 to supplement and then replace the five boats of the older and less capable 'Valiant' class. The design was a development of the 'Valiant' class design with a shorter and fuller hull form for deeper-diving capability and higher submerged speed at the expense of one of the six torpedo tubes carried in the 'Valiant' class.

The Cruise Missile

AFTER a brief flirtation with the submarine-launched cruise missile (the Regulus I and II weapons launched from two conventionally powered and one nuclear-powered submarines) in the late 1950s and early 1960s, the US Navy virtually ignored the cruise missile until the mid-1980s when it adopted conventionally armed versions of the General Dynamics BGM-109 Tomahawk weapon for submarine-launched attacks on ship and land targets, the latter predominating in the extensive use of the weapon as part of the USA's contribution to the UN-led war of 1991 to oust the Iraqi invaders from Kuwait. The USSR, on the other hand, from the mid-1950s devoted considerable attention to the cruise missile for strategic tasks. These tasks fell into two main categories as attacks on major land targets and the destruction of operationally vital maritime targets, most notably the carrier battle groups and amphibious task forces that the USSR saw as a major threat to its survival in the face of supposed American aggression. In order of their appearance in the combined US and NATO terminology for such weapons, these were the SS-N-3 'Shaddock' anti-ship missile with a conventional or 350-kiloton nuclear warhead, the SS-N-7 'Starbright' anti-ship missile with a conventional or 200-kiloton nuclear warhead, the SS-N-9 'Siren' anti-ship missile with a conventional or 200-kiloton nuclear warhead, the SS-N-12 'Sandbox' anti-ship missile with a conventional or 350-kiloton nuclear warhead, the SS-N-19 'Shipwreck' anti-ship missile with a 500-kiloton nuclear warhead, the SS-N-21 'Samson' dual-purpose weapon with a conventional or 250/350-kiloton nuclear warhead, and the SS-N-24 dual-purpose weapon with a conventional or nuclear warhead. Most of these weapons use inertial guidance (with the possibility of mid-course command update) for the mid-course phase of their flights in conjunction with some type of terminal guidance (active radar, passive radar or infra-red) for better accuracy in the attack phase of the flight. Weapons with a nuclear warhead do not need as accurate a terminal-guidance package as the versions with a conventional warhead.

Completed between 1961 and 1968 at Gorky, the 15 nuclear-powered submarines of the 'Juliett' class were designed for the interception and destruction of US Navy carrier battle groups with the aid of a primary armament of four large nuclear-tipped cruise missiles that can be launched only after the submarine has surfaced. These comprise either the SS-N-3C 'Shaddock' with active radar or infra-red terminal guidance for the delivery of a 350 kiloton nuclear or 2,205lb (1,000kg) warhead over a range of 290 miles (467km), or the SS-N-12 'Sandbox' with active radar terminal guidance for the delivery of a 350 kiloton nuclear or 2,205lb (1,000kg) conventional warhead over a range of 345 miles (555km). The missiles are accommodated in two side-by-side pairs of elevating launchers located ahead and abaft of the small sail with distinctive blast deflectors to channel the exhaust gases upward and outward when the missiles are launched at an elevation of about 20 degrees.

these boats introduced a number of detail improvements, and from the late 1970s were revised to carry the Trident I missile in place of the Poseidon.

The last word in SLBM submarines of Western origins is the current mainstay of the US Navy, the altogether larger and more formidable 'Ohio' class of boats, of which 18 are in the process of being commissioned with the main missile battery increased to 24 weapons of the Trident I type in the first eight submarines and the improved Trident II in the remaining 10 submarines. The size of the missile section is so much greater than those of the preceding classes that the overall dimensions and displacement of the 'Ohio' class are increased dramatically: whereas the 'Lafayette' and 'Benjamin Franklin' classes were based on a hull 425ft (129.5m) long with a beam of 33ft (10.05m) and a draught of 31ft 6in (9.6m) for a submerged displacement of 8,250 tons, the 'Ohio' class submarine is based on a hull 560ft (170.7m) long with a beam of 42ft (12.8m) and a draught of 36ft 5in

(11.1m) for a submerged displacement of 18,750 tons. The greater size and displacement of the 'Ohio' class meant that a more powerful propulsion arrangement had to be incorporated lest the performance of the submarine fell to unacceptably low levels: the 'Lafayette' and 'Benjamin Franklin' classes had been based on the use of a single propeller receiving 15,000hp (11,185kW) from the two geared turbines powered by steam from a single Westinghouse S5W reactor for a submerged speed of about 25 knots, but in the 'Ohio' class the single propeller receives 60,000hp (44,736kW) from the two geared steam turbines powered by steam from a single General Electric S8G reactor for a submerged speed of 30 knots. Like its predecessors, the 'Ohio' class submarine also carries torpedo armament in the form of four 21in tubes in the bows for Mk 48 wire-guided torpedoes.

Compared with the Americans, who opted for exclusive use of the ballistic missile for its strategic purposes after a brief flirtation with the winged cruise missile that ended with the one-off Halibut nuclear-powered boat completed in 1960 with a primary armament of two Regulus

The 'Oscar' class submarine of the Soviet navy was designed for the strategic cruise missile role with a very large hull to allow the incorporation of container-launchers four 24 SS-N-19 'Shipwreck' long-range anti-ship missiles.

Below: Built to a Danish design and here epitomised by the lead submarine, the four 'Delfinen' class coastal submarines were built between July 1954 and October 1964 by the Copenhagen Naval Dockyard, with surfaced and submerged displacements of 595 and 643 tons, a length of 178ft 10in (54.5m), a two-shaft propulsion arrangement with 1,200hp (805kW) diesel engines and 1,200hp (895kW) electric motors for surfaced and submerged speeds each of 15 knots, a crew of 33, and an armament of four 21in (533mm) torpedo tubes in the bows.

Built to the extent of six boats produced by Kockums and Karlskrona Navy Yard between 1957 and November 1962, and here epitomised by the *Gripen*, the 'Draken' class was basically an improved version of the 'Hajen' class with one large propeller for reduced noise and improved submerged speed.

Built from December 1976 by Kawasaki and Mitsubishi, the Japanese submarines of the 'Yuushio' class were built to an improved 'Uzushio' class design with deeper-diving capability and more advanced electronics.

Above: The *Pijao* is one of two 'Type 209/1' or 'Type 1200' class conventionally powered submarines operated by the Colombian navy with German and Dutch electronics together with an armament of German torpedoes.

The *Cakra* is one of two 'Type 209/2' or 'Type 1300' class conventionally powered submarines operated by the Indonesian navy with German, French and Dutch electronics together with an armament of German torpedoes.

Above: The Japanese 'Uzushio' class is notable for its teardrop-shaped hull and generally good streamlining.

The Western designation 'Zulu IV' was allocated to the class of Soviet conventionally powered submarines adapted from the original 'Zulu I', 'Zulu II' and 'Zulu III' subclasses without any deck gun or similar exterior impediment.

The 'Sauro' class of four boats, here epitomised by the *Nazario Sauro*, was built between June 1974 and September 1982 by Italcantieri to a design optimised for sea-going operations along the whole length of the Mediterranean. The details of the class include surfaced and submerged displacements of 1,455 and 1,630 tons respectively, a length of 210ft 0in (63.9m), a single-shaft diesel-electric propulsion arrangement with 3,645hp (2,718kW) diesel engine and one 3,220hp (2,400kW) electric motor for surfaced, snorting and submerged speeds of 11, 12 and 20 knots respectively, the capability to dive to a maximum of 1,345ft (410m) although 820ft (250m) is the operational limit, a crew of 45 with provision for four trainees, and an armament of six 21in (533mm) tubes in the bows for twelve A 184 wire-guided torpedoes.

Built as cruise missile submarines, the 'Echo II' class of nuclear-powered submarines was originally armed with container-launchers for SS-N-3 'Shaddock' missiles that were replaced in 10 or more boats by the same number of container-launchers for SS-N-12 'Sandbox' missiles.

Opposite: The *Georgia* is the fourth unit of the US Navy's extremely capable 'Ohio' class. The markings on the upper part of the forward hull section are aiming marks so that a rescue submarine can find the docking port in the event of an underwater accident.

Below: Lead boat of the US Navy's largest ballistic missile submarine type, the *Ohio* is exceeded in size only by the boats of the Soviet (now Russian) 'Typhoon' class and carries vertical launch tubes for 24 Trident I missiles.

II or five Regulus I missiles, the Soviets opted for a two-handed approach that saw the development of both conventionally powered and nuclear-powered submarines for the carriage of ballistic missiles for the strategic role, and winged cruise missiles for the strategic role and also for the operational-level role of tracking the American carrier battle groups whose nuclear-armed aircraft were seen as another major threat to the survival of the USSR.

The first of the cruise missile types were the conventionally powered 'Whiskey Long Bin', conventionally powered 'Juliett' and nuclear-powered 'Echo I' classes. The first comprised a number of 'Whiskey' class boats converted between 1961 and 1963 with four SS-N-3 'Shaddock' anti-ship missiles in a process that reduced the type's submerged speed to 8 knots; the second totalled 16 boats built between 1961 and 1969 with four SS-N-3 or later four SS-N-12 missiles and a submerged displacement of 3,750 tons and

Above: This photograph shows the *Ohio* under way on the surface, the size of the submarine and its immense power being readily evident from its considerable bow wave and turbulent wake.

Above: The missile tube covers are clearly visible in this photograph of the *Yankee II*. The object on the large mast at the after end of the fin is an aerial for electronic warfare. Satellite navigation equipment is contained in the large sphere at the forward end.

Left: The massive section immediately abaft the sail on the 'Ohio' class ballistic missile submarine is occupied by the two longitudinal rows each of 12 tubes for the primary armament, which comprises 24 Trident I missiles in the first eight boats and 24 considerably more powerful and accurate Trident II missiles in the last nine boats.

a submerged speed of 14 knots; and the third amounted to five boats built between 1960 and 1962 with an armament of eight SS-N-3 missiles, a submerged displacement of 5,500 tons, and a submerged speed of 25 knots with two propellers receiving 25,000hp (18,640kW) from two sets of geared steam turbines powered by a single reactor. Between 1962 and 1967 there followed 29 'Echo II' class boats with an enlarged sail carrying the type of radar that could provide mid-course guidance updates for the eight SS-N-3 missiles, and with a submerged displacement of 6,000 tons the boats could achieve a submerged speed of 23 knots on basically the same propulsion arrangement as the 'Echo I' class boats.

The primary limitation of the 'Echo' class boats was that they had to surface to fire their missiles, and this tactical limitation was addressed in the following 'Charlie' class of 21 boats delivered between 1968 and 1980 in three subvariants, each armed with eight underwater-launched anti-ship missiles: in the 10 units of the 'Charlie I' class these are SS-N-7 'Starbright' weapons, in the six units of the 'Charlie II' class they are SS-N-9 'Siren' weapons, and in the five units of the 'Charlie III' class they are SS-N-22 'Sunburn' weapons. The 'Charlie I' class has a submerged displacement of 5,000 tons and a submerged speed of 27 knots, while the longer 'Charlie II' and 'Charlie III' classes each have a submerged displacement of 5,500 tons and a submerged speed of 26 knots, in each case with 15,100hp (11,260kW) delivered to one propeller from a set of geared steam turbines powered by a single pressurised water-cooled reactor.

The last of the Soviet cruise missile submarines was the six-strong

Numerically the most important nuclear-powered ballistic missile submarine class in Soviet (now Russian) service, the 'Delta IV' class carries a primary armament of 16 vertically launched SS-N-18 'Stingray' missiles. This has liquid propellants and carries a MIRVed warhead system (with three or seven 200-kiloton warheads as an alternative to one 450-kiloton warhead) by comparison with the solid propellants and non-MIRVed warhead system (one 1.2-megaton or two 800-kiloton warheads) of the SS-N-8 'Sawfly' carried by the preceding 'Delta I' and 'Delta II' classes. The greater length of the SS-N-8 is reflected in the fact that the after casing of the 'Delta III' rises 29ft 6in (9.0m) above the waterline whereas in the two earlier subclasses it was 'only' 25ft 5in (7.75m) above the water.

Built to the extent of only one boat that was lost in 1989, the 'Mike' class design of nuclear-powered attack submarine had a titanium-reinforced hull for a considerable deep-diving capability, and is thought to have used explosive charges rather than compressed air to blow the main ballast tanks at the extremely high pressures encountered at great depths.

'Oscar' class of very large boats built in two subclasses as two 'Oscar I' and four 'Oscar II' class boats, each with a primary armament of 12 two-round launchers for SS-N-19 'Shipwreck' missiles. The 'Oscar I' class has a submerged displacement of 12,500 tons and a submerged speed of 30 knots on the 90,000hp (67,105kW) delivered to two propellers by geared steam turbines powered by two pressurised water-cooled reactors, while the 'Oscar II' class has a submerged speed of 28 knots on the same propulsion arrangement and incorporates improved quietening features that have increased the submerged displacement to 13,400 tons.

Now deleted from service, the *Lafayette* was the lead boat of an extremely important class of nuclear-powered ballistic missile submarines that, with the basically very similar 'Benjamin Franklin' class boats, bore the brunt of the USA's naval deterrent capability between the mid-1960s and mid-1980s.

The *Tireless* is the third unit of the seven-strong 'Trafalgar' class that is the Royal Navy's newest nuclear-powered attack submarine class, all built by Vickers. The class is designed to complement the 'Swiftsure' class, and is notable for its extremely low radiated noise levels resulting largely from the use of a wraparound coating of anechoic tiles and reliance on a pumpjet propulsor rather than a propeller.

Opposite top: Seen with two deep-submergence rescue vehicles (DSRVs) in wells on the after casing, the 'India' class submarine was designed for the rescue role. Only two of the submarines were built, single boats operating with the Soviet (now Russian) Pacific and Northern Fleets, which are the main operators of the deep-ocean submarines that might need the aid of the DSRVs.

Right: The 'Golf II' class has now disappeared from service, although two 'Golf I' class boats remained in service into the early 1990s as command and communications submarines.

Below: Commissioned in January 1983 after construction between September 1979 and April 1981 by the Electric Boat Division of the General Dynamics Corporation, the *City of Corpus Christi* was the eighteenth unit of the 'Los Angeles' class, eventually to number 62 boats as the largest class of nuclear-powered submarines yet envisaged.

After development and initial deployment of ballistic missiles in the conventionally powered 'Golf' class, of which 22 were completed between 1958 and 1962 with a primary armament of three SS-N-4 or later SS-N-5 missiles, both of which had to be launched on the surface, the USSR moved into the field of nuclear-powered ballistic missile submarines with the 'Hotel' class, of which eight were completed between 1958 and 1962 with a primary armament of three SS-N-4 missiles, a submerged displacement of 6,000 tons, and a submerged speed of 26 knots on the 30,000hp (22,370kW) delivered to two propellers by geared steam turbines driven by two pressurised water-cooled reactors. Between 1963 and 1970 the boats were modified to the more capable 'Hotel II' standard with the primary armament revised to three SS-N-5 'Sark' missiles that could be launched while the boats were still submerged.

Although these boats provided an operational capability of types, the first genuine SLBM capability was attained by the USSR with the 34 'Yankee' class submarines delivered between 1963 and 1972, with a submerged displacement of 9,600 tons, a submerged speed of 27 knots on the 50,000hp (37,280kW) delivered to two propellers by geared steam turbines powered by two pressurised water-cooled reactors. The primary armament of these boats was 16 underwater-launched SS-N-6 'Serb' missiles, which may be regarded as having been roughly equivalent to the Polaris weapon used by the US Navy, thus making the 'Yankee' class the Soviet counterpart of the 'Lafayette' class, although the Soviet boats were significantly more noisy and, with a 30 per cent larger propulsion section and 30 per cent smaller missile section, were generally less efficient than their American rivals.

The next series of Soviet SLBM submarines comprised the four subvariants of the 'Delta' class. Built between 1972 and 1977, the 18 'Yankee I' class boats had a submerged displacement of 10,200 tons and a submerged speed of 26 knots on the 50,000hp (37,280kW) delivered to two propellers by the geared steam turbines powered by two pressurised water-cooled reactors, and carried a primary armament of 12 SS-N-8 'Sawfly' underwater-launched missiles. The four 'Delta II' class boats that followed in 1974 and 1975 were lengthened to allow the carriage of 16 rather than 12 missile launch tubes, and with the submerged displacement increased to 11,300 tons, had a submerged speed of 25 knots with the same propulsion arrangement. Next came 14 'Delta III' class boats built between 1974 and 1982, with a slightly longer hull and revisions to carry 16 SS-N-18 'Stingray' missiles with liquid rather than solid propellants, a submerged displacement of 11,700 tons and a submerged speed of 24 knots with an unchanged propulsion arrangement. Finally, there were the six submarines of the 'Yankee IV' class delivered from 1984 as a development of the 'Yankee III' class with the SS-N-23 'Skiff' missile, which is a moderately advanced weapon combining the range of the SS-N-8 with the multiple independently targeted warhead capability of the SS-N-18. The 'Yankee IV' class carries 16 of these weapons, with a submerged displacement of 12,150 tons has a submerged speed of 23.5 knots with an unchanged propulsion arrangement.

The final class of SLBM submarines designed in the USSR is the 'Typhoon' class, which is the largest submarine yet designed and built, with a submerged displacement of 26,500 tons, a submerged speed of 27 knots on the 80,000hp (59,650kW) delivered to two propellers by the geared steam turbines powered by two pressurised water-cooled reactors, and a primary armament of 20 SS-N-20 'Sturgeon' missiles each carrying up to nine independently targeted warheads. Six of the boats have been delivered since 1982. The three other countries that have built nuclear-powered SLBM submarines are China, France and the UK. China's current strength is just one 'Xia' class submarine with a submerged displacement of

Opposite: The largest submarine type yet planned and built, the Soviet (now Russian) 'Typhoon' class boat carries a primary armament of 20 SS-N-10 'Sturgeon' vertically launched ballistic missiles in missile compartments located forward of the sail, and is in essence two pressure hulls and nuclear propulsion plants located side-by-side and connected by a free-flooding outer hull.

Left: The 'Victor' class was built in three subclasses totalling some 48 nuclear-powered boats to provide the Soviet (now Russian) navy with its most important attack submarine type.

8,000tons, a submerged speed of 22 knots, and a primary armament of 12 CSS-N-3 missiles.

France has developed and built three classes of SLBM submarine in the form of the five-strong 'Le Redoutable' class delivered between 1974 and 1980, with a submerged displacement of 8,940 tons, a submerged speed of 25 knots, and a primary armament of 16 M20 or, in one boat, M4 missiles; the single 'L'Inflexible' class submarine developed from the 'Le Redoutable' class with 16 M4 (later M45) missiles; and the planned six units of the 'Le Triomphant' class entering service in the second half of the 1990s with a submerged displacement of 14,335 tons, a submerged speed of 25 knots, and a primary armament of 16 M45 missiles.

Finally there is the UK, which entered the field of the SLBM submarine in 1967 with the commissioning of the first of four 'Resolution' class submarines with a submerged displacement of 8,400 tons, a submerged speed of 25 knots, and a primary armament of 16 Poseidon missiles. From the mid-1990s these are being replaced by the four submarines of the 'Vanguard' class with a submerged speed of 25 knots and a primary armament of 16 Trident II missiles.

With the ending of the confrontation between the two superpower blocs in the late 1980s, the rationale behind the construction and operation of nuclear-powered ballistic missile submarines has been weakened considerably, and it is probable that boats of this type will now be kept in lengthy service with improvements introduced in the form of better equipment and updated versions of the current generation of missiles. The flexibility offered by attack and patrol submarines of the nuclear-powered and conventionally powered types is now more important than ever, however, and it is possible that this will result in continued development of these types.

Opposite: *HMS Triumph* rendevous with a US Navy SSN at the North Pole, pictured with a RAF Nimrod flying overhead. The Trafalgar class SSN has the ability to stay at sea for long periods without the necessity for dedicated forward support.

Left and below: *HMS Vanguard*, a Trident SSBN is powered by a Pressurised Water Reactor, and has a very low noise footprint which makes it more difficult to detect. The Vanguard class is fitted with the Trident 2 SLBM with 16 tubes. It also has Spearfish and Tigerfish torpedoes and Sub-Harpoon SGM.

Inset: The control consul in the *Vanguard* is positively spacious when compared with that of its predecessor, the O class, which was only finally decommissioned in 1993.

Glossary

ASDIC original type of equipment, otherwise known as Asdic, for the detection of submerged targets by acoustic means, and then in improved versions the gathering of data about their bearing and range from the listener

BALLAST in submarine terms, water that is admitted into the outer part of the hull to replace buoyancy air and thus cause the boat to submerge until the time that the command to surface is givem, whereupon vents at the tops of the ballast tanks are closed and compressed air is released into the tanks, expelling the water and giving the boat positive buoyancy

BALLISTIC MISSILE missile that flies a ballistic trajectory after motor burn-out

BARBETTE fixed circular mounting carrying a revolving turret

BREECH-LOADING GUN type of gun in which the projectile and propellant are loaded through an opening breech mechanism

BUNKERAGE volume for the carriage of the submarine's fuel oil

CASING external flat decking and its support structure added above the pressure hull on older submarines to provide a flooring for crew movement outside the pressure hull for the purposes of manning the deck gun, revictualling and rearming the boat, and mooring and unmooring the submarine

CONNING TOWER raised structure carrying the bridge of the submarine above the pressure hull and also accommodating the periscope(s) and any other such extending/raisable unit

CRUISE MISSILE winged missile that flies an aerodynamic trajectory

DEPTH CHARGE anti-submarine weapon comprising a large high esxplosive charge packed into a cylindrical steel container and initiated at a pre-set depth (or rather pre-set pressure of water) by a hydrostatic pistol

DIESEL ENGINE type of internal combustion engine operating on the basis on compression ignition of heavy oil rather than the spark ignition of light petroleum, and therefore better suited to submarine propulsion for its lack of highly volatile petroleum gases as well as its considerably greater operating economy

DIESEL-ELECTRIC   type of propulsion arrangement in which the diesel engines are not geared to the propeller shafts but instead drive electric generators that supply current to the electric motor(s) powering the propeller shaft(s)

DUAL-PURPOSE GUN   gun capable of engaging low-angle (surface) and high-angle (aerial) targets

GUN HOUSE   portion of the turret accommodating the gun or guns

GUN MOUNTING   rotating semi-enclosed or open housing for one or more guns

'HEDGEHOG'   weapon throwing a pattern of small impact-fused bombs into the water ahead of an attacking warship with the target submarine still located in the Asdic (sonar) beam

HYDROPLANE   horizontal control surface, normally installed as two sets of surfaces near the bows and stern, to control the submarine's attitude in the water

'LIMBO'   trainable weapon throwing a pattern of large depth-fused bombs into the water ahead and/or to the side of an attacking warship with the target submarine still located in Asdic (sonar) beam

MIRV   this Multiple Independently targeted Re-entry Vehicle warhead comprises a bus carrying several warheads that are independently targeted on individual targets after re-entry

MUZZLE-LOADING GUN   type of gun in which the propellant and projectile are loaded through the muzzle

PERISCOPE   primary external vision device of a submarine comprising a tall vertical tube containing two inward-facing mirrors angled at 45 degrees to transmit the image gathered by the horizontal lens at the head of the periscope to the eyepiece used by the operator

PRESSURE HULL   basically cylindrical structure bearing the main compression loads as the submarine dives

RAM   waterline forward extension of the bow designed to penetrate the hull of an enemy warship

RIFLED GUN   gun with a rifled barrel and therefore firing a projectile that is spin-stabilised and thus more accurate over long range than a projectile fired from a smooth-bore barrel

279

SAIL   modern version of the conning tower with a more streamlined outer shell and usually containing part of the control space

SHELL   hollow projectile containing explosive initiated by a fuse mechanism

SHOT   solid projectile containing to explosive

SMOOTH-BORE GUN   gun without a rifled barrel and therefore firing a projectile that is not spun and thus less accurate over long range than a projectile fired from a rifled barrel

SNORKEL   mast-mounted device, originally known to the Germans as the Schnorchel and the British as the snort, allowing air to be drawn into a submarine just under the surface of the water for the purposes of running the diesel engines for a higher submerged speed and also for recharging of the batteries

SONAR   American name, now universal, for Asdic

TORPEDO   in submarine terms, two types of offensive weapon in the forms of the 'spar torpedo' that was a large explosive charge extended over the bows of the boat on a long spar, and the 'locomotive torpedo' that is a self-propelled weapon of basically cylindrical form containing a gyroscopic control mechanism, rear-mounted stabilising fins with attached control surfaces, a propulsion system, a large warhead and, in more modern torpodoes, either a homing system or an external wire-guidance package

'SQUID'   weapon throwing a pattern of large depth-fused bombs into the water ahead of an attacking warship with the target submarine still located in the Asdic (sonar) beam

TRIPLE-EXPANSION STEAM ENGINE   type of reciprocating steam engine

TURBINE STEAM ENGINE   type of non-reciprocating steam engine with less volume and vibration than a triple-expansion engine

TURRET   rotating enclosed and generally armoured housing for one or more guns

Index

'Capitani Romani' class 73
'Carlisle' class 59
'Caroline' class 58-59
'Casablanca' class 129
'Castle' class 92
'Centaur' class 58-59
'Ceres' class 59
'CH' class 89
'Challenger' class 53-54
'Chapayev' class 78
'chariot' human torpedo 203
'Charles F. Adams' class 104
'Charlie' classes 268
'Chester' class 58
'Chikuma' class 58
'Chiyoda' class 137
'Claud Jones' class 103
'Clemson' class 93
'Cleveland' class 66-67, 69-70, 76
'Cleveland' class 127
'CO' class 89
'Colbert' class 77-78
'Colossus' class 17
'Commencement Bay' class 129
'Condottieri' type 72
'Conte di Cavour' class 19, 44
'Courbet' class 19, 29
'CR' class 89
'Craven' class 93
'Curtatone' class 97

D

'D' class 59-60, 82
'D' class 179
'Dagger' class 115
'Danae' class 60, 68
'Dante Alighieri' class 18
'Daphné' class 227
'Dardo' class 97
'David' types 143
'de Grasse 'class 77
'de Ruyter' class 78
'Dealey' class 103
'Delaware' class 17
'Delhi' class 55-56, 60, 68

'Delta' classes 273-276
'Derfflinger' class 20
'Des Moines' class 67, 73
'Deutschland' class 45, 46
'Diadem' class 53-54
'Diaz' class 72
'Dido' class 48, 61, 69, 73
'Dolfijn' class 227
'Draken' class 227
'Dresden' class 57, 68
'Duguay Trouin' class 70, 72
'Dunkerque' class 45, 46, 48
'Duquesne' class 64, 70, 71

E

'E' class 60, 83
'E' class 156, 159, 163, 166
'E/F' class 88
'Echo' classes 266-268
'Edsall' class 94-95
'Elbing' class 96
'Electro' type 199
'Emile Bertin' class 70
'España' class 18
'Essex' class 125
'Ethan Allen' class 257
'Evarts' class 94-95

F

'F' class 83-84
'Fargo' class 70
'Farragut' class 93, 104
'Fiji' class 61-62
Fisher, Admiral Sir John 10-11, 14
'Fletcher' class 93, 103
'Florida' class 17
'Flower' class 91-92
'Folgore' class 97
'Forrest Sherman' class 104
'Forrestal' class 131
'Foxer' decoy 201
'Foxtrot' class 223-224

'FPB/TNC-45' class 108-109
'Frauenlob' class 56-57
'Fubuki' class 98-99

G

'G' class 84
'G/H' class 88
'G3' class 41, 44
'Gangut' class 19
'Garcia' class 103
'Garibaldi' class 72
'Gato' class 207, 218
'Gazelle' class 56-57
'Gearing' class 93-94, 103
'Generale' class 96-97
'George Washington' class 256
'Glorious' class 35
'Gneisenau' class 46
'Golf' class 222, 273
'Guépard' class 95
'GUPPY' programme 218

H

'H' class 84
'H' class 163-164
'H145' class 87
'H3' class 117
'Hai' class 228
'Häjen' class 227
'Han' class 244
'Harushio' class 231-232
'Hatsuhara' class 100
'Hayashio' class 230
'Hecht' class 201
'Hegu' class 108
'Helgoland' class 17
'Hercules' class 17
'Hermes' class 121-122
'Hiyo' class 136
'Hotel' classes 273
'Huangfen' class 116
'Hyuga' class 43

Index of Ships Names

Index of Boat Names